essays on the structure of social science models

by Albert Ando
Franklin M. Fisher
Herbert A. Simon

The M.I.T. Press, Massachusetts Institute of Technology, Cambridge, Massachusetts

[redacted]
Second [redacted]
[redacted]

Library of Congress Catalog Card Number 63-19112

Printed in the United States of America

ACKNOWLEDGMENTS

The authors and publishers wish to thank the following for permission to reprint copyrighted material:

John Wiley & Sons, Inc., for "Causal Ordering and Identifiability," by Herbert A. Simon, in Studies in Econometric Method, William C. Hood and Tjalling C. Koopmans, eds. (1953).

Econometrica, for "On the Cost of Approximate Specification in Simultaneous Equation Estimation," by Franklin M. Fisher, and "Aggregation of Variables in Dynamic Systems," by Herbert A. Simon and Albert Ando, in Vol. 29, No. 2 (April, 1961), and "Decomposability, Near Decomposability, and Balanced Price Change under Constant Returns to Scale," by Franklin M. Fisher, in Vol. 31, No. 1-2 (January-April, 1963).

International Economic Review, for "Near-Decomposability, Partition and Aggregation, and the Relevance of Stability Discussions," by Albert Ando and Franklin M. Fisher, in Vol. 4, No. 1 (January, 1963).

The American Political Science Review, for "Two Theorems on Ceteris Paribus in the Analysis of Dynamic Systems," by Franklin M. Fisher and Albert Ando, in Vol. 56, No. 1 (March, 1962).

CONTENTS

1

INTRODUCTION

To most of us who spend our professional lives in scientific inquiry, questions of epistemology and methodology tend to be as remote and distasteful as the most recent discoveries in biochemical research laboratories are to ordinary farmers. Many scientists make significant contributions to knowledge unhindered by, even aided by, their disinterest in formal problems of methodology. Yet, unlike farmers who can confidently depend on others to be concerned with the biochemistry of porcine metabolism, scientists must, when it becomes necessary, face the methodological and epistemological questions themselves.

Social science, because it developed much later than did natural science, benefited greatly from the adaptation of the systematic methodology developed for the latter. But, with progress in social science, it has become increasingly clear that some changes of emphasis in methodology are necessary.

Among the methodological problems that are much more acute in the social than in the physical sciences are those having their origin in the difficulty in performing controlled experiments on social phenomena. In the absence of such experiments, social scientists must use the data generated by a single, complex, uncontrolled experiment that is the history of society in its entirety. Under such a circumstance, a number of familiar notions become rather ambiguous and must be redefined carefully if we are to use them in formulating and analyzing problems in social sciences.

One of the concepts that seems quite indispensable in our thinking is "causality." It is quite true that we could conceive of a system described by a set of simultaneous equations, in which all variables are determined simultaneously. However, even in such a system, we often talk of "solving the system in terms of parameters," implying in some sense that parameters are the "cause" of a specific solution for the variables of the system. When an analyzed system is used as a datum for normative analysis, it becomes crucial to pick out those variables and parameters that are either (1) under the direct control of the decision maker, or (2) "given" in the sense that they are not influenced by other variables within the system under consideration, and distinguish them from those variables that are (3) influenced by other variables in the system.

The possibility of identifying "causal" relations is intimately related to the possibility of classifying variables into a hierarchy of sets, levels I, II, III, and so on. Variables belonging to higher-numbered sets are influenced by those in the lower-numbered sets, but the former do not influence the latter. (Variables within any set may, but need not, influence each other.) When such a stratification exists, then we may say that the variables in the lower-numbered sets are the "causes" of the variables in the higher-numbered sets. This type of hierarchical structure also provides the justification for ignoring the variables in higher-number groups when the object of an investigation is restricted to the behavior of variables in lower-numbered sets. Laboratory experimentation is a technique for artificially creating a particularly simple form of hierarchy among variables. The second chapter in this volume undertakes to define rigorously the structural relations and meaning of "causality" in this context.

As mentioned earlier, in dealing with social phenomena, it is frequently impossible to define such a hierarchical structure, partly because social systems are often more complex than physical systems, and because the laboratory experiments which artificially create a hierarchical structure are not available to the social scientist.

However, nature is not completely unkind to social science. While exact hierarchical structures are not likely to be encountered, many of the situations that social scientists are interested in can be represented by "approximately" hierarchical systems. But the question immediately arises: do only approximately hierarchical systems exhibit characteristics similar to those possessed by exactly hierarchical systems? More fundamentally, what do we mean by "approximately" hierarchical?

Alternatively, nature may sometimes present us with a situation that can be represented by two or more subsystems which are "approximately" unrelated to each other. Here again the same questions arise. In what sense, if any, are the results valid when one of such a set of "approximately" unrelated subsystems is analyzed as though it existed in complete isolation? What do we mean by "approximately" unrelated?

We deal with these questions in the fourth and fifth chapters in this book. It turns out that the answer depends crucially on the time period over which the system is observed and on the closeness of approximation to the hierarchical structure (to a collection of unrelated subsystems). More specifically, suppose that we treat an "approximately" hierarchical system as though it were exactly hierarchical (a set of "approximately" unrelated subsystems as though such subsystems were completely unrelated) and require that the resulting predictions we make about the behavior of the system be within a predetermined accuracy.

Then, for any required degree of accuracy (not exact), we can specify: (1) a time period and (2) the largest deviation permitted from the exact hierarchical structure (or the set of completely unrelated subsystems) such that within this time interval the specified accuracy of the prediction will be maintained. One can trade between the length of the time interval and the degree of approximation; i.e., for a given degree of accuracy of prediction, the closer the system is to the exact structure required, the longer the time interval over which the accuracy of prediction will be maintained.

A second but equally important result obtained in the fourth and fifth chapters in this book is concerned with the behavior of the approximate system after the above time interval is over. It is shown that for any approximate system there exists a time interval (which, of course, depends on the degree of approximation and the accuracy demanded) such that, after it has passed, scalar indices representing sets of variables at different levels of hierarchy (in different, nearly unrelated, subsystems) can be defined, and the behavior of the system defined entirely in terms of these indices, or aggregates.

Finally, and this is perhaps the most important result, it is shown that even after all the "approximately" zero causal relations in the system have worked themselves out, the internal structure of each set of variables at a particular causal level (or of each of the "approximately" unrelated subsystems) will be almost the same as would have been the case had the approximations been exact, even though the levels and rates of change of such sets of variables as a whole will generally be quite different. In other words, short-run equilibrium configurations within such sets of variables are approximately maintained as part of the long-run behavior of the system as a whole. This is what makes possible the aggregation into indices just mentioned.

These results are rigorously stated and proved for linear systems in the fourth and fifth chapters in this book. The sixth chapter presents the theorems in rather less technical form and applies them to the analysis of two illustrative examples drawn from the field of political science. The seventh and eighth chapters extend the results to the von Neumann model of production, both in terms of prices and in terms of outputs; the restriction to linearity is removed in that context, so that the results are known to hold for certain classes of nonlinear systems as well. In addition, since little is known about the behavior of such models in the exact hierarchical case, much of the seventh and eighth chapters consists in examining such behavior.

One of the major consequences of the unavailability of controlled experiments in social sciences is the lack of a powerful technique that often permits physical scientists to measure parameters of their systems. During the past twenty years, economists have developed statistical methods designed to deal with the problems created by the fact that their data are generated not by simple experimental settings but by complex simultaneous equation systems. Although the point was not emphasized initially, it can be shown that the method developed cannot cope with the data generated by a completely simultaneous system. In fact, the method presupposes that the system generating the data is an exactly hierarchical one. As stated previously, the systems generating economic data are not likely to be exactly hierarchical but only approximately so. Under the circumstances, how good are the simultaneous equation methods?

The third chapter in this book attempts to answer this question. It is shown that the properties associated with the simultaneous equation estimators hold approximately for approximately hierarchical systems. (The exact meaning of this statement is rather technical and is given the third chapter.

The essays collected here are concerned primarily with the logical foundations for choosing a methodology, and not with more practical problems of actually defining criteria that can be used to choose one methodology over another. While the latter are undoubtedly important, we have limited ourselves to the more abstract question discussed in this introduction, as it is in itself a difficult enough and important enough problem — one that must be dealt with if social sciences are to make systematic contributions to our knowledge of man and society and to our techniques for guiding social and economic progress.*

---

*A word about terminology is certainly in order here. In this introduction, we have spoken of "hierarchical" structures and "sets of unrelated subsystems." These correspond to what are called in most of the essays "decomposable" and "completely decomposable" systems, respectively. Unfortunately, however, as these papers were not written originally for this book, Chapter 4 uses "decomposable" in place of "completely decomposable." This corresponds to one of two fairly common usages (in which our "decomposable" is called "reducible") but is not consistent with the terminology of the other essays. The context will always prevent confusion.

2

Causal Ordering and Identifiability[1]

HERBERT A. SIMON

1. INTRODUCTION

In careful discussions of scientific methodology, particularly those carried on within a positivist or operationalist framework, it is now customary to avoid any use of the notion of causation and to speak instead of "functional relations" and "interdependence" among variables. This avoidance is derived, no doubt, from the role that the concept of causality has played in the history of philosophy since Aristotle, and particularly from the objectionable ontological and epistemological overtones that have attached themselves to the causal concept over the course of that history.

Empiricism has accepted Hume's critique that necessary connections among events cannot be perceived (and hence can have no empirical basis). Observation reveals only recurring associations. The proposition that it is possible to discover associations among events that are, in fact, invariable ceases to be a provable statement about the natural world and becomes instead a working rule to guide the activity of the scientist. He says, "I will seek for relationships among events that seem always to hold in fact, and when it occurs that they do not hold, I will search for additional conditions and a broader model that will (until new exceptions are discovered) restore my power of prediction." The

[1] I am indebted to Tjalling C. Koopmans for his valuable suggestions and comments on earlier drafts of this chapter, particularly with regard to the discussion of the relation between causal ordering and identifiability. A distinction between endogenous and exogenous variables similar to the concept of causal ordering here developed was made by Orcutt [1952]. For a discussion of the incorporation of the notion of causality in a system of formal logic, see Simon [1952].

only "necessary" relationships among variables are the relationships of logical necessity that hold in the scientist's model of the world, and there is no guarantee that this model will continue to describe the world that is perceived.

Even this narrower notion of causality—that causal orderings are simply properties of the scientist's model, properties that are subject to change as the model is altered to fit new observations—has been subjected to criticism on two scores. First of all, the viewpoint is becoming more and more prevalent that the appropriate scientific model of the world is not a deterministic model but a probabilistic one. In quantum mechanics and thermodynamics, and in many social science models, expressions in terms of probabilities have taken the place of completely deterministic differential equations in the relationships connecting the variables. However, if we adopt this viewpoint, we can replace the causal ordering of the variables in the deterministic model by the assumption that the realized values of certain variables at one point or period in time determine the probability distribution of certain variables at later points or periods.

The second criticism is in one sense more modest; in another, more sweeping. It has already been alluded to above. It is simply that "causation" says nothing more than "functional relationship" or "interdependence," and that, since "causation" has become encrusted with the barnacles of nonoperationalist philosophy, it is best to abandon this term for the others.

In view of the generally unsavory epistemological status of the notion of causality, it is somewhat surprising to find the term in rather common use in scientific writing (when the scientist is writing about his science, not about its methodology). Moreover, it is not easy to explain this usage as metaphorical, or even as a carry-over of outmoded language habits. For, in ordinary speech and writing the causal relationship is conceived to be an asymmetrical one—an ordering—while "functional relationship" and "interdependence" are generally conceived as entirely symmetrical. When we say that A causes B, we do not say that B causes A; but when we say that A and B are functionally related (or interdependent), we can equally well say that B and A are functionally related (or interdependent). Even when we say that A is the independent variable in an equation, while B is the dependent variable, it is often our feeling that we are merely stating a convention of notation and that, by rewriting our equation, we could with equal propriety reverse the roles of A and B.

The question, then, of whether we wish to retain the word "cause" in the vocabulary of science may be narrowed down to the question of whether there is any meaning in the assertion that the relationship between two variables in a model is sometimes asymmetrical rather than symmetrical. If the answer to this question is in the negative, there would seem to be good reason for abandoning "cause" in favor of its synonyms. If the answer is affirmative, the term "cause," carefully scrubbed free of any undesirable philosophical adhesions, can perform a useful function and should be retained.

It is the aim of this chapter to show how the question just raised can be answered in the affirmative and to provide a clear and rigorous basis for determining when a causal ordering can be said to hold between two variables or groups of variables in a model. Two preliminary remarks may help to clarify the approach that will be taken.

First, the concepts to be defined all refer to a model—a system of equations—and not to the "real" world the model purports to describe. Hence both Hume's critique and the determinism-indeterminism controversy are irrelevant to the question of whether these concepts are admissible in scientific discourse. The most orthodox of empiricists and antideterminists can use the term "cause," as we shall define it, with a clear conscience.

Second, it might be supposed that cause could be defined as functional relationship in conjunction with sequence in time. That is, we might say that if A and B are functionally related and if A precedes B in time, then A causes B. There is no logical obstacle to this procedure. Nevertheless, we shall not adopt it. We shall argue that time sequence does, indeed, sometimes provide a basis for asymmetry between A and B, but that the asymmetry is the important thing, not the sequence. By putting asymmetry, without necessarily implying a time sequence, at the basis of our definition we shall admit causal orderings where no time sequence appears (and sometimes exclude them even where there is a time sequence). By so doing we shall find ourselves in closer accord with actual usage, and with a better understanding of the meaning of the concept than if we had adopted the other, and easier, course. We shall discover that causation (as we shall define it) does not imply time sequence, nor does time sequence imply causation.

We conclude these introductory comments with two examples of relationships that "common sense" would regard as causal. First, the classical work of the biologists Henderson, Cannon, and others on homeostasis is replete with references to asymmetrical relationships among the variables. On thirst, Cannon [1939, pp. 62–66] states: "Thirst is a sensation referred to the inner surface of the mouth and throat, especially to the root of the tongue and the back part of the palate .... When water is lacking in the body the salivary glands are unfavorably affected ...

[They] are therefore unable to secrete, the mouth and pharynx become dry and thus the sensation of thirst arises."

The causal chain clearly implied by this statement is

deficiency of water in body tissues→reduction in salivation→dryness of tongue and palate→stimulation of nervous system (sensation of thirst).

To this Cannon adds elsewhere:

→activity of drinking→restoration of water content of tissues.

It is difficult to think or write of these functional relationships as symmetrical, or as asymmetrical but running in the opposite direction. For example, if there is normal salivation but the saliva is prevented from reaching the tongue and palate, thirst is produced, but this neither reduces salivation nor produces a deficiency of water in the body tissues.

Similarly, in economics we speak of relations like

poor growing weather→small wheat crops→increase in price of wheat

and we reject the notion that by changing the price of wheat we can affect the weather. The weather is an "exogenous" variable, the price of wheat an "endogenous" variable.

2. Self-Contained Structures

The task we have set ourselves is to show that, given a system of equations and a set of variables appearing in these equations, we can introduce an asymmetrical relationship among individual equations and variables (or subsets of equations and variables) that corresponds to our common-sense notion of a causal ordering. Let us designate the relationship by an arrow, →. Then we shall want to construct our definition in such a manner that $A \rightarrow B$ if and only if A is a direct cause (in ordinary usage of the term) of B.

In the following discussion we shall seek mathematical simplicity by limiting ourselves to systems of linear algebraic equations without random disturbances. Later we shall indicate how the concepts can readily be extended to nonlinear systems, but a discussion of stochastic systems is beyond the scope of this chapter.

Definition 2.1: *A* linear structure *is a system of linear nonhomogeneous equations* (cf. Marschak [1950, p. 8]) *that possesses the following special properties:*

(a) *That in any subset of k equations taken from the linear structure at* *least k different variables appear with nonzero coefficients in one or more of the equations of the subset.*

(b) *That in any subset of k equations in which $m \geqslant k$ variables appear with nonzero coefficients, if the values of any $(m - k)$ variables are chosen arbitrarily, then the equations can be solved for unique values of the remaining k variables.*

In particular, a linear structure is an independent and consistent set of linear nonhomogeneous equations, independence and consistency being guaranteed by properties (a) and (b).[2]

DEFINITION 2.2: *A linear structure is* self-contained *if it has exactly as many equations as variables* (cf. Marschak [1950, p. 7]).

Because of (b), a self-contained linear structure possesses a unique solution—there is precisely one set of values of the variables that satisfies the equations.

A linear structure can be represented by the matrix of the coefficients (augmented to include the constant terms) of the equations of the structure. We have already required that the system be nonhomogeneous (that not all the constant terms be zero) and that a sufficient number of variables appear with nonzero coefficients in one or more of the equations in any subset of the structure.

DEFINITION 2.3: *A* linear model *is the class of all linear structures that can be obtained from a given structure by the substitution of new nonzero coefficients for the nonzero coefficients of the original structure* [*without, of course, violating* (*a*) *or* (*b*)].[3]

With these terms defined we can undertake to introduce the notion of a causal ordering of the variables, and a corresponding precedence ordering of the equations, of a self-contained linear structure. We shall

[2] It should be noted that Conditions (a) and (b), incorporated in Definition 2.1, are absent from the definitions of linear structure employed in other chapters. This slight difference in definition simplifies the exposition and should cause the reader little difficulty. The relevant theorems on independence and consistency will be found in Bôcher [1907, pp. 43–49]. Condition (b) can be omitted if we exclude from consideration certain exceptional sets of values of the coefficients of the equation system; in this case we can develop properties of the system, parallel to those described in the present chapter, which hold "almost everywhere" (see Koopmans, Rubin, and Leipnik [1950, p. 82]) in the space of these coefficients.

[3] Again this definition, for purposes of simplification, is somewhat narrower than in other chapters.

then see at once that all the linear structures belonging to the same linear model possess the same causal ordering. Hence, we shall see that the causal ordering is determined as soon as we know which variables appear with nonzero coefficients in which equations.

3. Causal Ordering

3.1. Consider any subset A of the equations of a linear structure (alternatively, a subset of the rows of the augmented coefficient matrix) and the corresponding subset α of the variables that appear with a nonzero coefficient in at least one of the equations of A. Let N_A be the number of equations in A, and n_α the number of variables in α. By (a), $n_\alpha \geqslant N_A$. If we extend Definition 2.2 to subsets of equations in a linear structure, then we may say:

Definition 3.1: *A subset A of a linear structure is* self-contained *if and only if $n_\alpha = N_A$.*

Definition 3.2: *If $n_\alpha > N_A$, we shall say that A is* sectional [Marschak, 1950, p. 7].

Now suppose that A and B are two subsets of equations of the same linear structure. We prove the theorem:

Theorem 3.1: *Let A be self-contained and B be self-contained. Then their intersection C (the set of equations belonging to both A and B) is self-contained.*

Designate by α the set of variables that appear in A, by β the set in B, and by γ the set in C; let $A \cap B$ designate the intersection of the sets A and B, and $A \cup B$ their sum (i.e., the set of elements belonging either to A or to B). Then the theorem states that if $n_\alpha = N_A$, $n_\beta = N_B$, and $C = A \cap B$, then $n_\gamma = N_C$.

Proof: Designate by N_S the number of equations in $(A \cup B)$, and by n_σ the number of variables in $(\alpha \cup \beta)$. Then we have

$$N_A + N_B - N_C = N_S . \tag{3.1}$$

Designate by $n_{(\alpha \cap \beta)}$ the number of variables belonging to both α and β. Then, similarly, we have for the sets of variables

$$n_\alpha + n_\beta - n_{(\alpha \cap \beta)} = n_\sigma . \tag{3.2}$$

But by hypothesis we have $N_A = n_\alpha$ and $N_B = n_\beta$, while, by (a), $N_S \leqslant n_\sigma$. Substituting these relations in (3.1) we get

$$n_\alpha + n_\beta - N_C = N_S \leqslant n_\sigma . \tag{3.3}$$

Finally, γ is included in $(\alpha \cap \beta)$ since if a variable is in γ it must appear in C, and hence in both A and B. Therefore, $n_{(\alpha \cap \beta)} \geqslant n_\gamma$. Employing this relationship together with (3.2), we get

$$n_\sigma \leqslant n_\alpha + n_\beta - n_\gamma , \tag{3.4}$$

whence, combining (3.3) and (3.4) and eliminating identical terms from both sides of the resulting inequality, we obtain

$$N_C \geqslant n_\gamma . \tag{3.5}$$

But since, by (a), $n_\gamma \geqslant N_C$, (3.5) implies

$$n_\gamma = N_C , \tag{3.6}$$

which proves the theorem.

DEFINITION 3.3: *We call those self-contained subsets of a linear structure that do not themselves contain self-contained* (*proper*) *subsets the* minimal self-contained subsets of the structure.

From Theorem 3.1 there follows immediately

THEOREM 3.2: *The minimal self-contained subsets A_i of the equations of a linear structure, and likewise the subsets of variables that appear in these minimal subsets of equations, are disjunct.*

That the subsets of equations are disjunct is obvious from Theorem 3.1. That the subsets of *variables* appearing in the several minimal self-contained subsets of equations are also disjunct follows from the observation that, if this were not so, the sums of minimal subsets with common variables would contain fewer variables than equations, contrary to (a). That is, let A and B be minimal self-contained subsets and let $C = A \cup B$. Then, since A and B are disjunct, $N_C = N_A + N_B$, while $n_\gamma = n_\alpha + n_\beta - n_{(\alpha \cap \beta)}$. But $n_\alpha = N_A$, $n_\beta = N_B$. Hence $n_{(\alpha \cap \beta)} > 0$ implies $n_\gamma < N_C$, which contradicts (a).

3.2. We can now decompose a self-contained linear structure A containing variables α into two parts: a part A', which is the sum of all the minimal self-contained subsets, $A' = A_1 \cup A_2 \cup \cdots \cup A_k$ (containing variables $\alpha' = \alpha_1 \cup \alpha_2 \cup \cdots \cup \alpha_k$); and a remainder, B. Since the A_i are disjunct, $N_{A'} = \sum N_{A_i}$. Similarly, $n_{\alpha'} = \sum n_{\alpha_i} = \sum N_{A_i}$. Hence $N_{A'} = n_{\alpha'}$, i.e., the number of variables appearing in A' is equal to the number of equations in A'. Further, if B is not null ("empty"), we must have $n_\beta > N_B$; otherwise B would be self-contained, contrary to its definition. Hence, at least one of the variables of α' must belong to β.

It is convenient to distinguish three cases:

I. A' consists of a single self-contained set, which coincides with the entire structure; i.e., the structure A contains no self-contained proper subset. In this case B is null, and we may say that the structure is completely *integrated.*

II. A' consists of one or more proper subsets of the structure and B is not null. In this case we may say that the structure is *causally ordered.*

III. A' consists of more than one proper subset of the structure and B is null. In this case we may say that the structure is *unintegrated.*

In all three cases we shall call the minimal self-contained subsets belonging to A' the (minimal) *complete subsets of zero order.*

DEFINITION 3.4: *If in Case II we solve the equations of A' for the unique values of the variables in α', and substitute these values in the equations of B [by (b) this is always possible], the linear structure we obtain is the* derived structure of first order, *a self-contained structure of N_B equations in $n_{(\beta-\beta\cap\alpha')} = N_B$ unknowns. We can now find the minimal self-contained subsets of the first derived structure, $B' = B_1 \cup B_2 \cup \cdots \cup B_m$* (complete subsets of first order), *and proceed as before, obtaining Case I, II, or III. If Case II holds, we repeat the process with the* derived structure of second order, *and so forth. Since the number of equations in the original structure was finite, we must finally reach a derived structure that falls under Case I or Case III.*

DEFINITION 3.5: *The minimal self-contained subsets of the derived structure of k-th order will be called the* complete subsets of kth order.

3.3. By the process just described we have arrived at a complete ordering of disjunct subsets of the equations of A, so that $A = A' \cup B' \cup \cdots \cup N$, where N, the derived structure of highest order, is either unintegrated or completely integrated. Each of the minimal complete subsets, of whatever order, reached in the process may be interpreted in either of two ways. The subset, taken by itself, may be regarded (as above) as a self-contained structure with as many variables as equations, the remaining variables having been eliminated by substitution after solution of the equations of the lower-order structures. Alternatively, it may be viewed as a *complete* subset, in which case the variables in question are not eliminated by substitution but are regarded as *exogenous variables,* the remaining variables (equal in number to the equations of the subset) being regarded as *endogenous variables.* (It will be clear that these terms are used in a sense relative to the complete subset of equations in question.[4])

Adopting the latter interpretation of subsets in the derived structures, it is clear that each complete subset of first order must contain at least one variable in α', for if it did not, the subset would be a complete subset of zero order. Similarly, each complete subset of kth order must contain at least one variable that appears in a complete subset of $(k - 1)$th order and that does not appear in any complete subset of order less than $(k - 1)$.

Since the concepts of endogenous and exogenous variables will play an important role in the following discussion, it will be useful to have for these terms a definition more formal than that just given.

DEFINITION 3.6: *If D is a complete subset of order k, and if a variable x_i appears in D but in no complete subset of order lower than k, then x_i is* endogenous *in the subset D. If x_i appears in D but also in some complete subset of order lower than k, then x_i is* exogenous *in the subset D.*

From our previous discussion (in particular, the paragraph following Theorem 3.2) it can be seen that each variable in a self-contained linear structure appears as an endogenous variable in one and only one complete subset of the structure, that it appears in no complete subset of order lower than the one in which it is endogenous, and that it appears in complete subsets of higher order (if at all) as an exogenous variable. Therefore, there exists a one-to-one correspondence between the complete subsets of equations and the subsets of variables occurring as endogenous variables in these equations.

We can now employ the distinction between exogenous and endogenous variables to define a causal ordering of the sets of variables endogenous to the corresponding complete subsets of equations.

DEFINITION 3.7: *Let β designate the set of variables endogenous to a complete subset B, and let γ designate the set endogenous to a complete subset C. Then the variables of γ are* directly causally dependent *on the variables of β ($\beta \rightarrow \gamma$) if at least one member of β appears as an exogenous variable in C. We can say also that the subset of equations B has* direct precedence *over the subset C.*

We have now partitioned the equations of a self-contained structure into disjunct subsets (the minimal complete subsets of various orders);

[4] This usage of "complete," "exogenous," and "endogenous" is consistent with Marschak's definition of those terms [Marschak, 1950, pp. 7–8].

we have similarly partitioned into disjunct subsets the variables of the structure (the sets of endogenous variables corresponding to the complete subsets of equations); and we have partially ordered these minimal subsets of equations and corresponding sets of variables by means of the (isomorphic) relations of direct precedence and direct causal dependence, respectively.

4. Analysis of Examples

4.1. Our first example is the simple one mentioned in the introduction to this chapter:

poor growing weather → *small wheat crops* → *increase in price of wheat.*

We may translate this into the form of a self-contained linear structure as follows: Let x_1 be an index measuring the favorableness of weather for growing wheat; x_2, the size of the wheat crop; and x_3, the price of wheat. We suppose the weather to depend only on a parameter; the wheat crop, upon the weather (we ignore a possible dependence of supply on price); and the price of wheat, on the wheat crop; and we suppose all relations to be linear. The resulting equations are

$$a_{11}x_1 = a_{10}, \tag{4.1}$$

$$a_{21}x_1 + a_{22}x_2 = a_{20}, \tag{4.2}$$

$$a_{32}x_2 + a_{33}x_3 = a_{30}. \tag{4.3}$$

Equation (4.1) contains only one variable and hence is a minimal complete subset of zero order, with x_1 as the endogenous variable. There are no other such subsets. Solving (4.1) for x_1 and substituting this value in (4.2) and (4.3), we get the derived structure of first order,

$$a_{22}x_2 = a_{20} - a_{21}(a_{10}/a_{11}), \tag{4.2a}$$

$$a_{32}x_2 + a_{33}x_3 = a_{30}. \tag{4.3a}$$

We see that equation (4.2a) is a minimal complete subset of first order, with x_2 as its endogenous variable. Solving (4.2a) for x_2 and eliminating x_2 from the third equation, we are left with a single equation as the minimal complete subset of second order. Applying Definition 3.7, we may write:

$$(4.1) \rightarrow (4.2) \rightarrow (4.3)$$

[read: "(4.1) has direct precedence over (4.2), and (4.2) over (4.3)"], and

$$x_1 \rightarrow x_2 \rightarrow x_3$$

(read: "x_1 is the direct cause of x_2, and x_2 of x_3").

4.2. A less trivial example, which also shows that our definitions correspond with common-sense notions of causality, is the structure whose coefficients are estimated by Girshick and Haavelmo in Chapter V, pages 107–110. In writing their system we omit the random terms and employ a different notation for the coefficients:

$$a_{11}y_1+a_{12}y_2+a_{13}y_3+a_{18}z_8+a_{19}z_9=a_{10}\,, \tag{4.4}$$

$$a_{21}y_1+a_{22}y_2+a_{24}y_4+a_{28}z_8=a_{20}\,, \tag{4.5}$$

$$a_{33}y_3+a_{37}z_7+a_{39}z_9=a_{30}\,, \tag{4.6}$$

$$a_{44}y_4+a_{45}y_5+a_{46}z_6+a_{48}z_8=a_{40}\,, \tag{4.7}$$

$$a_{52}y_2+a_{55}y_5+a_{58}z_8=a_{50}\,, \tag{4.8}$$

$$a_{66}z_6=a_{60}\,, \tag{4.9}$$

$$a_{77}z_7=a_{70}\,, \tag{4.10}$$

$$a_{88}z_8=a_{80}\,, \tag{4.11}$$

$$a_{99}z_9=a_{90}\,. \tag{4.12}$$

Analysis of this structure, which the reader may wish to carry out as an exercise, shows that there are four single-equation subsets of zero order: equations (4.9), (4.10), (4.11), (4.12), and one subset of first order: equation (4.6). The four remaining equations form a single subset of second order in the endogenous variables y_1, y_2, y_4, and y_5. In terms of equations, the precedence relations are

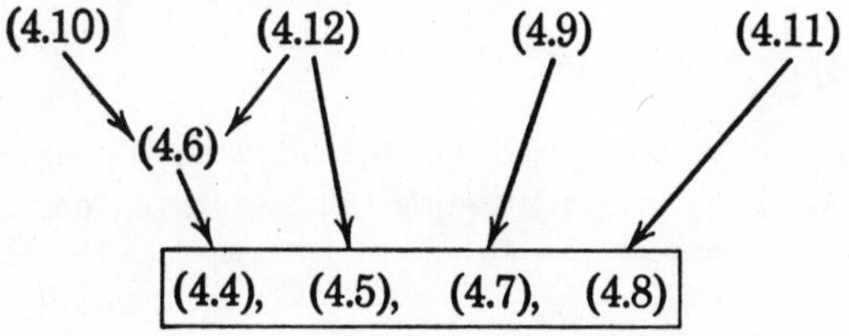

Interpreting this result in terms of the corresponding sets of variables, we find that Girshick and Haavelmo are asserting:

1. That food consumption (y_1), retail food prices (y_2), food production (y_4), and food prices received by farmers (y_5) are interdependent (members of the same minimal complete subset of second order) and directly causally dependent upon disposable income (y_3), last year's food prices received by farmers (z_6), time (z_8), and last year's disposable income (z_9).

2. That disposable income (y_3) is directly causally dependent upon net investment (z_7) and last year's disposable income (z_9).

4.3. We present, without interpretation, a final example:

$$\alpha_{11}x_1 + \alpha_{12}x_2 + \alpha_{13}x_3 + \alpha_{16}x_6 = \alpha_{10}\,, \tag{4.13}$$

$$\alpha_{24}x_4 + \alpha_{25}x_5 = \alpha_{20}\,, \tag{4.14}$$

$$\alpha_{32}x_2 = \alpha_{30}\,, \tag{4.15}$$

$$\alpha_{43}x_3 = \alpha_{40}\,, \tag{4.16}$$

$$\alpha_{51}x_1 + \alpha_{52}x_2 + \alpha_{53}x_3 + \alpha_{54}x_4 = \alpha_{50}\,, \tag{4.17}$$

$$\alpha_{66}x_6 + \alpha_{67}x_7 = \alpha_{60}\,, \tag{4.18}$$

$$\alpha_{71}x_1 = \alpha_{70}\,. \tag{4.19}$$

It can be shown that there are three complete subsets of zero order: equation (4.15) and variable x_2, equation (4.16) and variable x_3, and equation (4.19) and variable x_1. There are two complete subsets of first order: equation (4.13) and x_6, and equation (4.17) and x_4. Finally, there are two complete subsets of second order: equation (4.14) and x_5, and equation (4.18) and x_7. In this case each complete subset consists of one equation in one endogenous variable, and we can represent the precedence and causal partitioning alternatively as follows:

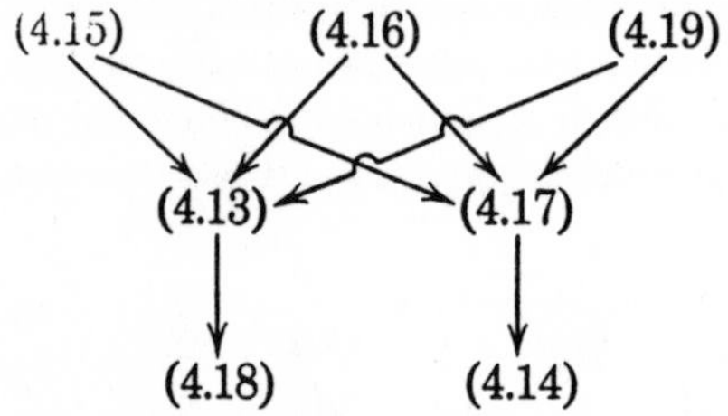

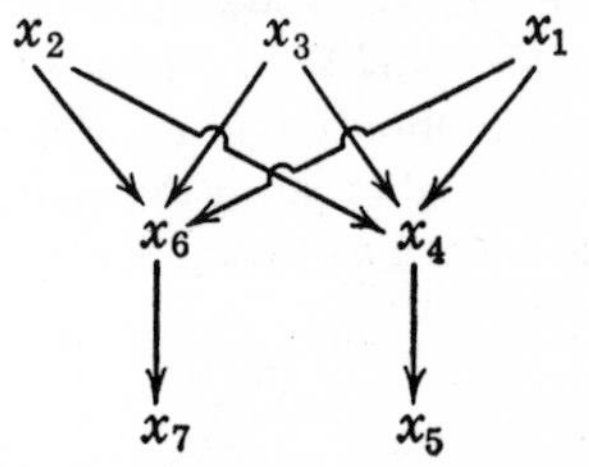

Reordering our equations to correspond with the order of the corresponding variables, the partitioning can also be represented as follows:

	x_1	x_2	x_3	x_4	x_6	x_5	x_7
(4.19)	×	0	0	0	0	0	0
(4.15)	0	×	0	0	0	0	0
(4.16)	0	0	×	0	0	0	0
(4.17)	×	×	×	×	0	0	0
(4.13)	×	×	×	0	×	0	0
(4.14)	0	0	0	×	0	×	0
(4.18)	0	0	0	0	×	0	×

In this table, nonzero coefficients in the matrix are designated by ×, zero coefficients by 0. The coefficients of the constant term are not displayed.

4.4. We see from this last representation that ordering the equations and variables according to their precedence and causal relations places the matrix in a canonical form that in a certain sense is as nearly triangular as the structural equations permit. This suggests that calculation of the causal relations in a structure may have some value in indicating the optimum arrangement of equations and variables in fixing the sequence of computation of their solutions. It would be easy to construct an electrical computing device which, even for very large structures, would rapidly locate the complete subsets from this matrix representation.

The blocks of zeros above and to the right of the main diagonal in the canonical form of the matrix show clearly also that our concept of causal ordering is essentially identical with the concept of unilateral coupling, employed in connection with dynamical systems.[5]

4.5. The blocks of zeros in the lower left-hand corner are really accidental properties of the particular partitioning we are studying—that variables of zero order appear only in equations of zero and first order, not in equations of second order.

The causal relation we have defined is a nontransitive relation— $\alpha \rightarrow \beta$ and $\beta \rightarrow \gamma$ does not imply $\alpha \rightarrow \gamma$. We may wish to introduce, among sets of endogenous variables, a transitive relationship meaning "directly or indirectly caused."

DEFINITION 4.1: *$\alpha \supset \gamma$ (read: "α is a cause of γ") if there exist β_1, $\beta_2, \cdots, \beta_k$ such that $\alpha \rightarrow \beta_1 \rightarrow \beta_2 \rightarrow \cdots \rightarrow \beta_k \rightarrow \gamma$. We may also speak of a relationship of* precedence *holding between the corresponding subsets of equations; for instance, $A \supset C$.*

5. Causality in Systems Not Self-Contained

5.1. We now proceed to show that it is essential that we assume a self-contained structure in order to introduce the notion of causal ordering.

Consider the structure used as an example in Section 4.3. Suppose that we omit equations (4.15) and (4.19) and replace them with

$$\alpha_{85}x_5 = \alpha_{80}, \tag{5.1}$$

$$\alpha_{99}x_7 = \alpha_{90}. \tag{5.2}$$

[5] As a matter of fact, the writer originally approached his problem from the standpoint of unilateral coupling (cf. Goodwin [1947, pp. 183–184]).

We then obtain the following causal structure:

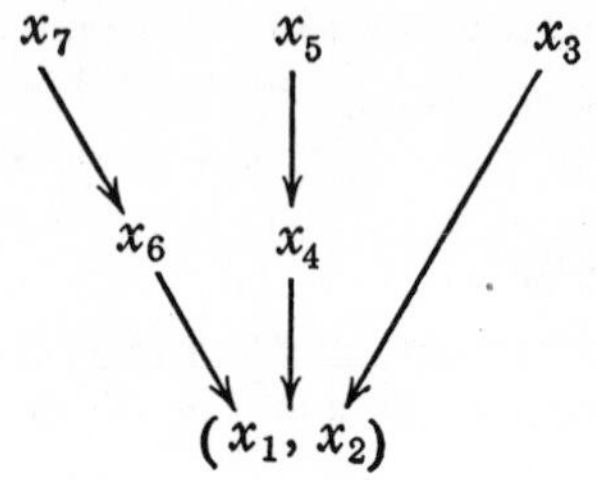

where (x_1, x_2) represents the complete subset of second order comprising the variables x_1 and x_2. We see that we have not only reversed the direction of causation between x_5 and x_7, on the one hand, and x_1 and x_2 on the other, but have also changed the relation of x_3 to the remainder of the structure. Hence we cannot speak of an "internal" causal structure among the variables of a sectional (not self-contained) structure apart from the particular self-contained structure in which it is imbedded. In our new case the canonical form of matrix is

	x_3	x_5	x_7	x_4	x_6	x_1	x_2
(4.16)	×	0	0	0	0	0	0
(5.1)	0	×	0	0	0	0	0
(5.2)	0	0	×	0	0	0	0
(4.14)	0	×	0	×	0	0	0
(4.18)	0	0	×	0	×	0	0
(4.13)	×	0	0	0	×	×	×
(4.17)	×	0	0	×	0	×	×

Of the five equations common to both structures, only equation (4.16) has retained the same order. Moreover, the complete subsets of equations are associated with subsets of variables different from those before.

5.2. In general, we can complete a sectional structure by adding an appropriate number of additional equations, and in general we can do this in a number of different ways. Each of the resulting self-contained structures is likely to have different causal relationships among its variables. One way to complete a sectional structure is to specify which variables are exogenous and to add a sufficient number of equations in which these exogenous variables alone occur [Marschak, 1950, p. 8].

6. Operational Significance of Causal Ordering

6.1. An important objection to our definition of causal ordering remains to be examined—the objection that it is essentially artificial, since the same set of observations could be represented by different structures with different causal orderings of the variables. Consider the following three sets of two equations each:

$$\left.\begin{array}{l}(6.1)\\(6.2)\end{array}\right\} \qquad \left\{\begin{array}{l} a_{11}y_1 + a_{12}y_2 = a_{10}\ ,\\ a_{21}y_1 + a_{22}y_2 = a_{20}\ ;\end{array}\right.$$

$$\left.\begin{array}{l}(6.3)\\(6.4)\end{array}\right\} \qquad \left\{\begin{array}{l} b_{11}y_1 = b_{10}\ ,\\ a_{21}y_1 + a_{22}y_2 = a_{20}\ ,\end{array}\right.$$

with $b_{11} = a_{11} - (a_{12}/a_{22})a_{21}$, $b_{10} = a_{10} - (a_{12}/a_{22})a_{20}$;

$$\left.\begin{array}{l}(6.5)\\(6.6)\end{array}\right\} \qquad \left\{\begin{array}{l} b_{11}y_1 = b_{10}\ ,\\ a_{22}y_2 = c_{20}\ ,\end{array}\right.$$

with $c_{20} = a_{20} - (a_{21}/b_{11})b_{10}$.

All three sets of equations are satisfied by precisely the same set of values of y_1 and y_2 , namely,

$$y_1 = b_{10}/b_{11}\ , \qquad y_2 = c_{20}/a_{22}\ . \tag{6.7}$$

Yet the causal ordering in the three sets is different. Equations (6.1) and (6.2) comprise a single minimal complete set of zero order. Equation (6.3) is a complete set of zero order, while (6.4) is a complete set of first order to which (6.3) is directly precedent. Equations (6.5) and (6.6) each constitute a complete set of zero order. The first structure is completely integrated, the second causally ordered, and the third unintegrated. If the three sets are to be regarded as operationally equivalent, because each can be obtained from either of the others by algebraic manipulation without altering the solution, then causal ordering has no operational meaning.

Closer inspection of the three sets of equations, (6.1)–(6.6), suggests a possible basis for distinguishing them even though they have an identical solution. Consider the first pair of equations. Suppose that equation (6.1) were altered (say, by a change in the constant term or one of the other coefficients). Then the values of both y_1 and y_2 would, in general, be altered. The same would be true if (6.2) were altered.

Consider next the second pair of equations. Suppose that equation (6.3) were altered. Again, both y_1 and y_2 would be changed in value. On the other hand, if (6.4) were altered, only y_2 would be affected and y_1 would remain unchanged.

Finally, consider the third pair of equations. Suppose that equation (6.5) were altered. This would change the value of y_1 but not of y_2. However, if (6.6) were altered, this would change the value of y_2 but not of y_1.

The principle illustrated by the example above can easily be generalized.

THEOREM 6.1: *Let A be a self-contained linear structure, let A_1 be a complete subset of order k in A, and let A' be a self-contained linear structure that is identical with A except for a single equation belonging to A_1. (We assume that the set of variables appearing in A_1 is unaltered.) Consider the (unique) solutions of A and A', respectively. Then (a) the values of all variables in A that are neither endogenous variables of A_1 nor causally dependent, directly or indirectly, on the endogenous variables of A_1 are identical with the values of the corresponding variables in A'; and (b) the values of all variables in A that are endogenous in A_1 or are causally dependent on the endogenous variables of A_1 are (in general) different from the values of the corresponding variables in A'.*

PROOF: We can solve the equations of a linear structure for the values of the variables appearing in a particular complete subset A_2 by (1) solving successively the complete subsets (starting with those of zero order) that have precedence over A_2, and finally (2) substituting in A_2 the values of all the exogenous variables appearing in A_2 and solving the equations of A_2 for the endogenous variables. Hence, altering an equation belonging to one of these complete subsets will, in general, alter the values of the variables in A_2; but altering an equation in a complete subset that does not have precedence over A_2 cannot alter the values of the variables in A_2.

6.2. Let us apply this notion to the example used in Section 4.1. The structure represented by equations (4.1)–(4.3) might be altered by changing any one of the three equations, each of which constitutes a complete subset.

I. If (4.1) is altered (e.g., rainfall is increased by sowing carbon dioxide crystals in clouds), this will also affect the wheat crop and the price of wheat.

II. If (4.2) is altered (e.g., a drought-resistant variety of wheat is introduced), this will affect the wheat crop and the price of wheat but not the weather.

III. If (4.3) is altered (e.g., a population increase shifts upward the demand schedule for wheat), the price of wheat will change but not the size of the wheat crop or the weather.

The causal relationships have operational meaning, then, to the extent that particular alterations or "interventions" in the structure can be associated with specific complete subsets of equations. We can picture the situation, perhaps somewhat metaphorically, as follows. We suppose a group of persons whom we shall call "experimenters." If we like, we may consider "nature" to be a member of the group. The experimenters, severally or separately, are able to choose the nonzero elements of the coefficient matrix of a linear structure, but they may not replace zero elements by nonzero elements or vice versa (i.e., they are restricted to a specified linear model). We may say that they *control directly* the values of the nonzero coefficients. Once the matrix is specified, the values of the n variables in the n linear equations of the structure are uniquely determined. Hence, the experimenters *control indirectly* the values of these variables. The causal ordering specifies which variables will be affected by intervention at a particular point (a particular complete subset) of the structure.

We see that, in addition to a language describing the linear model, we require, in order to discuss causality, a second language (a "metalanguage") describing the relationship between the "experimenters" and the model. The terms "direct control" and "indirect control" are in this metalanguage. Thus, in our metalanguage we have an asymmetrical relationship ($>$)—behavior of experimenters $>$ equation coefficients $>$ values of variables—that must be introduced in order to establish the asymmetrical causal relationship ($\rightarrow$).

In one sense we have moved our problem from the language of the original model to the metalanguage. In order to establish a causal ordering we must have a priori knowledge of the limits imposed on the "experimenters"—in this case knowledge that certain coefficients of the matrix are zeros. If the causal ordering is to have operational meaning it is necessary that, within these limits, the "experimenters" be able to alter at least some equation in each complete subset in some way.

7. Causal Ordering and Identifiability

The concept of identifiability has been introduced in Chapter II. In the present chapter no hint has been given thus far as to the relationship between identifiability and causal ordering. In fact, however, there appears to be a very close relationship between the two concepts, and it is the task of the present section to describe it.[6]

7.1. In Section 6 we sought an operational basis for the concept of causal ordering, a basis that would make of the ordering something more than an arbitrary property of a particular (and arbitrary) way of writing the equations governing certain empirical variables. We found that we could provide the ordering with an operational basis if we could associate with each equation of a structure a specific power of intervention, or "direct control." That is, any such intervention would alter the structure but leave the model (and hence the causal ordering) invariant. Hence, causal ordering is a property of models that is invariant with respect to interventions within the model, and structural equations are equations that correspond to specified possibilities of intervention.

The usual notion of operationalism requires us to associate with each *variable* of an empirical system a method (set of operations) for measuring it. The extended notion introduced in Section 6 requires us to associate with each *equation* a procedure (set of operations) for altering its constant term or coefficients. It is by virtue of such procedures that we can distinguish between "structural" and "nonstructural" sets of equations describing the same set of observations.

But it is precisely this same notion of intervention, and this same distinction between structural and nonstructural equations, that lies at the root of the identifiability concept.[7] As long as structure remains unaltered, identifiability is not required in order to estimate the parameters that are needed for prediction. When a recognizable change in structure occurs, however, identifiability of at least some of the parameters of the structural equations is necessary if correct predictions are to be made in the new structure. From these epistemological considerations we conclude that the conditions under which the causal ordering of a structure is operationally meaningful are generally the same as the conditions under which structural equations can be distinguished from nonstructural equations, and the same as the conditions under which the question of identifiability of the equations is meaningful.

[6] In addition to the logical connection, to be discussed in the text, between causal ordering and identifiability, it may be of interest to point to a number of historical connections. Pioneering work on identifiability was done by Ragnar Frisch [1934], who explored the problem discussed in Section 8.1 below. Other authors in econometrics began to use the concept of causality in their writings without explicit definition; for example, Haavelmo [1944, especially p. 22] and Wold [1949]. An explicit causal ordering for a special class of cases was introduced by Tinbergen [1940].

[7] See Marschak [1950, pp. 8–18], Hurwicz [1950b, pp. 266–273], Chapter I of this volume, and Section 8 of Chapter II.

7.2. Parallel with the epistemological relationship just described, we should expect to find a mathematical relationship between the two concepts. In this we are not disappointed.

Identifiability of a linear structure is obtained when certain a priori constraints are placed on the model. For complete identifiability of a structure these restraints must preclude the existence in the model of a different equivalent structure, that is (in linear models), a different set of equations whose members are linear combinations of the original equations.[8]

The simplest basis for identifiability is obtained if we can specify a priori that certain coefficients appearing in the model must be zero. But if the jth coefficient in the ith equation is zero, then the jth variable does not appear in the ith equation. Hence, these specifications may be regarded as determining which variables appear in which equations. In a self-contained structure specification of which variables appear with nonzero coefficients in which equations determines the causal ordering. (In the present section we shall restrict ourselves to a priori specifications of the kind just described.)

7.3. The argument just set forth may be restated in a more formal way, which will perhaps clarify further the operational status of the terms "causal ordering" and "identifiability." An important guiding principle in the relationship between mathematical models and empirical data is that a property of a mathematical model cannot be regarded as reflecting a property of the empirical world the model purports to describe unless this property is invariant under permissible (operationally nonsignificant) transformations of the equations specified by the model.

For example, in Newtonian mechanics it is meaningless to ask whether a body is at rest or in uniform motion in a straight line, for by a trivial transformation of the reference system the motion of the body can be transformed from the first state to the second.[9] It is meaningful

[8] The definition of identifiability from which this statement is derived (see Chapter II, Section 3, and Koopmans, Rubin, and Leipnik [1950, Definition 2.1.5.3]) refers to stochastic models. We shall see in Section 8 that the statement remains valid for an equivalent identifiability concept formulated for nonstochastic models [Marschak, 1950, Section 1.3]. In either case, the concept of identifiability always refers to a complete structure, whose equations may be a complete subset (Definition 3.5) of a (stated or unstated) structure consisting of a larger number of equations. The implications of this fact have not received sufficient emphasis in the literature on identifiability, and will be elaborated in Section 8.

[9] This is the classical problem of "absolute" versus "relative" motion. The notion of invariance under transformation as a necessary condition for a "real" property of a physical system has provided a leading motivation for the development of relativistic mechanics and other branches of modern physics. For the identification problems that arise in classical mechanics, see Simon [1947].

however, to ask whether the body is accelerated or unaccelerated since this property is invariant under transformation from one physically admissible reference system to another.

In the classical theory of systems of linear equations we are interested in properties of a system that are invariant under certain groups of transformations of the coefficients of its matrix. In particular, we may be interested in the solutions of any given system (the sets of values of the variables satisfying the system). These are invariant under elementary row transformations of the matrix.

DEFINITION 7.1: *Elementary row transformations of a matrix are those which (1) interchange rows of the matrix (i.e., reorder the equations), (2) add to a given row multiples of another row or rows, (3) multiply a row by a nonzero scalar. These all amount to premultiplication of the coefficient matrix by a nonsingular matrix.*[10] *The group of transformations thus generated we will call the R-transformations.*

DEFINITION 7.2: *Any two coefficient matrices that are obtainable from one another by R-transformations we will call R-equivalent.*

Concentration of interest on those properties (e.g., solutions) that are invariant under the group of R-transformations has led to the replacement of the notion of causality by the notion of mutual dependence. For, given a (consistent and independent) set of k linear equations in n ($n \geqslant k$) variables, then, in general, each variable belonging to any subset [Bôcher, 1907, p. 46] of k variables can be expressed as a function of the remaining $(n - k)$.

We have seen that the causal ordering in a linear structure is not invariant under the group of R-transformations (cf. Sections 6.1, 6.2). Hence, to give invariant meaning to this causal ordering we must restrict ourselves to a more limited group of transformations than the R-transformations.

DEFINITION 7.3: *We say that two coefficient matrices are structurally equivalent (S-equivalent) if the second can be obtained from the first by premultiplication by a nonsingular diagonal matrix (i.e., by row transformations of the third type only). The group of transformations thus admitted we shall call the group of S-transformations.*

It is clear that if only the S-transformations are admitted (multiplication of each equation by a constant), the positions of the zero and

[10] Albert [1941, pp. 24, 43].

nonzero coefficients cannot be affected. That is, the causal ordering of a linear structure and the identifiability of its several equations are invariant under the group of S-transformations but not under the wider group of R-transformations.

Now the operational significance of distinguishing between these two groups of transformations has already been suggested in Sections 6.2 and 7.1. If with each equation of a structure we associate a specific power of intervention, then, under S-transformations, this one-to-one correspondence between equations and interventions will not be disturbed—each equation will retain its identity. But, under R-transformations of types (1) or (2), the equations will be scrambled and combined. Suppose that the jth and kth equations belong to different complete subsets. If the jth equation is interchanged with the kth, the interventions will have to be correspondingly reordered; while if the jth equation is replaced by a sum of multiples of the jth and kth, the kth power of intervention will now not be associated with a single equation but with both the jth and the kth.

The definition of identifiability implies that a linear structure is completely identifiable if and only if the a priori restrictions on the model (e.g., the zeros of the coefficient matrix) are such as to permit only S-transformations upon the matrix. If the identifiable structure is self-contained, there will then be a unique causal ordering associated with it, and this ordering will be invariant under any transformations permitted by the a priori restrictions.[11]

8. Identifiability in Complete Subsets

The relationship, just explored, between causal ordering and identifiability casts some light upon the conditions under which the coefficients of a structure can be determined from data in the case of nonstochastic models. First, some preliminary explanations are necessary.

8.1. We suppose that we have a large number of observations of the simultaneous values of n variables entering in a linear model. Each observation may be regarded as a point in an n-dimensional space whose coordinates are the values of the n variables. We suppose, further, that the model specifies k equations ($k < n$) which are assumed to govern

[11] On the other hand, the causal ordering may be defined even if the structure is not completely identifiable. Since the causal ordering depends only on which subsets of variables appear in which complete subsets of equations, it will also be invariant over the group of R-transformations upon the equations of any complete subset.

the behavior of the variables; any single observation must satisfy the k equations. Under what conditions will the observations be sufficient to determine the unknown coefficients of all k equations, that is, the unknown structure within the model?

The answer to this question can be obtained from geometrical considerations. If each observation is to satisfy all the equations, all observations must lie in a hyperplane of not more than $(n - k)$ dimensions. This hyperplane must be the intersection of the k $(n - 1)$-dimensional hyperplanes representing the k equations. (For example, if there are three variables and two equations, each equation will be represented by a plane, and all observations will lie on the straight line that is the intersection of the two planes.)

Now if the observations do not lie in a hyperplane of *fewer* than $(n - k)$ dimensions, the criteria for identifiability of equations that have been derived for linear stochastic models[12] are also sufficient to assure unique determination of the coefficients of these equations in the present nonstochastic case. For a model satisfying these criteria restricts transformations of the equations to the group of S-transformations (which do not affect the location of the planes represented by the equations), and hence only one set of k admissible hyperplanes can intersect in the $(n - k)$-dimensional hyperplane defined by the observations. That is to say, any other set of k $(n - 1)$-dimensional hyperplanes intersecting in the same $(n - k)$-dimensional hyperplane must consist of linear combinations of the original set, and this possibility is ruled out by the a priori restrictions, specified by the model, that produce identifiability.

However, if the observations are "degenerate" [i.e., lie in a hyperplane of fewer than $(n - 1)$ dimensions], it may be impossible to determine all the coefficients of the structure. Hence, to insure the possibility of determining these coefficients we must require that the variables not be subject to any equations in addition to those of the structure.[13]

8.2. We shall now see how a knowledge of the causal ordering of a set of variables can be used to help determine whether the coefficients of a linear structure governing these variables can be determined. In the discussion of criteria for identifiability of a structural equation by a linear model, given in Chapter II and in Section 4.4 of Chapter VI, a necessary order condition and a necessary and sufficient rank condition for identifiability are derived. For simplicity, in the following discussion

[12] Chapter II, Section 4; Chapter VI, Section 4.4 and Appendix A.

[13] This requirement is a sufficient, but not a necessary, condition for determinacy. If the a priori restrictions are more than the minimum required for identifiability, determinacy may be present even if the variables are subject to additional, unknown restrictions. The problem under discussion here is the question of "confluence," first studied intensively by Frisch [1934].

we shall consider only the order condition. The exposition would be considerably complicated, and the results not materially altered, if the rank condition were included as well. In the following theorem we restate the order condition, which, in view of the discussion of Section 8.1, applies also to the present nonstochastic case.

THEOREM 8.1: *In a linear model with a priori restrictions in the form of exclusions of variables from equations, a necessary condition for the identifiability of the k-th equation of a structure A consisting of m equations in n variables is that at least* $(m - 1)$ *of the variables in A be excluded from the k-th equation.*

It follows immediately that, if A is a self-contained structure, the only equations belonging to it that are identifiable are those containing a single variable (i.e., the equations that constitute complete subsets of zero order). Hence, the prospects of determining the coefficients of a self-contained structure (unless it is made up entirely of one-variable equations) are nil as long as all observations are restricted by the entire system of equations. In fact, in a nonstochastic structure, repeated observations could in this case only produce the same set of values for all variables that was obtained in the first observation. This suggests that we shall need to intervene (see Section 6.2) to "relax" certain of the relationships in order to obtain observations adequate for determining the coefficients of the remaining equations.

In a self-contained structure A consider an identifiable complete subset S of k equations in n variables. [By Theorem 8.1, no equation of S contains more than $(n - k + 1)$ variables.] If we can produce a set of observations of the variables that satisfies these k equations, and no others independent of these, then we can determine the coefficients of S. Now let us add to S any number of additional equations of A which either (1) belong to complete subsets of the same or higher order than S, or (2) do not contain any of the variables of S. Designate by S' this structure (which includes S). Then the equations of S also satisfy the order condition of identifiability in this new system. For the number of variables in S' must exceed the number of variables in S by at least the number of equations added [by (a)]. None of these new variables appear in the equations of S. Therefore, the equations of S still satisfy the condition of Theorem 8.1 and hence, as far as the order condition is concerned, are still identifiable in S'. We have proved

THEOREM 8.2: *If each equation of a complete subset S of a linear structure A is identifiable in that subset, it also satisfies the order condition of identifiability in the larger set S′ that is formed by adding to S any equations* *of A which either* (1) *belong to complete subsets of the same or higher order than S or* (2) *do not contain any of the variables of S.*

By virtue of this theorem we see that in order to permit the determination of the coefficients of an identifiable complete subset of equations we need to relax, at most, the equations that are precedent to this subset. This theorem makes clear the point, referred to in footnote 8, that identifiability has reference to complete subsets of equations.[14] As a matter of fact, the condition of Theorem 8.2, while sufficient for the preservation of the order condition, is not necessary. Without pursuing the matter in detail, we may illustrate the situation with an example. Consider a complete subset S of k equations in k endogenous and m exogenous variables. Suppose the m exogenous variables to be endogenous to a complete subset T (of lower order of precedence) of m equations in $m + p$ $(p \geqslant m)$ variables. Then it is easy to see that, if an equation of S is identifiable in S, it is identifiable in the system consisting of S and T together. To guarantee that the order condition of identifiability will be satisfied when we add new equations to an identifiable complete subset we need merely make sure that we add as many new variables as equations.

8.3. The rationale of the identifiability concept with reference to a complete subset A_k of a self-contained structure A would appear to be the following. We suppose the equations of A_k of order k to be identifiable in A_k, and we wish to determine their coefficients. All the variables of A of order less than k that appear in A_k are exogenous variables relative to A_k. We now suppose that these variables can be arbitrarily varied (by relaxing the structural equations of order less than k) to produce a set of observations of the highest dimensionality consistent with the relations of A_k. This set of observations, together with the condition that the equations of A_k be identifiable, permits us to determine the coefficients.

It is to be noted that we have here again implicitly introduced the notion of an experimenter who, by his direct control over the parameters of the equations in A of order less than k (or by selection of observations provided by "nature"), can bring about independent variations in the variables that are exogenous to A_k. If this procedure is operationally meaningful, the experimenter, confronted with a self-contained structure

[14] In the stochastic case discussed in Chapter II, Section 3, and in Koopmans, Rubin, and Leipnik [1950, Definition 2.1.3.2] this is reflected in the stipulation that structures are regarded as equivalent only if they give rise to identical distributions of the observations for all values of the "exogenous" variables, i.e., exogenous with reference to the subset considered (Definition 3.6 above).

A, can partition the structure into its complete subsets and, isolating each of these from the whole, proceed to determine its parameters. This seems to correspond exactly to the procedure of a physiologist who (in the example used in the introduction) prevents an animal's saliva from reaching the palate and in this way explores the thirst mechanism.

In the stochastic case nature may provide some of the necessary variability of exogenous variables that escape experimental control. In fact, the discussion of identifiability of complete structures in the stochastic case is meaningful only if sufficient independent variation of "exogenous" variables is provided by nature.[15]

9. Causality in Nonlinear Systems

Thus far we have considered only the case of linear, nonstochastic structures. In this chapter the problem of causal ordering in the stochastic case will not be considered, but a few comments may be made on the nonlinear case.

We consider a system of functional relations of the form

$$\phi_i(x, \cdots, x_n) = 0 \qquad (i = 1, \cdots, n). \tag{9.1}$$

We assume further that the system has, at most, a denumerably infinite set of solutions. Now we can again decompose the system into complete subsets of equations of various orders, such that each subset contains as many variables not appearing in subsets of lower order as it contains equations. If appropriate conditions are imposed on our system, this decomposition will again be unique.

In our linear structure we assumed that an experimenter could directly control the parameters appearing in the equations. In the present case we assume that an experimenter can relax or modify any equation or set of equations in the system. In this way we have the same general relationship as in the linear case between the problem of defining the causal ordering and the problem of identification.

10. Conclusion

In this chapter we have defined a concept of causality that corresponds to the intuitive use of that term in scientific discussion. Causality is an asymmetrical relation among certain variables, or subsets of variables, in a self-contained structure. There is no necessary connection between the asymmetry of this relation and asymmetry in time, al-

[15] See footnote 13 above and also Chapter II, footnotes 7 and 13, from which it will be clear that "exogenous" as used in the sentence to which this footnote is appended corresponds to "predetermined" in the context of Chapters II and VI.

though an analysis of the causal structure of dynamical systems in econometrics and physics will show that lagged relations can generally be interpreted as causal relations.

In models specifying which variables are excluded from which equations, the concept of causality has been shown to be intimately connected with the concept of identifiability, although the conditions under which a self-contained structure possesses a nontrivial causal structure are somewhat weaker than the conditions under which it is completely identifiable.

A study of the operational meaning of the causal ordering (or of the concept of "structural" equations) appears to require a metalanguage that permits discussion of the relation between the structure and an experimenter who has direct control over some of the parameters of the structure. As the brief discussion of the nonlinear case implies, the distinction between parameters and variables can be disregarded if the former are regarded as exogenous variables (determined by a larger system) with respect to the latter. In this case the experimenter must be regarded as being able to relax or alter particular equations in this larger system.

REFERENCES

Albert, A. A., *Introduction to Algebraic Theories*, Chicago: University of Chicago Press, 1941, 137 pp.

Bôcher, Maxime, *Introduction to Higher Algebra*, New York: The Macmillan Co., 1907.

Cannon, Walter B., *The Wisdom of the Body*, New York: W. W. Norton & Co., 1939 (revised ed.), 333 pp.

Frisch, Ragnar (1934), *Statistical Confluence Analysis by Means of Complete Regression Systems*, Oslo: Universitetets Økonomiske Institutt, 1934, 192 p.

Goodwin, Richard M., "Dynamical Coupling with Especial Reference to Markets Having Production Lags," *Econometrica*, *15*, July 1947, pp. 181–204.

Haavelmo, Trygve (1944), "The Probability Approach in Econometrics," *Econometrica*, *12*, Supplement, July, 1944, 118 pp. (reprinted as Cowles Commission Paper, New Series, No. 4).

Hurwicz, Leonid (1950b), "Prediction and Least Squares," Chapter VI in *Statistical Inference in Dynamic Economic Models*, Cowles Commission Monograph 10, T. C. Koopmans, ed., New York: John Wiley & Sons, 1950, pp. 266–300.

Koopmans, T. C., H. Rubin, and R. B. Leipnik, "Measuring the Equation Systems of Dynamic Economics," Chapter II in *Statistical Inference in Dynamic Economic Models*, Cowles Commission Monograph 10, T. C. Koopmans, ed., New York: John Wiley & Sons, 1950, pp. 53–237.

Marschak, J. (1950), "Statistical Inference in Economics: An Introduction," Chapter I in *Statistical Inference in Dynamic Economic Models*, Cowles Commission Monograph 10, T. C. Koopmans, ed., New York: John Wiley & Sons, 1950, pp. 1–50.

Orcutt, Guy H. (1952), "Toward Partial Redirection of Econometrics," *Review of Economics and Statistics*, *34*, August 1952.

Simon, Herbert A. (1947), "The Axioms of Newtonian Mechanics," *Philosophical Magazine*, *27*, December 1947, pp. 888–905.

________ (1952), "On the Definition of the Causal Relation," *Journal of Philosophy*, *49*, July 31, 1952.

Tinbergen, Jan (1940) "Econometric Business Cycle Research," *Review of Economic Studies*, 7, 1939–40, pp. 73–90.

Wold, Herman O. A., "Statistical Estimation of Economic Relationships," *Econometrica*, *17*, Supplement, July 1949, pp. 1–22.

3

ON THE COST OF APPROXIMATE SPECIFICATION IN SIMULTANEOUS EQUATION ESTIMATION[1]

By Franklin M. Fisher

This paper considers the question of whether simultaneous equation estimation is possible in view of the fact that specification errors are always made in the construction of models which are supposed only to hold approximately. It is shown that, so far as consistency is concerned, good approximations give good results, but that different estimators have different sensitivities to specification errors of the types considered. It follows that the choice of an estimator may depend crucially on its properties in such situations.

The problem leads naturally to a consideration of the positions of T. C. Liu and H. Wold on the prevalence of underidentification and recursiveness, respectively. The concept of recursiveness is generalized as is the Proximity Theorem, and it is shown that a position intermediate between the two just mentioned is highly tenable, such a position permitting the use of simultaneous equation estimators. The whole problem turns out to be related to the question of almost unilateral coupling of dynamic systems and some conjectures are presented on the possibility of generalizing the recent aggregation and partition theorem of H. Simon and A. Ando.

1. T. C. LIU'S OBJECTIONS TO SIMULTANEOUS EQUATION METHODS

In recent years, there has been growing discussion of the techniques and problems of simultaneous equation estimation.[2] Most of this discussion has been concerned primarily with the techniques of estimation in the overidentified case. An important exception to this, however, is the work of T. C. Liu.

In a 1955 article[3] Liu advanced a disturbing argument which he has vigorously maintained ever since.[4] This argument is disturbing because its premises apparently cannot be doubted and because its conclusions, if accepted, imply that the hope of structural estimation by any techniques whatsoever is forlorn indeed.

It is perhaps best to emphasize immediately that this paper *only* takes issue with the very general and most disturbing form of Liu's position. The

[1] I am indebted to Paul A. Samuelson for suggesting this study. This paper was written while I was a member of the University of Chicago Department of Economics and was supported in part by the Ford Foundation Econometrics Workshop of that department.

[2] See, for example, Sargan [**10**], and Theil [**16**, Chapter 6].

[3] Liu [**7**, pp. 436–437, 464–466].

[4] For example, in his contribution to the Roundtable Discussion of Simultaneous Estimation Techniques at the Chicago Meeting of the Econometric Society, December, 1958 published as [**9**]. Liu has also given his detailed argument in [**8**]. A partial but still inadequate reply along the lines of the present paper is given in S. Valavanis [**18**, pp. 130–132].

fact that I argue that such a *general* position is largely untenable should not be taken to mean that I think the problems to which Liu calls attention are not important in many particular instances. Some of these Liu has pointed out.

The argument is as follows. Econometric models are only approximations to reality. Of necessity, they abstract from the real world by limiting the number of variables included in each equation and in the system as a whole. In fact, however, there are always more variables "really" in each equation —either variables included in other equations of the model or variables excluded altogether therefrom—than are assumed in the practical approximations. Furthermore, the equations stated in the model are not a complete set of equations. In fact, other, outside equations always exist, either relating variables in the model alone or relating them to unincluded variables.

Now, Liu goes on to argue, these points have serious consequences which are of three types. First, the usual form of *a priori* restriction used for identification—the restriction that some parameters in a structural equation are zero, that is, that some variables included elsewhere in the system do not enter into that equation—is likely to be incorrect. Such restrictions, at best, will only hold approximately, and approximately is not good enough. If the variables in question really belong in the equation being studied, then that equation is underidentified and its parameters cannot be estimated by any reasonable technique.

Secondly, the existence of other variables in the equation that are not included elsewhere in the system, together with the existence of unincluded equations relating those variables to the included ones or relating the included variables to each other, means that the number of equations in the system has been understated so that the necessary order condition for identifiability[5]—which runs in terms of the number of *a priori* restrictions and the number of equations—is not satisfied in fact. Finally, few variables are truly exogenous to the complete system; to count only the explicitly stated equations is to treat endogenous variables as exogenous. Once again it follows that identification and, *a fortiori*, overidentification is the unusual case and underidentification the usual one.

Therefore, says Liu, the current emphasis on techniques of estimation in overidentified systems is entirely misplaced. Structural estimation is generally not possible in simultaneous systems, and only reduced forms can be obtained. Furthermore, unrestricted least squares estimation of the reduced form is the appropriate method, for restricting the reduced form by

[5] See Koopmans, Rubin and Leipnik [**5**, p. 79 and pp. 81–82]. Actually, Liu generally states the order condition in terms of the number of endogenous variables included in and the number of exogenous variables excluded from a given equation, which is an equivalent statement.

the *a priori* restrictions not only adds no more information, it is positively harmful, as it adds *mis*information. Forecasting should therefore always be done with the unrestricted reduced form which, as is well known, has smallest error variance for the sample observations, as there is no reason to expect mistakenly oversimplified and restricted models to do as well or better.

Now, this is a powerful and disturbing argument. There can be no doubt that econometric models do in fact abstract from reality in the way described by Liu and thus that *a priori* restrictions which exclude variables from equations are frequently misspecified. Further, there can be no doubt that Liu is largely correct in stating that the treatment of certain variables as exogenous is also likely to be misspecification. The economic system even considered as a whole is embedded in a far larger socio-physical framework. If Liu is right in his conclusions, then there must be serious doubt as to the possibility of structural estimation.

Nor do two counter-observations which might be advanced here seem very helpful in a direct way. The first of these is that it has now been shown that *a priori* restrictions of a far more general kind than those considered by Liu may be used for identification.[6] The usual case is certainly the one which Liu considers, and even the use of inequalities (which are common restrictions) will not directly help very much.

The second observation is that variables need not be exogenous to the system as a whole to be exogenous with respect to some subset of equations. It is therefore not sufficient to argue that few variables are exogenous to the complete system; one must also hold that there are excluded equations specifically providing some "feedback" effect (however weak) from endogenous to assumed exogenous variables or connecting the latter with variables influencing the error terms. Otherwise, the system may be what we shall define below as "block recursive." However, since the existence of such excluded equations cannot be denied in general—especially equations connecting the variables in the error terms of the original system and the exogenous variables—this remark is also not directly helpful save as a reservation to Liu's argument in special cases.

While these counter-arguments are, however, not of much help directly, they do provide aid in an indirect way, for they indicate that the problem may not be quite so dichotomous as Liu makes it. Thus, in the next section, we use the above mentioned results on general restrictions to show that the proper question is not whether certain parameters assumed to be zero are in fact so; the issue is rather whether they are in some sense sufficiently small—whether the restriction that the corresponding variables do not appear is or is not a good approximation. We show that the problem is not

[6] See Fisher [**2**].

the discontinuous one of just or overidentification if the restrictions hold exactly and underidentification if they do not, but rather one of diminishing estimation inconsistency as the restrictions are better and better approximations.

Similarly, in later sections, we go on to consider the problems of omitted variables and of exogenous variables and show that the issue is not whether a variable assumed exogenous is "really" so, or whether omitted variables "really" have zero coefficients but rather whether these things are sufficiently so in an approximate sense. We thus justify the practice of breaking down a complete system into parts by assuming certain variables exogenous that are only approximately so, and by assuming certain variables absent that truly appear with very small coefficients.

These results have several consequences. First, of course, structural estimation is seen to be entirely possible in general, so that discussion and criticism must be directed toward the goodness or badness of the approximate assumptions in a particular case and not toward the truth or falsity thereof.

Secondly (and this is a somewhat different way of looking at the matter), we may say that whereas, hitherto, estimation techniques required the knowledge or assumption that certain things (parameters, covariances, and so forth) were zero, the results here presented allow estimation with negligible inconsistency provided only that such things are known (or assumed) to be small. Since the latter kind of knowledge is easier to come by than the former and the assumption involved is likely to be held with greater confidence, this is a reassuring and perhaps not insignificant result.

Thirdly, even if it is considered obvious that small errors have small consequences,[7] it is always of interest to know exactly where errors must be small and thus to clarify assumptions.

Finally, an objection to simultaneous equation estimation somewhat better known than that of Liu is the position of H. Wold[8] which states that the real world is not truly simultaneous at all, but that causation is unilateral and that true systems are always recursive. Part of the Liu objection, on the other hand, can be crudely put as the argument that the real world is always more simultaneous than we think—that no economic model ever fully states the true simultaneity—and therefore that estimation is impossible since the world is truly underidentified. It would seem at first glance as though no middle ground between these two positions is possible, that once the possibility of simultaneous causation is admitted, one cannot stop short

[7] That the obvious is not always true in this area has been shown by R. H. Strotz who has recently provided us with an example of a case where the limit of the maximum likelihood estimator as specification error goes to zero is *not* the maximum likelihood estimator of the limit. See [**14**].

[8] [**19**, chapter 2], for example.

of an explicit statement of the total set of equations explaining the socio-physical universe. We shall see, however, that this is not the case; a position intermediate between Wold and Liu is indeed possible, for systems—and highly plausible systems at that—do exist in which simultaneity is present but not completely overriding. Estimation of the usual simultaneous type is thus entirely possible.[9]

2. MISSPECIFICATION IN THE *a priori* RESTRICTIONS

We first consider in isolation the problem of the misspecification of the *a priori* restrictions. Throughout this section it will be assumed that the system is correctly specified save for the *a priori* restrictions. We shall remove this assumption below.

Consider the system of equations:

$$u(t) = Ax(t) \tag{2.1}$$

where $u(t)$ is an $(m+1)$ dimensional column vector of disturbances, A is an $(m+1) \times (n+1)$ matrix of coefficients with first row A_1, and $x(t)$ is an $(n+1)$ dimensional column vector of variables. Without loss of generality we may renumber the variables so that

$$x(t) = \begin{bmatrix} y(t) \\ \hline z(t) \end{bmatrix} \tag{2.2}$$

where $y(t)$ is an $(m+1)$ dimensional column vector of endogenous variables and $z(t)$ an $(n-m)$ dimensional column vector of exogenous variables. Then A may be partitioned accordingly into:

$$A = [B \mid G] \tag{2.3}$$

where B is a square nonsingular matrix of rank $m+1$. We further assume that there are no linear identities connecting the exogenous variables.

Now, let ϕ' be a matrix with K columns and $n+1$ rows, where $n \geqslant K \geqslant m$. Each column of ϕ' is to contain precisely one unit element and have all other elements zero.[10] Impose (incorrectly) the *a priori* restrictions on A_1:

$$A_1\phi' = 0\,, \tag{2.4}$$

[9] Although, of course, this does not remove the possibility that either Liu or Wold is correct; the real world may be constructed as one of them describes it. The point is that it need not be so constructed and that it is very plausible that it should not.

[10] In fact, ϕ' can be any constant matrix so that all remarks and theorems apply *mutatis mutandis* to any consistent set of misspecified linear homogeneous restrictions. The case given in the text is the usual one of excluding variables from equations and is thus of greatest interest. Linear but inhomogeneous restrictions could obviously be handled with but a slight change in notation. Nonlinear restrictions present certain formal complexities which would unduly obscure the discussion, but the basic theorem is always the same. For a general treatment of the latter two types of restrictions see Fisher [**2**].

and assume that the rank of the matrix $A\phi'$ is m, so that the necessary and sufficient conditions for unique identifiability of A_1 are satisified if (2.4) holds. Select some endogenous variable not excluded from the first equation of (2.1) by (2.4)—of course, such must exist—and normalize by setting the corresponding element of A_1 equal to unity.[11] Without loss of generality, we may assume that it is the first variable which is thus treated. Extend the definition of ϕ' by adding to it a new first column which has a one at the top and zeros elsewhere. ϕ' now has $K+1$ columns and (2.4) is replaced by

$$A_1\phi' = (1,0,\ldots,0) . \tag{2.4'}$$

It is easy to see that the new $A\phi'$ must have rank $m+1$.

We now assume that (2.4) and hence (2.4′) are misspecified so that the variables excluded from the first equation of (2.1) are really in that equation, so that (2.4) is only approximately true at best. Let the *true a priori* restrictions corresponding to (2.4′) be

$$A_1\phi' = (1\ \bar{\eta}) \tag{2.5}$$

where $\bar{\eta}$ is a K-dimensional row vector.

It will be convenient at this stage to rewrite the first equation of (2.1). Let $y_1(t)$ be the first variable. Let $y^1(t)$ be the vector of endogenous variables whose coefficients in the first equation are not specified by (2.5); similarly, let $z^1(t)$ be the vector of exogenous variables whose coefficients in the first equation are not specified by (2.5). Let B_1^1 and G_1^1 be the corresponding vectors of true coefficients. Finally, let $w(t)$ be the vector of variables (other than $y_1(t)$) whose coefficients are specified by (2.5). Then the first equation of (2.1) can be written:

$$y_1(t) + B_1^1 y^1(t) + G_1^1 z^1(t) + \bar{\eta}w(t) = u_1(t) . \tag{2.6}$$

Now, let $a_{1j}(\eta,\bar{\eta})$ be the probability limit—if it exists—of the estimate of A_{1j} obtained by imposing

$$A_1\phi' = (1\ \eta) \tag{2.7}$$

when (2.5) is true and using one of the standard estimation techniques.[12] Thus, $a_{1j}(0,\bar{\eta})$ is the probability limit—if it exists—of the estimate of A_{1j} obtained by imposing (2.4′) and using one of the standard techniques.

[11] By Fisher [**2**, Lemmas 4 and 5, pp. 436–437], this is always possible no matter what ϕ' is, so long as the rank condition holds.

[12] It is shown in what follows that two different estimation techniques (in particular, two-stage least squares and limited information) for both of which $a_{1j}(0,0) = A_{1j}$ (in general, $a_{1j}(\bar{\eta},\bar{\eta}) = A_{1j}$), may have different $a_{1j}(\eta,\bar{\eta})$ for $\eta \neq \bar{\eta}$. We shall discuss this below; however, it would unduly complicate the notation to take explicit account of it here.

Similarly, $a_{1j}(\bar{\eta},\bar{\eta})$ is the probability limit—if it exists—of the estimate of A_{1j} obtained by imposing the true restrictions.

In what follows, we restrict our attention to estimators of Theil's k-class.[13] This class includes two-stage least squares and limited information, maximum likelihood as well as other estimators. Similar theorems could obviously be proved for estimators not in the k-class, save that for full information, maximum likelihood misspecifications elsewhere in the system must be assumed to go to zero.

Now, choose a set of T values for $u(t)$ and for those predetermined variables which are not lagged endogenous variables; further, choose a set of initial values for those predetermined variables which are lagged endogenous variables. The values of the endogenous variables are then completely determined by the matrix A. We shall assume that all asymptotic variances and covariances (between variables or between variables and residuals) are finite.

Next, fix all rows of A other than the first and all elements of B_1^1 and G_1^1. Consider an infinite sequence of equation systems differing only in $\bar{\eta}$, such that $\bar{\eta}$ converges to the zero vector as we move along the sequence. We shall assume that there exists a neighborhood of the zero vector, such that all systems in the sequence for which $\bar{\eta}$ lies within that neighborhood are stable.

This assumption requires some discussion. We shall show that it is a sufficient condition for $a_{1j}(0,\bar{\eta})$ to approach A_{1j} as a limit as $\bar{\eta}$ goes to zero, and hence that it implies that simultaneous equation estimators are only negligibly inconsistent for all elements of $\bar{\eta}$ sufficiently small (i.e., for (2.4′) a good enough approximation to (2.5)). The assumption may not be necessary, however; indeed, it seems quite clear that the theorem in question holds provided that there exists a neighborhood of zero for which consistent estimation is possible under correct specification (provided that identifiability is present). Whether there exist unstable systems for which the usual estimators are not consistent under correct specification is as yet an open question save in special cases. Our assumption should be regarded as a declaration that we are not here concerned with answering this question, but that we are dealing with only one problem at a time.[14]

[13] [**16**, pp. 227–229, 334–336].

[14] I am indebted to H. Uzawa for calling this problem to my attention by pointing out the incompleteness of an earlier proof that ignored it and to J. D. Sargan for helpful discussion of the present proof. The stability assumption is implicitly made in all later theorems.

In general, the proof given will be valid for the non-stable consistent estimator case if T can be replaced by some $f(T)$ such that the required probability limits exist and are nonzero. We should ordinarily expect this, provided that the estimator involved is consistent under correct specification for $\bar{\eta}$ in some neighborhood of the zero vector.

THEOREM 1.

$$\lim_{\bar{\eta}\to 0} |a_{1j}(0,\bar{\eta}) - A_{1j}| = 0 \textit{ for all } j = 1,\ldots, n+1 .$$

Proof: It is shown in [**2**, Theorem 13, p. 444] that a necessary and sufficient condition for the identifiability of A_1 under (2.5) is that the rank of $A\phi'$ be $m+1$. We have already observed that this is the case for $\bar{\eta} = 0$; it must therefore also be the case for $\bar{\eta}$ sufficiently close to zero, for the elements of $A\phi'$ are either constant or continuous functions of $\bar{\eta}$ and the value of a determinant is a continuous function of its elements. Hence, for $\bar{\eta}$ sufficiently close to zero, A_1 is identifiable under (2.5).

Now, the theorem is trivially true for those elements of A_1 which are also elements of $\bar{\eta}$. We may therefore restrict our attention to the elements of $\overset{1}{B_1}$ and $\overset{1}{G_1}$.

Following Theil,[15] define a new endogenous variable, $q(t)$, as:

$$q(t) \equiv y_1(t) + \bar{\eta}w(t) \tag{2.8}$$

and rewrite (2.6) as:

$$q(t) + \overset{1}{B_1}\overset{1}{y}(t) + \overset{1}{G_1}\overset{1}{z}(t) = u_1(t) . \tag{2.9}$$

We call the system of equations formed by (2.8) and (2.1) with the first equation of the latter set replaced by (2.9) the *auxiliary* system to (2.1). It is evident that (2.1) and its auxiliary system are equivalent and that the inhomogeneous restrictions (2.5) corresponding to (2.1) have been replaced with equivalent restrictions of the usual zero-coefficient type in the auxiliary system. Further, observe that the variables that are included in $y^1(t)$ and $z^1(t)$ do not depend on the value of $\bar{\eta}$ or on statements about that value. That is, the auxiliary equation (2.9) differs from the original equation (2.6) with the misspecified restrictions $\bar{\eta} = 0$ imposed only in that $q(t)$ and not $y_1(t)$ appears.

Now consider an estimator of the k-class. Let $\overset{1}{a_1}(\eta,\bar{\eta})$ be the column vector of those $a_{1j}(\eta,\bar{\eta})$ corresponding to the elements of $\overset{1}{B_1}$ and $\overset{1}{G_1}$. Let V be a matrix of observations on the residuals from the least squares estimates of the reduced form equations explaining the elements of $y^1(t)$. Let all other capital letters denote the observation matrices of the corresponding lower case variables. Then the typical k-class estimator of (2.9) is given by:

$$\begin{bmatrix} (Y^1)'Y^1 - kV'V & (Y^1)'Z^1 \\ (Z^1)'Y^1 & (Z^1)'Z^1 \end{bmatrix}^{-1} \begin{bmatrix} (Y^1 - kV)'Q \\ (Z^1)'Q \end{bmatrix} . \tag{2.10}$$

Letting H be the matrix whose inverse is taken, this may be rewritten:

$$(TH^{-1})(1/T\begin{bmatrix} (Y^1 - kV)'Q \\ (Z^1)'Q \end{bmatrix}) \tag{2.11}$$

[15] [**16**, pp. 341–342].

and, under the stability and identifiability assumptions made, the probability limit of (TH^{-1}) exists for $\bar{\eta}$ sufficiently close to zero, as does the probability limit of the second factor. Further, the probability limit of the product is $\overset{1}{a_1}(\bar{\eta},\bar{\eta})$ and

$$(2.12) \qquad \overset{1}{a_1}(\bar{\eta},\bar{\eta}) = \begin{bmatrix} (B_1^1)' \\ (G_1^1)' \end{bmatrix}$$

provided that the probability limit of k is one.

There are now two cases to consider. The first case is that in which the probability limit is independent of η—that is, independent of our misspecification. This is the case of two-stage least squares (k identically equal to one) and of certain other members of the k-class.[16] The case in which the probability limit of k does depend on $\bar{\eta}$ is exemplified by limited information, maximum likelihood, and we shall restrict our attention in the second case to this example.

Suppose now that the probability limit of k is independent of η. Form the k-class estimator of (2.6) on the assumption that $\bar{\eta} = 0$—i.e., under misspecification. This estimator can be written as:

$$(2.13) \qquad (TH^{-1})(1/T\begin{bmatrix} (Y^1 - kV)'Y_1 \\ (Z^1)'Y_1 \end{bmatrix}).$$

The crucial point here is that H is unaltered by the misspecification; hence the probability limit of (TH^{-1}) exists as does the probability limit of the second factor which involves only asymptotic moment matrices. The probability limit of the product is $\overset{1}{a_1}(0,\bar{\eta})$, and we have:

$$(2.14) \qquad \overset{1}{a_1}(\bar{\eta},\bar{\eta}) - \overset{1}{a_1}(0,\bar{\eta}) = \operatorname{P\,lim}\left\{(TH^{-1})\,(1/T\begin{bmatrix} (Y^1 - kV)'W \\ (Z^1)'W \end{bmatrix})\,(\bar{\eta}')\right\},$$

and this clearly approaches zero as a limit as $\bar{\eta}$ goes to zero, thus proving the theorem in this case in view of (2.12).

The case of limited information, maximum likelihood is similar, save that here k is not independent of η, since it is equal to $(1 + \varrho)$ where ϱ is the smallest root of the determinantal equation

$$(2.15) \qquad |M_1 - (1 + \varrho)M| = 0$$

where M_1 and M are different for the auxiliary and the misspecified systems. For the auxiliary system, they are the moment matrices of the estimated residuals in the least squares regressions of $q(t)$ and the elements of $y^1(t)$ on the elements of $z^1(t)$ and on all the exogenous variables, respectively. For the misspecified system, on the other hand, they are the same with $y_1(t)$ in place of $q(t)$. Of course, the two coincide for $\bar{\eta} = 0$.

[16] For example, where k depends only on the number of variables in $y^1(t)$ and $z^1(t)$ and on the total number of exogenous variables in the system. See [**16**, p. 229].

The probability limits of M_1 and M and hence of ϱ and k exist in either case. It is clear, moreover, that the two cases differ only in the first rows and columns of M_1 and M. As $\bar{\eta}$ approaches zero, these first rows and columns approach each other, in view of (2.8), as do the probability limits of the corresponding k's. For $\bar{\eta}$ sufficiently close to zero, therefore, the probability limit of k in the misspecified system will be sufficiently close to that in the auxiliary system (unity) to insure the existence of the probability limit of (TH^{-1}) when H is computed using the k corresponding to the misspecified system. The proof now proceeds as before.

Some remarks are now in order. First, it is clear that the theorem could easily be generalized to the case where $\bar{\eta}$ approaches η for given η. We should then merely have $(\bar{\eta} - \eta)'$ in place of $\bar{\eta}'$ on the extreme right of (2.14). Moreover, the same generalization shows that the theorem remains true if we allow η to approach $\bar{\eta}$ for fixed $\bar{\eta}$, that is, allow our statement to approach the truth rather than (as above) allowing the truth to approach our statement. (We have adopted the latter course because of the context of the problem.)

Secondly, we have now shown that it is not the case that the use of *a priori* restrictions which only hold approximately necessarily leads to the abandonment of simultaneous equation methods of estimation. It is true that such use leads to inconsistency in the estimates, but, provided the approximations involved are good enough, such inconsistencies will be negligible.

What is involved in deciding whether particular approximations are "good enough" is an interesting but complex and difficult question. It has been answered by Theil[17] for the case of a single equation with misspecified *a priori* restrictions. The answer for simultaneous equations is far more difficult to obtain and is a fit subject for further work, especially in view of the fact (brought out in the above proof) that different estimators may have different sensitivities to this kind of misspecification. We shall return to this below. Here we are concerned only to show that some "good enough" approximation does exist, so that simultaneous equation methods need not be discarded simply because restrictions are only approximate. It may indeed be true that many or all *a priori* restrictions actually used are not "good enough" approximations (in the sense that they lead to inconsistencies too large to be tolerated); however, this must be decided on a case by case basis and no general *a priori* argument can be made to this effect.

Thirdly, it follows from our theorem and discussion that Liu is wrong in claiming that the unrestricted least squares estimates of the reduced form should be used for prediction because the use of *a priori* restrictions adds only misinformation. The reduced form matrix is a continuous transformation

[17] [**16**, pp. 331–333].

of the coefficient matrix of the system; it follows that as inconsistencies in the estimates of the elements of the latter go to zero, so do inconsistencies in the estimates of the reduced form coefficients. The use of *a priori* restrictions which are approximate thus leads to negligible inconsistencies in such estimates also—for good enough approximations. It follows that the restricted estimates of the reduced form obtained from structural equation estimates converge more rapidly to probability limits that differ slightly or negligibly from the true reduced form coefficients than the unrestricted least squares reduced form estimates converge to the true reduced form parameters. Here is a case in which a slightly or negligibly inconsistent estimator is more efficient than a consistent estimator. In applying the restrictions in the estimation of the reduced form, one trades consistency for efficiency. Such a trade of precise accuracy for convenient closeness is always the price of approximate assumptions. Provided the approximations are close enough, the efficiency properties of simultaneous equation estimators will more than compensate for their inconsistency. Here again, there is no general *a priori* argument that approximations will not be "close enough"; this can only be decided in particular cases.

3. BLOCK RECURSIVE SYSTEMS: OMITTED VARIABLES

The last section considered the effect of misspecification in the *a priori* restrictions alone. Throughout this section, unless otherwise stated, we assume that the *a priori* restrictions are correctly specified and turn to the next type of approximate misspecification considered by Liu.

It will be convenient to alter our notation somewhat and to define some new concepts. A triangular matrix is a square matrix with zeros everywhere below the main diagonal. As is well known, an equation system whose matrix is triangular is a recursive system; its equations may be treated singly or sequentially rather than simultaneously and may be estimated by least squares. The equations of the system form a unilateral causal chain.[18]

We now generalize these concepts in the following way. For any matrix, M, let $r(M)$ be the number of rows of M and $c(M)$ be the number of columns. Consider a square matrix

$$W = \begin{bmatrix} R^1 & S^1 & & & \\ 0^{21} & R^2 & S^2 & & \\ 0^{31} & 0^{32} & R^3 & S^3 & \\ \cdot & \cdot & \cdot & \cdot & \\ \cdot & \cdot & \cdot & \cdot & \cdot \\ \cdot & \cdot & \cdot & \cdot & \cdot \\ 0^{N1} & 0^{N2} & 0^{N3} & \cdot & \cdot \quad R^N \end{bmatrix} \tag{3.1}$$

[18] See H. Wold in association with L. Juréen [**19**, pp. 14, 49–53, and elsewhere].

where the R^i are nonsingular (and hence square) matrices and the S^i are matrices which may or may not be zero. The 0^{ij} are zero matrices; clearly,

$$\begin{aligned} r(0^{ij}) &= r(R^i)\,, \\ c(0^{ij}) &= c(R^j) = r(R^j) \end{aligned} \qquad (i,j = 1,\dots,N)\,. \tag{3.2}$$

Such a matrix is said to be *block triangular*; it is triangular in blocks rather than in single elements.[19] The reason for imposing nonsingularity on the R^i is one of convenience and will be apparent shortly.

Observe that each of the submatrices:

$$R^N, \begin{bmatrix} R^{N-1} & S^{N-1} \\ 0^{NN-1} & R^N \end{bmatrix}, \begin{bmatrix} R^{N-2} & S^{N-2} & \\ 0^{N-1N-2} & R^{N-1} & S^{N-1} \\ 0^{NN-2} & 0^{NN-1} & R^N \end{bmatrix}, \dots, W$$

is square and nonsingular and is block triangular (the last property holding in an empty sense for R^N which has only one block).

Now consider the equation system

$$u = Ax\,. \tag{3.3}$$

(We have dropped the time argument for convenience; it is to be understood.) As in the last section, partition A and x to correspond to endogenous and exogenous variables, the endogenous variables coming first. Thus rewrite (3.3) as:

$$u = [B \ \ G]\begin{bmatrix} y \\ z \end{bmatrix}. \tag{3.4}$$

Now assume that B is block triangular with N blocks and partition u and y into N corresponding blocks, thus:

$$u = \begin{bmatrix} u^1 \\ u^2 \\ u^3 \\ \vdots \\ u^N \end{bmatrix}; \quad y = \begin{bmatrix} y^1 \\ y^2 \\ y^3 \\ \vdots \\ y^N \end{bmatrix}. \tag{3.5}$$

We call an equation such as (3.3) in which the part of the coefficient matrix corresponding to the endogenous variables is block triangular, *block*

[19] The term is evidently a natural one. Since first using it, it has been pointed out to me by Jerome Rothenberg that "block triangularity" has already been suggested by Walter Jacobs and used by George Dantzig to describe rather similar matrices occurring in linear programming. (See Dantzig [**1**, p. 176]). Save for the requirement that the R^i be nonsingular, my block triangularity property is the same as the well-known property of decomposability (See Solow [**13**]), a fact that will be of interest below.

recursive. Any equation system (block recursive or not) which has a square coefficient matrix (in our notation, where G is null) will be called *self-contained.*

Block recursive systems have the property that—given the exogenous variables, if any—the variables in y^N are (stochastically) determined solely by the equations corresponding to B^N; the variables in y^{N-1} are then determined by the exogenous variables, the variables in y^N, and the equations corresponding to B^{N-1}; and so forth. Accordingly, it is clear that if all the equations that involve the variables have been included in the system and the system itself correctly specified, the parameters of the subset of equations with u^j as left hand member (say the jth subset) may be estimated with regard only for the equations in that subset and without regard for the existence of the remaining equations.[20] The variables in any y^i may clearly be considered exogenous to the jth subset of equations provided that $i > j$, or to any union of such subsets as may be seen by solving (3.4) for y in terms of z and u. It is clear that ordinary recursive systems are special cases of block recursive systems with the B^i single rows and the 0^{ij} single elements.

The analysis of causation for self-contained block recursive systems has been given by H. Simon.[21] He argues (considering more general systems as well) that the variables in y^N can plausibly be regarded as "causing" the variables in y^{N-1} in such a case; the variables in y^N and y^{N-1} can be regarded as "causing" the variables in y^{N-2}; and so forth, a concept of causality which Strotz and Wold have aptly termed "vector causality."[22] The dynamic properties of block recursive systems are obviously closely related to those of unilaterally coupled systems considered by R. Goodwin;[23] indeed, block

[20] This assumes that the elements of any u^i are independent of the elements of any u^j for $j \neq i$. Actually, since we shall be explicitly investigating the effects of all omitted variables, we could well assume that all elements of u are independent of each other. This is an innocuous assumption since any dependence here can always be expressed in terms of some variable wrongly omitted from two or more equations (and thus present in the error term). Of course, this assumption is only meant to apply to cases where explicit account is taken of all omitted variables. Aside from being innocuous, however, this strong assumption is unnecessary; all that is needed for the results is the assumption in the first sentence of this footnote for block recursive systems and for systems supposed to be block recursive. A similar problem arises with ordinary recursive systems, and a similar assumption is always made in practice —although without the explicit sufficient justification given here, since omitted variables are not excluded from the error term. See Wold and Juréen [**19**, pp. 52–53]. Of course, the theorems given below provide justification for this practice when the specification of no omitted variables is approximately correct.

[21] [**11**]. The question of whether any system is really part of a self-contained system is a metaphysical one which need not concern us here.

[22] [**15**, pp. 421–422].

[23] [**3**]. See also Solow [**13**].

recursive systems are the generalization of unilaterally coupled systems to more than two markets. We shall have something to say about such dynamic properties in a later section.

We turn now to the second issue of specification error raised by Liu, that of the incorrect or only approximately correct omission of relevant variables from the whole system of equations being studied. As observed above, Liu argues that such omitted variables are likely to be connected with the included variables by equations other than those explicitly included. It will be convenient both now and later to frame our discussion (which is quite general) in terms of block recursive systems.

Consider the system of equations explicitly under investigation:

$$u^2 = [D^{21}\ B^2\ G^2] \begin{bmatrix} x^1 \\ y^2 \\ z^2 \end{bmatrix} \tag{3.6}$$

where B^2 is square and nonsingular; G^2 and D^{21} are rectangular; and the reason for the superscripts will appear shortly. In (3.6), y^2 is a vector of explicitly endogenous and z^2 a vector of explicitly assumed exogenous variables. x^1, on the other hand, is a vector of variables assumed absent from the system. In other words, D^{21} is incorrectly assumed to be a zero matrix.

In what follows we shall assume that the specification of z^2 as a vector of exogenous variables is correct, leaving the alternative case to a later section. We further suppose that sufficient *a priori* restrictions of the usual type have been imposed on the first equation of the system to identify it when D^{21} is in fact zero, that is (where ϕ' is, as before, the transposed matrix of the coefficients of the restrictions), we suppose that the rank of the matrix $[B^2\, G^2]\phi'$ is $r(B^2)-1$. For the present we continue to assume that all such *a priori* restrictions are true ones so that the problems studied in the last section do not arise.

We now consider all equations relating the variables of x^1 to the included variables of y^2 and z^2. We do this in the following way: consider equations explaining each of the elements of x^1 (y^2 is explained by (3.6) and z^2 is exogenous). If such equations involve variables not in (3.6) expand the definition of x^1 and hence of D^{21} to include all such variables. Continue this process until either there are as many new independent equations as there are variables in the expanded x^1, or until all variables left unexplained in the expanded x^1 are exogenous to the entire system. (There may be very many equations in the result.) Now partition x^1 into a vector of variables endogenous to the complete system, y^1, and a vector (possibly null) of variables exogenous to the complete system, z^1. Correspondingly, partition D^{21} into E^{21} and F^{21}. The complete system of which (3.6) is a part is thus:

$$(3.7)\qquad \begin{bmatrix} u^1 \\ u^2 \end{bmatrix} = \left[\begin{array}{c|c|c|c} B^1 & H^1 & G^1 & \\ \hline E^{21} & F^{21} & B^2 & G^2 \end{array}\right] \begin{bmatrix} y^1 \\ z^1 \\ y^2 \\ z^2 \end{bmatrix}$$

where B^1 is square and corresponds to y^1. We shall assume B^1 to be non-singular for the present. It is easily seen that $r(E^{21}) = r(B^2)$ and $c(E^{21}) = r(B^1)$. It is thus clear (if you like, reshuffle columns to put all exogenous variables together) that the assumption that $E^{21} = 0$ is the assumption that the system (3.7) is block recursive so that the subsystem (3.6) can be estimated in isolation. Of course, the assumption that $F^{21} = 0$ is the additional assumption that all exogenous variables that appear in (3.7) have been explicitly included in (3.6).

Let n be the total number of variables and m be the total number of equations in (3.7). Let:

$$(3.8)\qquad A = [D^{21}\ B^2\ G^2] = [E^{21}\ F^{21}\ B^2\ G^2]$$

and consider the problem of estimating the first row of A, as before, A_1. Let the probability limit of the estimate of A_{1j} obtained by assuming that $D^{21} = 0$ and applying a standard technique[24] be $\alpha_{1j}(0,D^{21})$. As in the previous section, choose an indefinitely large set of values for u^1 and u^2 and for those elements of z^1 and z^2 that are not lagged endogenous variables; choose a set of initial values for all lagged endogenous variables in z^1 and z^2. Now fix B^1, H^1, G^1, B^2 and G^2, and consider a collection of systems differing only in D^{21}. Consider an infinite sequence of such systems such that D^{21} approaches the zero matrix. We prove that the inconsistency involved in assuming D^{21} zero—that is, in omitting x^1 from the equations—goes to zero as D^{21} goes to zero, as the approximation involved gets better and better.

THEOREM 2.

$$\lim_{D^{21}\to 0} |\alpha_{1j}(0,D^{21}) - A_{1j}| = 0 \textit{ for all } j = 1,\ldots,n\,.$$

Proof: We prove the theorem by showing it to be a special case of Theorem 1. Estimation of A_1 on the assumption that $D_1^{21} = 0$ is estimation applying as many new (though incorrect) *a priori* restrictions as there are elements in D_1^{21}, i.e., as many restrictions as there are variables in x^1. By assumption, however, there are already available at least $r(B^2) - 1$ restrictions on the other elements of A_1; hence the necessary order condition for the identifiability of A_1 *considered as a part of* (3.7) *rather than just of* (3.6) is certainly satisfied when $D_1^{21} = 0$ since

$$(3.9)\quad r(B^2) - 1 + c(D^{21}) \geqslant r(B^2) - 1 + c(E^{21}) = r(B^2) + r(B^1) - 1 = m - 1.$$

[24] A similar remark to that made in footnote 12 above applies here.

If F^{21} is not null, there are more restrictions than necessary (as there may also be if there were more than $r(B^2)-1$ original restrictions).

We must now show that the necessary and sufficient rank condition is also satisfied when $D_1^{21} = 0$. Arrange the restrictions $D_1^{21} = 0$ so that the coefficients thereof form a unit matrix with $c(D^{21})$ rows and columns. The rank condition will be satisfied if the rank of the matrix:

$$(3.10) \qquad \begin{bmatrix} B^1 & H^1 & G^1 \\ E^{21} & F^{21} & B^2 \mid G^2 \end{bmatrix} \begin{bmatrix} I & 0 \\ 0 & \phi' \end{bmatrix} = \begin{bmatrix} B^1 & H^1 & G^1\phi' \\ E^{21} & F^{21} & (B^2\, G^2)\phi' \end{bmatrix}$$

is $m-1$.

To see that this is the case for D^{21} sufficiently close to zero, strike out the row of the above product matrix that corresponds to A_1, denoting the result by the use of lower case instead of upper case letters. Further, select $r(B^2)-1$ independent columns from ϕ' and assume (for convenience only) that these are the only columns in ϕ'. Consider the following submatrix of the above matrix:

$$(3.11) \qquad \begin{bmatrix} B^1 & G^1\phi' \\ e^{21} & (b^2\ \ g^2)\phi' \end{bmatrix} = W(e^{21}), \quad \text{say} .$$

This is $(m-1) \times (m-1)$. Now consider $W(0)$, and suppose that it were singular. Then a nonzero row vector, say, λ, would exist such that $\lambda W(0) = 0$. Partition λ into $(\lambda^1\ \lambda^2)$ corresponding to the two rows of blocks in $W(0)$. Singularity of $W(0)$ then implies that

$$(3.12) \qquad (\lambda^1\ \lambda^2) \begin{bmatrix} B^1 & G^1\phi' \\ 0 & (b^2\ \ g^2)\phi' \end{bmatrix} = 0$$

and hence that

$$(3.13) \qquad \lambda^1 B^1 + \lambda^2 0 = \lambda^1 B^1 = 0$$

which is impossible unless $\lambda^1 = 0$, since B^1 was assumed nonsingular. It thus follows that

$$(3.14) \qquad \lambda^1 G^1\phi' + \lambda^2(b^2\ \ g^2)\phi' = \lambda^2(b^2\ \ g^2)\phi' = 0 .$$

This is impossible, however, unless $\lambda^2 = 0$, for $(b^2\ \ g^2)\phi'$ is also nonsingular by assumption. Hence $\lambda = 0$ and $W(0)$ must be nonsingular. It now follows immediately that $W(e^{21})$ must also be nonsingular for D^{21} (and hence e^{21}) sufficiently close to zero, for the determinant of a matrix is a continuous function of its elements. Therefore the product matrix in (3.10) has rank $m-1$ for D^{21} sufficiently close to zero and the rank condition is satisfied.

This being the case, estimation of A_1 on the assumption that $D_1^{21} = 0$ is estimation which involves incorrect *a priori* restrictions; however, for the remaining rows of D^{21} sufficiently close to zero, identification of A_1 is present when the restrictions are actually correct. *This is just the situation considered in Theorem* 1, *however*;[25] hence as *all* rows of D^{21} (including the first) approach zero, $\alpha_{1j}(0,D^{21})$ and A_{1j} approach each other for all j, by Theorem 1. *Q.E.D.*

It is thus the case that, when the specification that the variables in x^1 do not appear in the system (3.6) is a "good enough" approximation, the inconsistency involved in applying it will be negligible in estimating any equation of (3.6) which is otherwise identified. (Once again, it is far more difficult precisely to define "good enough.") Moreover, a more important result than this is readily available.

The theorem just proved dealt with the estimation of one equation on the assumption that *all* specification errors approached zero—that not only were the omitted variables nearly absent from the equation in question, but that they were nearly absent from the system (3.6)—that is, that *all* rows of D^{21} approached zero, not just the first. It is easy to show, however, that the negligibility of inconsistencies in the estimation of A_1 almost never depends on the closeness to zero of the last $r(B^2)-1$ rows of D^{21}. To see this, observe that the only use made of such closeness in the proof of the theorem was to show that $W(e^{21})$ was nonsingular, and hence that the rank condition was satisfied for the last rows of D^{21} close enough to zero. *The necessary order condition is always satisfied regardless of the value of* D^{21}, in view of (3.9). Furthermore, the closeness to zero of the last rows of D^{21} is a sufficient, but by no means a necessary condition for the rank condition to hold; $W(e^{21})$ can be nonsingular for other configurations. Indeed, since a determinant is a linear function of any element and of the elements in any row, and since $W(0)$ is known to be nonsingular, $W(e^{21})$ must be nonsingular for all points in the space of the elements of e^{21}, save for a set of measure zero. Hence the rank condition is satisfied almost everywhere in the space of the elements of the last $r(B^2)-1$ rows of D^{21} and we have:

THEOREM 3 (*Limited Effects of Other Errors Theorem*).

$$\lim_{D_1^{21}\to 0} |\alpha_{1j}(0,D^{21})-A_{1j}| = 0 \textit{ for all } j = 1,\ldots, n$$

almost always regardless of the last $r(B^2)-1$ *rows of* D^{21}.[26]

[25] It is necessary to add that in the present case, V in (2.10) refers to residuals from regressions on the elements of z^2 only, rather than on all exogenous variables. A similar remark applies to the interpretation of M_1 and M in (2.15). This amounts to using the elements of z^2 as instrumental variables and the remainder of the proof follows as before.

[26] This is a special case of the general remark made in Koopmans, Rubin, and Leipnik [**5**, p. 83].

This is an important theorem, for it shows that the mistaken omission of nonnegligible variables from a given structural equation generally affects only the estimates of the parameters of that equation and not the estimates of parameters of other equations in the system. Specification errors of this type are thus of limited effect, and the estimates of the parameters of a given equation can be judged with regard only for the question of the goodness of approximation in the specification of that equation.

Some further remarks are now in order. If F^{21} and H^1 are not null, i.e., if some of the omitted variables are exogenous to (3.7), then it can easily happen that even when e^{21} is such as to make $W(e^{21})$ singular, the rank condition holds, so that the preceding theorem is slightly stronger. Secondly, the assumption that B^1 is nonsingular seems an innocuous one. It can be discarded, however, and replaced with the statement that $W(0)$ (and hence $W(e^{21})$ for small e^{21}) will be nonsingular almost everywhere in the space of the elements of B^1. As before, the rank condition can hold even with singularity of $W(e^{21})$ if there are omitted exogenous variables so that H^1 is not null.

Finally, we observe that the proofs of Theorems 2 and 3 do not depend on the truth or falsity of the original *a priori* restrictions. If those restrictions only hold approximately, it suffices to observe that the rank of $(b^2\ g^2)\phi'$ will be $r(B^2)-1$ almost everywhere in the space of the elements of $(b^2\ g^2)$ and must be $r(B^2)-1$ if the original *a priori* restrictions are close enough approximations (this follows as in the proof of Theorem 1). Hence we may treat all *a priori* restrictions—the original ones and the restrictions that $D_1^{21}=0$—together. Let $(B_1^2\ G_1^2)\phi' = \bar{\eta}$ as in the preceding section. Denote by $\tilde{a}_{1j}(0,\bar{\eta};0,D^{21})$ the probability limit of the estimate of A_{1j} is obtained on the assumption that $D^{21}=0$ and $(B_1^2\ G_1^2)\phi'=0$. Consider the same sequence of systems as described before Theorem 2, save that B_1^2 and G_1^2 are only fixed in those elements not determined by the *a priori* restrictions. We have:

COROLLARY TO THEOREMS 1 AND 2:

$$\lim_{\substack{\bar{\eta}\to 0\\ D^{21}\to 0}} |\tilde{a}_{1j}(0,\bar{\eta};0,D^{21})-A_{1j}| = 0 \quad \textit{for all} \quad j=1,\ldots,n\,;$$

and

COROLLARY TO THEOREMS 1 AND 3:

$$\lim_{\substack{\bar{\eta}\to 0\\ D_1^{21}\to 0}} |\tilde{a}_{1j}(0,\bar{\eta};0,D^{21})-A_{1j}| = 0$$

for all $j=1,\ldots,n$ *almost always regardless of the last* $r(B^2)-1$ *rows of* D^{21}.

Thus as approximations of both kinds so far considered get better and better, the inconsistency of estimates goes to zero. It follows that for good enough approximations—both in the *a priori* restrictions and in the omission of variables—such inconsistencies will be negligible. The effects of the assumption of block recursiveness and of approximate *a priori* restrictions are thus independent in this regard.

All this has been on the assumption that all variables assumed exogenous really are. We shall investigate the consequences of misspecification in this area after further discussion in the next section of the effects of omitted variables.

4. GENERALIZATION OF PROXIMITY THEOREM I

In the last section, we established conditions under which the inconsistency of the structural parameter estimates is negligible, even though variables are mistakenly or approximately excluded from the equation system studied. Those conditions were essentially that the coefficients of the excluded variables in the true system be very close to zero. In this section, we ask a somewhat different question. Suppose that the true coefficients of the omitted variables are not very close to zero. Under what conditions can the coefficients of the included variables be estimated with negligible inconsistency? In other words, let $J^2 = [B^2 \;\; G^2]$ and rewrite (3.6) as:

$$u^2 = [D^{21} \;\; J^2] \begin{bmatrix} x^1 \\ x^2 \end{bmatrix} . \tag{4.1}$$

Continue to assume that the rank of $J^2\phi'$ is $r(J^2) - 1$, where ϕ' is the coefficient matrix of true linear homogeneous *a priori* restrictions, $J_1^2\phi' = 0$. We wish to ascertain the conditions under which J_1^2, the first row of J^2, can be estimated with negligible inconsistency when D^{21} is assumed zero, but is in fact *not* very close to zero.[27]

Now, define a new residual vector, v, as

$$v \equiv u^2 - D^{21}x^1 = J^2x^2 . \tag{4.2}$$

[27] The question may be raised of why estimation of J_1^2 is desirable in these circumstances. Since we shall show below that the estimates obtained are estimates of the gross effect of the variables in x^2 (both their direct effect and their effect through the variables in x^1), are not such estimates to be desired for all purposes? The answer here is the same as in the case of reduced form versus structural estimation (indeed, the question is a special case of that question): Measurement of such gross effects may indeed be helpful for prediction, but in the event of a partial structural break that disturbs the relation between the included and the (mistakenly) omitted variables, the use of gross estimates leads to serious error, whereas true structural knowledge can still be used. An example would be the imposition of a tax on one of the variables.

Estimation of J^2 on the assumption that $D^{21} = 0$ is thus seen to be estimation of (4.2) on the assumption that the elements of v are distributed independently of the exogenous variables z^2. Leaving the interpretation of what follows in terms of a complete system such as (3.7) to later discussion, suppose that in fact v is related to x^2 by:

$$v = Px^2 + u^2 + \mu = Ly^2 + Qz^2 + u^2 + \mu \,, \tag{4.3}$$

that is, the relations between the excluded and included variables are such that $D^{21}x^2 = -Px^2 + \mu$. We continue to assume that the true residuals —the elements of $(u^2 + \mu)$—are in fact distributed independently of the elements of z^2. It is easy to see, however, that this cannot generally be the case with the elements of v unless some rows of P are zero, since eliminating y^2 from (4.2) and (4.3) gives:

$$v = [I - L(B^2)^{-1}]^{-1}[Q - L(B^2)^{-1}G]z^2 + [I - L(B^2)^{-1}]^{-1}(u^2 + \mu) \,. \tag{4.4}$$

An element of v can thus only be independent of the elements of z^2 if some row of the matrix $[Q - L(B^2)^{-1}G]$ is zero. This will be the case if the corresponding row of $P = [L \;\; Q]$ is zero; otherwise, it can only happen (on a set of measure zero) if the effects of z^2 on v directly are exactly cancelled by the indirect effects through y^2.[28]

As before, choose an indefinitely large number of values for u^2 and μ and for such elements of z^2 as are not lagged endogenous variables, choosing initial conditions for the remaining elements of z^2. Fix J^2 and consider systems differing only in P. Let $j_1(0,P)$ be the vector of the probability limits of the estimates of J_1^2 obtained for given P by wrongly assuming that $P = 0$ and applying one of the standard simultaneous equation techniques.[29] *Note that this may, but need not be, the mistaken assumption that no variables have been omitted* (the assumption of the last section). We shall discuss this below. We prove:

[28] Should this exceptional case occur, in particular, should it be the first element of v that is distributed independently of z^2, it may happen that the first equation of (4.2) is underidentified unless there are more than enough *a priori* restrictions to begin with. This is so because the first row of (4.3) will be indistinguishable in form from the first row of (4.2). (This does not otherwise arise because of the dependence of the elements of v and of z^2.) The exceptional case is of no importance; one could never know that it was present in any practical problem. The possibility of its existence does not substantially affect our discussion, save as a curiosity, since we are concerned with the more interesting case where rows of P are near zero. The possible existence of the exceptional case, however, does mean that we are stating sufficient but not always necessary conditions for negligible inconsistency.

[29] A similar remark to that given in footnote 12, above, applies here.

THEOREM 4 (*Generalized Proximity Theorem I*).

(a) $\lim_{P \to 0} j_1(0,P) = \lim_{P \to 0} (\overset{2}{J_1} - P_1) = \overset{2}{J_1}$;

(b) $\lim_{P_1 \to 0} j_1(0,P) = \lim_{P_1 \to 0} (\overset{2}{J_1} - P_1) = \overset{2}{J_1}$

almost always regardless of the last $r(P) - 1$ *rows of* P.

Proof:
Solve (4.2) and (4.3) for $(u^2 + \mu)$, obtaining

(4.5) $$(u^2 + \mu) = (J^2 - P)x^2 .$$

This system of equations is in the same form as (4.2), and $(u^2 + \mu)$ meets the assumptions made about (4.2)—its elements are distributed independently of z^2. Hence some linear combination of the rows of (4.2) will be estimated. It remains to be shown that as P goes to zero, that estimate approaches $(\overset{2}{J_1} - P_1)$. Consider the vector $(\overset{2}{J_1} - P_1)\phi'$. As P approaches zero, this must approach $\overset{2}{J_1}\phi' = 0$ by assumption. Therefore, as P approaches zero, $(\overset{2}{J_1} - P_1)$ comes closer and closer to satisfying the *a priori* restrictions. Furthermore, as P approaches zero, the matrix $(J^2 - P)\phi'$ approaches $J^2\phi'$. The determinant of a matrix, however, is a continuous function of its elements; hence, for P close enough to zero, the rank of $(J^2 - P)\phi'$ and of $J^2\phi'$ will be the same, namely, $r(J^2) - 1$. It now follows that $j_1(0,P)$ is an estimate satisfying all the conditions of Theorem 1, for P sufficiently close to zero, and statement (a) of the Theorem has been proved.

Statement (b) now follows as in the last section by observing that the rows of P other than the first only enter in the above proof in consideration of the rank of $(J^2 - P)\phi'$.

Before going on to discuss the reason for naming the theorem as we have, some remarks are in order regarding its consequences. Let us return to the notation of the last section (of (3.7) in particular). Here, however, we make one change. Previously we agreed to expand x^1 until all its elements were either explained or exogenous; now we must expand it until all its elements are either explained or distributed independently of z^2. This is not the same thing, for functions of exogenous variables are themselves exogenous. We suppress all such independent variables (and also H^1 and F^{21}) by writing them as functions of x^1 with zero coefficients, and thus including them in y^1. From (3.7):

(4.6) $$y^1 = -(B^1)^{-1}G^1x^2 + (B^1)^{-1}u^1 .$$

Hence

(4.7) $$v = u^2 - D^{21}x^1 = u^2 - E^{21}y^1 = E^{21}(B^1)^{-1}G^1x^2 + u^2 - E^{21}(B^1)^{-1}u^1 ,$$

and this is precisely (4.3) with

$$P = E^{21}(B^1)^{-1}G^1 ,$$
$$\mu = -E^{21}(B^1)^{-1}u^1 . \tag{4.8}$$

It follows that the conditions of the second part of the theorem will be satisfied if the first row of $E^{21}(B^1)^{-1}G^1$ goes to zero; hence inconsistencies will be negligible in the estimation of J_1^2 if all elements in that first row are sufficiently close to zero. Let us ask what this means.

In the first place, observe that the row in question will be near zero if the first row of E^{21} is near zero. This is scarcely surprising. If that is the case, then clearly inconsistencies in the estimation of E_1^{21} on the assumption that the latter is zero will be negligible. Combined with the results of Theorem 4, this gives us Theorems 2 and 3 as a special case.[30]

Secondly, the row in question will be near zero if G^1 and thus $(B^1)^{-1}G^1$ is near zero. It is the second matrix which is of most interest. This is a quasi-reduced form matrix showing the full effects of the included variables on the omitted ones. Clearly, if all such effects are near zero, inconsistencies will be negligible.[31]

Finally, we can make a general statement covering all cases. Inconsistencies will be negligible if to each nonnegligible element of E_1^{21}, say E_{1k}^{21}, there corresponds a negligible row of $(B^1)^{-1}G^1$, the kth row. In other words, inconsistencies will be negligible provided that the only omitted variables that enter into the first equation with nonnegligible coefficients are those variables on which the influence of the included variables is slight.

We have called Theorem 4 a generalization of the Proximity Theorem. The latter theorem is due to Wold[32] and applies to a single equation. It states that the least squares regression coefficients of a single equation will be nearly unbiased either if the residuals from that equation are small or if they are nearly uncorrelated with the explanatory variables. The two effects reinforce each other. In the case of omitted variables, where only one equation is involved (i.e., $r(J^2) = 1$), it is easy to see that this is essentially the same as our theorem with unbiasedness substituted for consistency.[33]

[30] A special case which was worth proving separately, nonetheless, because of the way in which the omission of variables enters as providing just sufficient *a priori* restrictions.

[31] Note that this is equivalent to the statement that the system can be put in block-recursive form (possibly with three blocks) by an appropriate renumbering of equations and variables.

[32] [**19**, Theorem 12.1.3, p. 189. Also see pp. 37–38]; more precise results have been obtained by Wold and P. Faxér [**20**].

[33] We can only deal with consistency in general because simultaneous equation estimators are not generally unbiased under correct specification.

Clearly, in this case, the single row of P will be negligible if and only if the zero order least squares regression coefficients of $D^{21}x^1$ on the included variables x^2 are all zero. These regression coefficients are, however, the products of correlation coefficients and the ratio of the variance of $D^{21}x^1$ to the variance of the variable in question. P will therefore be close to zero if either all the correlations are near zero or if the variance of $D^{21}x^1$ is near zero; and the two effects reinforce each other (they multiply). Hence our theorem essentially reduces to the Proximity Theorem in the single equation case. This is not the only generalization of the Proximity Theorem to the simultaneous equations case, however. Another such will be given in the next section.[34]

We may emphasize that the regression coefficients and not simply the correlations of the residual with the explanatory variables are important here.[35] Even if all such correlations were perfect, if the effects on the residual of moving the explanatory variables were very small, relative to the direct effects of such movement on the dependent variable, the inconsistency involved would be very slight. A similar statement holds for the simultaneous equation case.[36]

Finally, we observe that Theorem 4 and Theorem 1 can hold at the same time, that is, all inconsistencies in the estimation of J^2 will go to zero as P_1 goes to zero and as the *a priori* restrictions become better approximations. Thus such inconsistencies will be negligible if P_1 is close to zero and all *a priori* restrictions are good enough approximations.

5. GENERALIZATION OF PROXIMITY THEOREM II

Thus far we have assumed that all variables assumed to be exogenous actually are so. The time has now come to remove that restriction. Until further notice, we shall assume that all *a priori* restrictions are correctly specified and that no variables have been omitted from the system. More general cases will be considered below.

[34] It is interesting to observe that taken together the results of the two sections imply that the conditions of the Proximity Theorem imply that the system being studied is nearly recursive or block-recursive, with the equation being estimated forming one block. It follows that a defense of least squares based on the Proximity Theorem differs in degree but not fundamentally in kind from the defense that the real world is recursive. (An exception to this occurs when there are no omitted variables and the variance of the true structural residual is near zero.)

[35] Although useful results may be obtained in the single equation case using the the correlation coefficients alone, see A. C. Harberger [**4**].

[36] A clear statement of the theorem in the single equation case in terms of omitted variables and regression coefficients has been given by J. Lintner [**6**, Ch. II]. As usual in this area of analysis H. Theil has proved a general theorem (for a single equation) of which this is a special case. [**17**, p. 43].

Consider the system of equations:

$$u^1 = A^1x = [B^1 \; G^1] \begin{bmatrix} x^1 \\ x^2 \end{bmatrix} \tag{5.1}$$

where, as usual, B^1 is assumed nonsingular. Here x^1 is assumed endogenous and x^2 is (incorrectly) assumed exogenous. We further assume that, were those assumptions correct, A_1^1 would be identified, that is, that there exist *a priori* restrictions, $A_1^1\phi' = 0$ and that the rank of $A^1\phi'$ is $r(A^1) - 1$.

Now, suppose that in reality (5.1) is part of a larger system:

$$\begin{bmatrix} u^1 \\ u^2 \end{bmatrix} = \begin{bmatrix} B^1 & G^1 \\ E^{21} & B^2 \end{bmatrix} \begin{bmatrix} x^1 \\ x^2 \end{bmatrix} . \tag{5.2}$$

For simplicity, we assume that B^2 is square and nonsingular, i.e., that no additional variables are needed to explain x^2. In short, we assume that (5.2) is self-contained. More complex and realistic cases will be considered below.

We have already investigated the effect of assuming that $E^{21} = 0$ on the estimates of the second block of equations in (5.2). We now consider the effect of the same assumption on the estimates of the first block. Note once more that this assumption is that of block recursiveness. Should we prove that the effects of the assumption are here negligible for E^{21} sufficiently close to zero, we shall be in a position to speak strongly about the effects of separating total systems for partial analysis.

Let the coefficient matrix of (5.2) be A, rewrite (5.2) as:

$$u = Ax . \tag{5.3}$$

Then (assuming A to be nonsingular, which it must be for E^{21} sufficiently close to zero):

$$x = A^{-1}u . \tag{5.4}$$

However,

$$A^{-1} = \left[\begin{array}{c|c} (B^1 - G^1(B^2)^{-1}E^{21})^{-1} & -(B^1 - G^1(B^2)^{-1}E^{21})^{-1}G^1(B^2)^{-1} \\ \hline -(B^2 - E^{21}(B^1)^{-1}G^1)^{-1}E^{21}(B^1)^{-1} & (B^2 - E^{21}(B^1)^{-1}G^1)^{-1} \end{array}\right] \tag{5.5}$$

which reduces when $E^{21} = 0$ to:

$$A^{-1} = \left[\begin{array}{c|c} (B^1)^{-1} & -(B^1)^{-1}G^1(B^2)^{-1} \\ \hline 0 & (B^2)^{-1} \end{array}\right] \tag{5.6}$$

so that, in the latter case, x^2 depends only on u^2 and not on u^1. It follows that only when $E^{21} = 0$ is the assumption that x^2 consists of variables exogenous to (5.1) correct.

Now, as usual, choose an indefinitely large set of values for the elements of u. Fix B^1, G^1, and B^2. Consider a sequence of systems differing only in E^{21} and allow the latter matrix to go to zero. Note that (in view of (5.5)) the values of x^1 and x^2, and hence all estimates, are continuous functions of the elements of E^{21}. Clearly, we can prove a theorem analogous to Theorem 1 if we can show that all estimates are continuous functions of the *assumed* value of E^{21} also.

This, however, is not hard to do. It will prove instructive to transform the problem slightly. Denote the true asymptotic variance-covariance matrix of the elements of u^1 by $\bar{M}_{u^1u^1}$[37] and the asymptotic covariance matrix of the elements of x^2 and u^1 by $\bar{M}_{x^2u^1}$, the rows corresponding to the elements of x^2 and the columns to the elements of u^1. Let Q be the matrix in the left-hand lower corner of A^{-1} in (5.5). Then, from (5.4) and the remarks in footnote 20 above,

$$\bar{M}_{x^2u^1} = Q\bar{M}_{u^1u^1}. \tag{5.7}$$

Furthermore, observe that given $\bar{M}_{x^2u^1}$ and $\bar{M}_{u^1u^1}$, Q is determined by (5.7) (we assume $\bar{M}_{u^1u^1}$ to be nonsingular; we are choosing u^1). Given B^1, G^1, and B^2, it is easy to show that E^{21} is determined by Q. It follows that with everything else fixed, E^{21}—and hence the values of the elements of x—is determined as a continuous function of $\bar{M}_{x^2u^1}$; further, that function is such that E^{21} is zero if and only if $\bar{M}_{x^2u^1}$ is zero.

The assumption that the elements of x^2 are exogenous with respect to (5.1) is precisely the assumption that $\bar{M}_{x^2u^1} = 0$. It is clear, however, that this is but a limiting assumption—one out of an infinite number that might be made. Given *any* value assumed for $\bar{M}_{x^2u^1}$, and a method of estimation consistent for $\bar{M}_{x^2u^1} = 0$, and making an appropriate stability assumption, estimates of A_1^1 will exist. Indeed, the latter estimates generally depend only on the first column of $\bar{M}_{x^2u^1}$. If the true value of $\bar{M}_{x^2u^1}$ and the assumed value coincide, such estimates will be consistent. This is most clearly seen in the case of the method of instrumental variables, where the covariances in question appear explicitly. Since limited information, maximum likelihood and two stage least squares estimators are equivalent to the method of instrumental variables for appropriate choices of instruments,[38] the same properties obviously hold for them. Such properties also hold for the full information, maximum likelihood method.

Let the assumed value of $\bar{M}_{x^2u^1}$ be $M_{x^2u^1}$. Let the vector of the probability limits of the estimates of the elements of A_1^1 obtained by making that

[37] By the strong assumption in footnote 20 above, this is a diagonal matrix. Equation (5.7) below follows from the weak assumption in footnote 20; it allows us to forget u^2 in computing covariances, which is all that is necessary.

[38] See J. D. Sargan [**10**, p. 393] and H. Theil [**16**, p. 336].

assumption and applying one of the standard methods[39] be $a_1^1(M_{x^2u^1}, \bar{M}_{x^2u^1})$. It is clear that each element of the latter vector is a continuous function of both (matrix) arguments. It now follows exactly as in the proof of Theorem 1 that:

THEOREM 5 (*Generalized Proximity Theorem II*):

$$\lim_{\bar{M}_{x^2u^1} \to 0} a_1^1(0,\bar{M}_{x^2u^1}) = A_1^1 .$$

Further, since $\bar{M}_{x^2u^1}$ and E^{21} are in a one-to-one relation and so are the assumed values thereof, we have (where the notation is obvious):

COROLLARY TO THEOREM 5:

$$\lim_{E^{21} \to 0} \alpha_1^1(0,E^{21}) \equiv \lim_{E^{21} \to 0} a_1^1(0,\bar{M}_{x^2u^1}) = A_1^1 .$$

It thus follows that inconsistencies in the estimation of A_1^1 will be negligible for E^{21} close enough to zero—for the variables in x^2 "nearly" exogenous to (5.1).

We have called Theorem 5 another generalization of the Proximity Theorem discussed in the last section. That it is so may be seen as follows. In the case of a single equation, $\bar{M}_{x^2u^1}$ consists of a single row, the vector of covariances between the single residual and the assumed exogenous variables. Any such covariance, however, may be written as the product of the corresponding correlation coefficient, the standard error of the residual, and, the standard error of the variable in question. Hence $\bar{M}_{x^2u^1}$ will go to zero in this case as both the correlations between the independent variables and the residual and the variance of the residual go to zero, the two effects reinforcing each other.[40]

We may now remove the assumption that (5.2) is self-contained. To begin with, it is clear that no problem whatsoever is created by the appearance of variables exogenous to (5.1) in the equations explaining x^2; we shall not include them explicitly to avoid unduly complicating our notation.

A problem does arise, however, when variables appear in the equations explaining x^2 which are not truly exogenous to (5.1). Call the vector of all such variables x^0; it is to be thought of as expanded to include variables

[39] A remark similar to that made in footnote 12 above applies here.

[40] It is truly the variance of the residual and not just its standard error that is important here since, other residual variances remaining equal, the variance of the independent variable involved is a linear function of the variance of the residual in question, by the remarks in footnote 20, above.

explaining x^2, variables explaining such variables, and so forth, until either a self-contained system is reached or all remaining unexplained variables are truly exogenous to (5.1). (As just stated, we may assume the first of these alternatives for simplicity.) Suppose that, instead of (5.2), (5.1) is a subsystem of:

$$\begin{bmatrix} u^0 \\ u^1 \\ u^2 \end{bmatrix} = \begin{bmatrix} B^0 & E^{01} & E^{02} \\ 0^{10} & B^1 & G^1 \\ E^{20} & E^{21} & B^2 \end{bmatrix} \begin{bmatrix} x^0 \\ x^1 \\ x^2 \end{bmatrix} \tag{5.8}$$

where B^0 is assumed nonsingular. Note the appearance of 0^{10}; we are still assuming that there are no omitted variables in (5.1) and that A_1^1 is identified under true *a priori* restrictions.

By an analysis similar to that just given it is not hard to show that all inconsistencies in estimating A_1^1 on the assumption that the elements of x^2 are exogenous will go to zero as both the matrices E^{21} and $E^{20}(B^0)^{-1}E^{01}$ go to zero. The interpretation of this condition is as follows: E^{21}, as before, represents the direct effects of x^1 on x^2. Negligible inconsistency clearly requires that these effects be close to zero. The matrix $E^{20}(B^0)^{-1}E^{01}$, however, represents the indirect effects of x^1 on x^2 by way of the effects of x^1 on x^0 and x^0 on x^2. For negligible inconsistency, these effects must be close to zero also.[41] The latter condition may be interpreted further.

Assume that $E^{21} = 0$. If $E^{20} = 0$, (5.8) is block recursive as it stands and we have (5.2), the case already considered. In this case, we already know that $E^{21} = 0$ is a sufficient condition for consistency of all estimates. Now suppose that $E^{20} \neq 0$ but that $E^{01} = 0$. In this case, the system is block recursive also, but x^0 and x^2 must be written in the same block. This is the case mentioned above, where the additional variables explaing x^2 are exogenous to (5.1). Finally, $E^{20}(B^0)^{-1}E^{01}$ can be near zero, even if E^{20} and E^{01} both contain nonnegligible elements. The full condition for this is that the jth column of E^{20} can be nonnegligible only if the jth row of E^{01} is negligible. In other words, any variable in x^0 which has nonnegligible influence on the variables in x^2 must be influenced only negligibly by all variables in x^1.[41a]

We observe that, as usual, nothing in the above analysis would be affected if the *a priori* restrictions held only approximately. We conclude that inconsistencies will be near zero if all *a priori* restrictions are sufficiently close approximations *and* the above conditions hold.

We may now remove the last restriction and consider the general case where there are variables omitted from (5.1). Without loss of generality,

[41] Actually, inconsistencies can be negligible if the indirect and direct effects just cancel out, that is, if $(E^{21} - E^{20}(B^0)^{-1}E^{01}) = 0$. This could only happen by accident if the conditions named in the text are not satisfied; moreover, one could never tell whether it were nearly the case in practice. We thus disregard it.

[41a] Note that the full condition also implies that the system is nearly block recursive.

we may expand x^0 to include such variables and all variables explaining them and so forth until either a self-contained system is reached or all unexplained variables are exogenous to (5.1). For simplicity, we continue to assume the first of these alternatives.[42] x^0 now contains all variables needed to explain x^1 and x^2 and all variables needed to explain such variables, and to forth. Replacing 0^{10} in (5.8) by E^{10}, we have the *perfectly general* system:[43]

$$\begin{bmatrix} u^0 \\ u^1 \\ u^2 \end{bmatrix} = \begin{bmatrix} B^0 & E^{01} & E^{02} \\ E^{10} & B^1 & G^1 \\ E^{20} & E^{21} & B^2 \end{bmatrix} \begin{bmatrix} x^0 \\ x^1 \\ x^2 \end{bmatrix}. \tag{5.9}$$

We continue to assume the B^i nonsingular; this is the general case.

It is easy to show that the conditions given for the near exogeneity of x^2 to the second block of equations in (5.9) and hence for negligible inconsistencies are unchanged. They are the same as those just discussed in the case of (5.8) (of course, the magnitudes of the inconsistencies involved may be different; the point is that the limit—zero— is the same in both cases). Further, as observed above, all inconsistencies will go to zero as both those conditions are satisfied *and* as all *a priori* restrictions are better approximations. It was shown in Section 3, above, however, that estimation of the first equation of the second block of (5.9) on the assumption that $E_1^{10} = 0$, that is, on the erroneous omission of x^0, is in general equivalent to estimation with erroneous *a priori* restrictions, and hence that as E_1^{10} goes to zero, so do the effects of this misspecification. It follows that all our theorems hold concurrently (a similar statement holds for Theorem 4). Thus, inconsistencies in the estimation of the first row of the second block of equations in (5.9) will be negligible if all of the following conditions hold:

(1) All *a priori* restrictions are close approximations.

(2) E_1^{10} is close to zero; that is, omitted variables have small coefficients (this is sufficient save on a space of measure zero).[44]

(3) E^{21} is near zero—that is, the endogenous variables have negligible direct effects on the assumed exogenous variables.

(4) $E^{20}(B^0)^{-1}E^{01}$ is close to zero—that is, the endogenous variables have negligible indirect effects on the assumed exogenous variables.

[42] The additional remarks necessary if the second alternative holds are given in Section 3, above.

[43] Perfectly general, save for the self-contained feature just discussed.

[44] Alternatively, if only estimates of B_1^1 and G_1^1 are required (greatly inconsistent estimates of E_1^{10} are acceptable), we might have:

(2′) The first row of the matrix $E^{10}(B^0)^{-1}[E^{01}\ E^{02}]$ is near zero, that is, any omitted variable with a nonnegligible coefficient is only negligibly influenced by the included variables.

If in addition, the other rows of E^{10} are near zero, so that all coefficients of omitted variables in the block of equations investigated are small, then conditions 2–4 imply that the system is nearly block recursive either as it stands or as rewritten with the first and third blocks of equations grouped together. In either case, analysis of the second block of equations is possible without explicit reference to the total system of which it is a part. *It is the existence of situations such as this which permits estimation of partial economic models,* indeed, which permits estimation of general economic models which are in turn embedded in models of the socio-physical universe. Liu's objections to simultaneous equation estimation are thus not generally damning. They cannot be taken as general objections, but as highly important criticisms which must be considered case by case in the light of how good the approximations involved are, not in the light of whether such approximations are exactly true or not.

Having said this much, however, we must go on to inquire whether the four conditions named above are easily fulfilled in practice. It seems clear that the first three are likely to be; any reasonably attentive investigator will pay fairly close attention to them. The fourth condition, on the other hand, is not so easily disposed of. It is very easy to overlook the possibility that the endogenous variables may have sizeable effects on the assumed exogenous variables by way of effects on a third set, which set may be exceedingly large. Therefore this is the point to which close attention must be paid in practice.

Finally, we may draw a further conclusion. Liu's objections, though not valid as stated, point to a redirection of some current work. The theorems in this paper speak only of consistency. They have no bearing on the variance of estimators nor on the small sample properties thereof. We have seen that different estimators can have different probability limits under misspecifications of the types discussed here. It is likely that their asymptotic variances are different and almost certain that their small sample properties are different. Even if the approximations involved in such misspecifications are very good (as they must be for negligible inconsistencies) one estimator may do better than another. That is, one estimator may be less sensitive than another to errors of this kind. The choice among estimators may therefore depend on their behavior under approximative misspecification, even though negligible inconsistencies are assured for all. To put it slightly differently, the goodness of a "good enough" approximation may depend, particularly in small samples, on the estimator used. Since the situations envisaged by Liu arise commonly (as he convincingly argues) it follows that, even though his specific conclusions are wrong, it is imperative that work be done along the lines indicated. In particular, a good deal of future work in Monte Carlo experiments should be directed towards discovering the small sample properties of various estimators under the types of approximative misspecification pointed out by Liu and discussed here.

6. CONJECTURES ON DYNAMICS

A good deal of this paper has been concerned with estimation problems in equation systems that are close to being block recursive. We have seen that such closeness is a sufficient condition to permit estimation of the usual kind to take place despite Liu's objections. Since such closeness is also a necessary condition, in general, it seems clear that a large part of the profession implicitly believes the world to be constructed in this way. Indeed, it is interesting that, considered from this point of view, Liu's objections to simultaneous equation estimation lie at the other extreme from the better known objections of Wold. Wold has insisted that the real world is recursive in the ordinary sense. Liu's objections, if they are to hold, must imply that the real world is not generally recursive in any sense. As just observed, the middle ground that the real world is nearly block recursive is implicitly held by those practicing simultaneous equation methods.

If the real world is nearly block recursive, however, it becomes interesting to consider the dynamics of block recursive systems. A first step in this direction is the consideration of the dynamics of a first degree difference or differential equation whose matrix is block triangular. Explicitly, consider the equation system:

(6.1)

$$x(t) \equiv \begin{bmatrix} x^1(t) \\ x^2(t) \\ \vdots \\ x^N(t) \end{bmatrix} = \begin{bmatrix} B^1 & G^1 & & & \\ 0^{21} & B^2 & G^2 & & \\ \vdots & \vdots & \vdots & \ddots & \\ 0^{N1} & 0^{N2} & 0^{N3} & \cdots & B^N \end{bmatrix} \begin{bmatrix} x^1(t-1) \\ x^2(t-1) \\ \vdots \\ x^N(t-1) \end{bmatrix} \equiv Ax(t-1)$$

where the B^i are nonsingular. Clearly, the subsystems obtained by dropping the first k rows and columns of matrices and the corresponding x^i have the property that their dynamic properties may be investigated without regard for the remainder of the system.

Now consider matrices that are nearly block triangular, that is, matrices such as:

(6.2)
$$A(\eta) = A + \eta D$$

where η is a positive scalar and D is any matrix with finite elements. We are interested in the dynamic properties of systems with such matrices for small η.

Now, a special case of (6.1) arises when all the G^i are zero. In this case, A is completely decomposable, and $A(\eta)$ is nearly completely decomposable for small η. For nearly completely decomposable matrices, H. Simon and A. Ando have proved an important theorem.[45] Crudely interpreted, this theorem states that equilibrium in a system with a nearly completely decomposable matrix (for small η) is approached in three stages. During the first stage the variables within each $x^i(t)$ adjust to reach equilibrium positions that are related to each other according to the limiting completely decomposable system—to the B^i. Following this, in the second stage, maintaining such equilibrium at all times, the variables adjust *en bloc*—the variables with each $x^i(t)$ moving together—until at the final stage, as in any linear system, the variables approach the rate of growth corresponding to the largest latent root. These properties permit Leontief-Hicks type aggregation of the variables within each $x^i(t)$ during and after the second stage.

It is clear that nearly completely decomposable matrices are a special case of nearly block triangular matrices. Indeed, the latter are far more apt to arise in practice. It follows that all our theorems about estimation inconsistency apply to nearly completely decomposable matrices. Further, it seems clear that the problem of estimation inconsistency and the problem of equilibrium adjustment are related here. Both the Simon-Ando Theorem and the theorems proved in this paper concern the strength of feed-back effects. It seems likely that this relationship is not accidental. We therefore offer the following conjectures for further investigation:

(1) The Simon-Ando Theorem holds, *mutatis mutandis*, for nearly block triangular and not just for nearly completely decomposable systems.[46]

(2) If the first conjecture is true, there exists a direct proof thereof which depends on the theorems on estimation here proved.

(3) If the first two conjectures are true, a general theorem exists concerning the relationship between negligible inconsistency for negligible misspecification on the one hand and the equilibrium properties of closely related systems on the other.

Since block triangular systems may be fairly generally encountered, the first conjecture alone is an important one. If linkages are far stronger one way than another between related markets, for example, this conjecture, if true, would provide valuable information about the dynamic properties of the whole system of markets considered and would allow easier handling of the solution of the system.

Massachusetts Institute of Technology

[45] [**12**].

[46] Since this was written, Professor Ando and I have proved that this conjecture is indeed correct. The precise theorem and proof will be given in a later paper.

REFERENCES

[1] DANTZIG, G. B.: "Upper Bounds, Secondary Constraints, and Block Triangularity in Linear Programming," *Econometrica*, Vol. 23, No. 2 (April, 1955), pp. 174–183.

[2] FISHER, F. M.: "Generalization of the Rank and Order Conditions for Identifiability," *Econometrica*, Vol. 27, No. 3 (July, 1959), pp. 431–447.

[3] GOODWIN, R. M.: "Dynamical Coupling with Especial Reference to Markets Having Production Lags," *Econometrica*, Vol. 15, No. 3 (July, 1947), pp. 181–204.

[4] HARBERGER, A. C.: "On the Estimation of Economic Parameters," Cowles Commission Discussion Paper: Economics No. 2088, 1953 (unpublished).

[5] KOOPMANS, T. C., H. RUBIN, AND R. B. LEIPNIK: "Measuring the Equation Systems of Dynamic Economics," Chapter II in *Statistical Inference in Dynamic Economic Models* (T. C. Koopmans, ed.), New York, John Wiley and Sons, 1950 (Cowles Commission Monograph No. 10).

[6] LINTNER, J.: "Dividends, Earnings and Retained Earnings, Common Stock Prices and Expectations," forthcoming supplement to the *Review of Economics and Statistics*.

[7] LIU, T. C.: "A Simple Forecasting Model for the U.S. Economy," International Monetary Fund, *Staff Papers*, Aug., 1955, pp. 434–466.

[8] ———: "Structural Estimation and Forecasting: A Critique of the Cowles Commission Method," *Tsing Hua Journal*, forthcoming.

[9] ———: "Underidentification, Structural Estimation, and Forecasting," *Econometrica*, Vol. 28, No. 4 (Oct., 1960), pp. 855–865.

[10] SARGAN, J. D.: "The Estimation of Economic Relationships Using Instrumental Variables," *Econometrica*, Vol. 26, No. 3 (July, 1958), pp. 393–415.

[11] SIMON, H. A.: "Causal Ordering and Identifiability," Chapter 3 in *Studies in Econometric Method* (W. C. Hood and T. C. Koopmans, eds.), New York, John Wiley and Sons, 1953 (Cowles Commission Monograph No. 14); reprinted as Chapter 1 in H. A. Simon, *Models of Man*, New York, John Wiley and Sons, 1957.

[12] SIMON, H. A., AND A. ANDO: "Aggregation of Variables in Dynamic Systems," *Econometrica*, this issue.

[13] SOLOW, R. M.: "On the Structure of Linear Models," *Econometrica*, Vol. 20, No. 1 (Jan., 1952), pp. 29–46.

[14] STROTZ, R. H.: "Interdependence As a Specification Error," *Econometrica*, Vol. 28, No. 2 (April, 1960), pp. 428–442.

[15] STROTZ, R. H., AND H. WOLD: "Recursive *Vs.* Nonrecursive Systems: An Attempt at Synthesis," *Econometrica*, Vol. 28, No. 2 (April, 1960), pp. 417–427.

[16] THEIL, H.: *Economic Forecasts and Policy*, Amsterdam, North-Holland Publishing Co., 1958.

[17] ———: "Specification Errors and the Estimation of Economic Relationships," *Review of the International Statistical Institute*, Vol. 25, 1957, pp. 41–51.

[18] VALAVANIS, S.: *Econometrics*, New York, McGraw-Hill Book Company, 1959.

[19] WOLD, H., in association with L. JURÉEN: *Demand Analysis*, New York, John Wiley and Sons, 1953.

[20] WOLD, H., AND P. FAXÉR: "On the Specification Error in Regression Analysis," *Annals of Mathematical Statistics*, Vol. 28, No. 1 (Mar., 1957) pp. 265–267.

4

AGGREGATION OF VARIABLES IN DYNAMIC SYSTEMS[1]

By Herbert A. Simon and Albert Ando

Previous studies have examined dynamic systems that are decomposable into independent subsystems. This article treats of systems that are *nearly* decomposable—systems with matrices whose elements, except within certain submatrices along the main diagonal, approach zero in the limit. Such a system can be represented as a superposition of (1) a set of independent subsystems (one for each submatrix on the diagonal) and (2) an aggregate system having one variable for each subsystem. This superposition separates short-run from long-run dynamics and justifies the ignoring of "weak" linkages in partial equilibrium studies.

I. INTRODUCTION

In many problems of economic theory we need to use aggregates. The general Walrasian system and its more modern dynamic extensions are relatively barren of results for macroeconomics and economic policy. Hence, in our desire to deal with such questions we use highly aggregated systems by sheer necessity, often without having much more than the same necessity as our justification. Perhaps the most important result to date for justifying aggregation under certain circumstances is the Lange–Hicks[2] condition, about which we shall say more later.

Concern with actual numerical coefficients in the Leontief input–output model renewed interest in aggregation. It was hoped at first, perhaps, that modern computers would handle matrices of about any desired size, and hence would obviate the need for aggregation. By now it is clear that our ambitions have outstripped the computers, for the time required to invert a matrix by known methods increases with the cube of the number of rows and

[1] An earlier version of this paper was the result of the research undertaken in the Graduate School of Industrial Administration, Carnegie Institute of Technology, for the project *Planning and Control of Industrial Operations*, under contract with the Office of Naval Research and was circulated as O. N. R. Research Memorandum, No. 31, December, 1956. Reproduction of this manuscript in whole or in part is permitted for any purpose of the United States Government. Contract N ONR-76001, Project NR 047001. It was also read at the meetings of the Econometric Society, December, 1956. We are indebted to Drs. Allen Newell, Franklin Fisher, and S. Chakravarty for several enlightening discussions on the subject of this paper, and to John Muth for valuable suggestion on the proof given in Section IV.

[2] Lange, O., *Price Flexibility and Employment*, pp. 103 ff., 1952.

columns. The high cost of inverting large matrices has led to a number of experiments[3] to determine whether aggregation can be used to obtain approximate inverses more economically.

Hence, aggregation is a topic of considerable importance regardless of whether we are interested in the general mathematical treatment of large systems—in which case aggregation is essential for conceptual clarity and for effective manipulation of the systems—or interested in numerical computation—in which case aggregation is often necessary to make computation feasible with available means.

Let us consider an example. Suppose that government planners are interested in the effects of a subsidy to a basic industry, say the steel industry, on the total effective demand in the economy. Strictly speaking, we must deal with individual producers and consumers, and trace through all interactions among the economic agents in the economy. This being an obviously impossible task, we would use such aggregated variables as the total output of the steel industry, aggregate consumption and aggregate investment. The reasoning behind such a procedure may be summarized as follows: (1) we can somehow classify all the variables in the economy into a small number of groups; (2) we can study the interactions within the groups as though the interaction among groups did not exist; (3) we can define indices representing groups and study the interaction among these indices without regard to the interactions within each group.

When thus explicitly written out, this reasoning appears rather bold. Yet, we implicitly use it almost every day in our analysis of the economy. We should at least make some attempt to specify the conditions that would justify the aggregation.

The conditions for exact aggregation are very severe. Whether these conditions are strictly satisfied in any practical situation is, of course, not important. We would be perfectly satisfied with aggregative models that were only approximate; we have no illusions that *any* model we might employ is more that an approximate description of reality. In exploring the aggregation problem we seek rules and criteria—exact or heuristic—that indicate what variables to aggregate and that show the circumstances under which aggregation will yield satisfactory approximations.

In the more general sense, justifications for approximation must be related to the decisions that depend on the approximating—if the decisions based on the approximate model are not much "worse" than the decisions based on the more elaborate model according to some criteria, then we may be justified in using the approximate, simpler model. This consideration is strengthened if, while the improvement of the final decision is very slight, the cost of

[3] Balderston, J. B., and T. M. Whitin, "Aggregation in the Input-Output Model," in *Economic Activity Analysis*, ed. by O. Morgenstern, 1954.

working with a larger model is very much greater than that of working with an approximate, simpler model. Furthermore, the relation between the aggregation problem here discussed and the identification problem when the structural equations are misspecified—a relation pointed out recently by Fisher[4]—can be better understood when both of these problems are viewed as parts of a larger decision problem. We shall come back to this point in the concluding section of this paper, but we must first make the statement of our problem more precise.

We shall restrict our attention to aggregation defined within the following algebraic model: We have two sets of (not necessarily all distinct) variables, $x = (x_1,\ldots,x_i,\ldots,x_n)$, and $y = (y_1,\ldots,y_j,\ldots,y_m)$, and a system of equations giving y as a function of x; $y = \phi(x)$. We wish to know under what circumstances there exist two sets of functions, $X_I(x)$, $I = 1,\ldots,N$, $N < n$, and $Y_J(y)$, $J = 1,\ldots,M$, $M < m$, such that a set of relations between X and Y: $Y = \xi(X)$, can be derived from the given system of equations, ϕ, relating x and y. X and Y are vectors: $X = (X_1,\ldots,X_N)$, and $Y = (Y_1,\ldots,Y_M)$. Sometimes additional conditions are imposed, e.g., that the functions X and Y are given; or that there exist also relations, $y = y(Y)$, such that if, for a given set of values of x, $\bar{x}$, $\bar{y} = \phi(\bar{x})$, $\bar{X} = X(\bar{x})$, $\bar{Y} = \xi(\bar{X})$, and $\bar{\bar{y}} = y(\bar{Y})$, then $|\bar{y}_j - \bar{\bar{y}}_j| < \varepsilon$ for all j, where ε is a given positive number.

In the special case where the relations are all linear and the y_i's are the values of the x_i's in the following period, the function ϕ can be written as

$$x(t+1) = x(t)P \tag{1.1}$$

where $x(t)$ is an n-dimensional row vector and P is an $n \times n$ matrix of constants. The question raised above will then be specialized to that of conditions under which there exist N functions,

$$X_I(t) = X_I[x(t)] \qquad (I = 1,\ldots,N < n) \tag{1.2}$$

and a new set of relations

$$X(t+1) = X(t)Q \tag{1.3}$$

where $X(t)$ is an N-dimensional row vector, and Q is an $N \times N$ matrix of constants. The elements of Q are functions of the elements of P. Further, we seek to define an additional set of n functions

$$x_i(t) = f_i[X(t)] \qquad (i = 1,\ldots,n) \tag{1.4}$$

such that the time path of the x_i's defined by (1.3) and (1.4) can be considered an acceptable approximation of the time path of the x_i's defined by (1.1) according to some predetermined criteria.

The Lange-Hicks condition is a criterion of this kind. It states: if two or

[4] Fisher, F. M., "On the Cost of Approximate Specification in Simultaneous Equation Estimation," *Econometrica*, Vol. 29, April, 1961.

more variables always move together they may be aggregated into a single variable, which will be an appropriately weighted average of the original variables. This is a useful criterion, since it tells us that we may aggregate classes of commodities that are perfect substitutes, or that are approximately so.

At another level, the Lange-Hicks condition is unsatisfactory, for it requires that we know in advance which variables move together. In reality, it may be part of our problem to discover this. We may be confronted with a dynamic system of many variables, and may have to infer from the equations of the system which variables will move together—or will move nearly enough together to warrant aggregation. This is the problem we shall set ourselves here: *to determine conditions that, if satisfied by a (linear) dynamic system, will permit approximate aggregation of variables.* Note that we shall be interested in sufficient, rather than necessary, conditions. Hence, we may also view our task as that of discovering one or more classes of dynamic systems whose variables may be aggregated.

In Section II, we shall present one such class of dynamic systems, which we call "nearly decomposable" systems, and suggest that in such systems, the aggregation of variables described by equations (1.1) through (1.4) can be performed. In Section III, we shall give a physical illustration of such a system. In Sections IV and V, the mathematical analysis underlying the propositions summarized in Section II will be given in some detail. Section VI will present a numerical illustration of the behavior through time of "nearly decomposable" systems, and, as a special case, an application of the aggregation procedure discussed in this paper to the problem of the inversion of matrices. Finally, in Section VII, we shall discuss some further implications of our results and their relations to the recent works of others.

II. PROPERTIES OF NEARLY DECOMPOSABLE MATRICES

The dynamic characteristics of the system (1.1) depend on the properties of the matrix of its coefficients, $P = \|P_{ij}\|$. More specifically, we will be interested in the patterns of zeros and near-zeros in the matrix P. Since we are concerned with closed systems, we assume P to be a square matrix.

Let us consider a matrix P^*, that can be arranged in the following form after an appropriate permutation of rows and columns:

$$(2.1) \qquad P^* = \left\| \begin{matrix} P_1^* & & & & \\ & \ddots & & & \\ & & P_I^* & & \\ & & & \ddots & \\ & & & & P_N^* \end{matrix} \right\|$$

where the P_I^*'s are square submatrices and the remaining elements, not displayed, are all zero. Then the matrix is said to be completely decomposable.

Let us denote the number of rows and columns in the Ith submatrix in P^* by n_I. Then

$$n = \sum_{I=1}^{N} n_I .$$

We shall also adopt the following notation for the vector $\{x_i^*(t)\}$ on which P^* operates:

$$x^*(t) = \{x_i^*(t)\} = \{[x_{i_1}^*(t)], \ldots, [x_{i_I}^*(t)], \ldots, [x_{i_N}^*(t)]\}$$

where $x_{i_I}[(t)]$ is the row vector of a subset of components of $\{x_i^*(t)\}$, so that if

$$x_{i_I}^*(t) = x_i(t)$$

then

$$i = \sum_{J=1}^{I-1} n_J + i_I .$$

It is clear that if the system (1.1) is specified to

$$x^*(t) = x^*(0) P^{*t} \tag{2.2}$$

then the subset $[x_{i_I}^*(t)]$ of $x(t)$ at any stage t depends only on $[x_{i_I}^*(0)]$ and P_I^* and is independent of $[x_{i_J}^*(0)]$ and P_J^*, $I \neq J$.

Let us next consider a slightly altered matrix P defined by

$$P = P^* + \varepsilon C \tag{2.3}$$

where ε is a very small real number, and C is an arbitrary matrix of the same dimension as P^*. In this introductory discussion, the phrase "a very small real number" is intentionally left unprecise; it will be defined later. We shall refer to matrices such as P as *nearly decomposable matrices*. Using P thus defined, we restate equation (1.1) below:

$$x(t+1) = x(t) P . \tag{2.4}$$

It is the dynamic behavior of the system given by (2.4) in which we are interested.

Let the roots of the submatrix P_I^* of P^* be designated as: $\lambda_{1_I}^*, \lambda_{2_I}^*, \ldots, \lambda_{n_I}^*$. We assume that these roots are distinct, and the subscripts are so arranged that $\lambda_{1_I}^* > \lambda_{2_I}^* >, \ldots, > \lambda_{n_I}^*$. In addition, if $\lambda_{1_1}^*, \lambda_{1_2}^*, \ldots, \lambda_{1_N}^*$ are all distinct, then without loss of generality, we can arrange rows and columns so that $\lambda_{1_1}^* > \lambda_{1_2}^*, \ldots, > \lambda_{1_N}^*$. When all these conditions are satisfied, i.e., when all roots of P^* are distinct, we can analyze the dynamic behavior of (2.4) with relative ease. In most cases, we feel that this assumption is not too restrictive as a description of reality. There is, however, an important exception, namely, the case where P^* is a stochastic matrix in which case all $\lambda_{1_I}^*$ are unity. It turns out, fortunately, that our analysis of the case with all distinct roots can readily be extended to the stochastic case. In the remainder of this section, we shall summarize the results of more detailed mathematical analysis presented in Sections IV and V.

Let us define

$$\min_{\substack{i,j \\ i\neq j}} |\lambda_i^* - \lambda_j^*| = \delta^* . \tag{2.5}$$

If P^* is stochastic, the N largest roots of P^* take the identical values of unity. In this case, (2.5) should be interpreted to mean the selection of the minimum of the differences among all roots whose values are not unity and their differences from unity.

Since the roots of a matrix are continuous functions of its elements,[5] we can define, for any positive real number δ, however small, a small enough ε so that, for every root of P^*, λ_i^*, there exists a root of P, λ_i, such that

$$|\lambda_i - \lambda_i^*| < \delta . \tag{2.6}$$

We can choose δ sufficiently smaller than δ^* so that there is no confusion as to which root of P corresponds to any particular root of P^*. The only exceptions to this proposition are the N largest roots of the stochastic P^*. If P^* is stochastic, we have

$$\lambda_{1_I}^* = 1 \qquad (I = 1,2,\ldots,N) , \tag{2.7a}$$

$$|1 - \lambda_{i_I}^*| > \delta^* \qquad (i_I = 2,\ldots,n_I \,;\; I = 1,\ldots,N) . \tag{2.7b}$$

Hence, for P, we must have

$$|1 - \lambda_{1_I}| < \delta \qquad (I = 1,2,\ldots,N) , \tag{2.8a}$$

$$|1 - \lambda_{i_I}| > \delta^* - \delta \qquad (i_I = 2,\ldots,n_I \,;\; I = 1,\ldots,N) . \tag{2.8b}$$

Because of the correspondence of the characteristic roots of P and P^* described above, we expect $x(t)$, when its time path is defined by (2.4), to exhibit the following dynamic behavior:

(1) In the short run, the behavior of $x_{i_I}(t)$ will be dominated by roots belonging to the Ith subset, so that the time path of $x_{i_I}(t)$ will be very close to the time path of $x_{i_I}^*(t)$, and almost independent of $x_{j_J}(t)$, $J \neq I$, and P_J, $J \neq I$. Here, P_J is defined to be the submatrix of P corresponding to P_J^* of P^*. If we are interested in the behavior of the system at this stage, we can treat the system as though it were completely decomposable.

(2) Unlike P^*, P is not completely decomposable, so that the weak links among the subsystems will eventually make their influence felt. But the time required for these influences to appear is long enough so that when

[5] See, for instance, E. C. Titchmarsh, *The Theory of Functions*, 2nd ed., 1939.

they do become visible, within each subsystem the largest root, λ_{1_I}, will have dominated all other roots, $\lambda_{2_I}, \ldots, \lambda_{n_I}$. Thus, at this stage, the variables within each subset, $[x_{i_I}(t)]$, will move proportionately, and the behavior of the whole system will be dominated by N roots, $\lambda_{1_I}, \ldots, \lambda_{1_N}$. Notice that, since the variables in each subsystem move roughly proportionately, the Lange-Hicks condition for aggregation is approximately satisfied.

(3) At the end, however, the behavior of $x(t)$ will be dominated by the largest root of P, as in any linear dynamic system.

It is quite clear that all these statements refer to the limiting properties of the system (2.4), and can be made more precise and meaningful only with more careful mathematical analyses of the system, which are presented in Sections IV and V.

III. A PHYSICAL ILLUSTRATION

Before we proceed with a more complete statement of the mathematics that underlies our analysis, it may be useful to provide an example of a physical system that can be approximately decomposed in the manner just described. We shall see that the principle of aggregation we are employing is essentially that which justifies the replacement of microvariables by macrovariables in classical thermodynamics.

Consider a building whose outside walls provide perfect thermal insulation from the environment. The building is divided into a large number of rooms, the walls between them being good, but not perfect, insulators. Each room is divided into a number of offices by partitions. The partitions are poor insulators. A thermometer hangs in each of the offices. Suppose that at time t_0 the various offices within the building are in a state of thermal disequilibrium—there is a wide variation in temperature from office to office and from room to room. When we take new temperature readings at time t_1, several hours after t_0, what will we find? At t_1, there will be very little variation in temperature among the offices within each single room, but there may still be large temperature variations *among* rooms. When we take readings again at time t_2, several days after t_1, we find an almost uniform temperature throughout the building; the temperature differences among rooms have virtually disappeared.

The well-known equations for the diffusion of heat allow us to represent this situation by a system of differential equations—or approximately by a system of difference equations. Let $F_{i_I}(t)$ be the temperature of the ith office which is in the Ith room, at time t. Let $F(t)$ be the vector consisting of these temperatures as components, $F(t) = [F_{1_1}, F_{2_1}, \ldots, F_{i_I}, \ldots, F_{1_N}, \ldots, F_{n_N}]$. Then

$$F(t+1) = F(t)R \tag{3.1}$$

where R is a matrix whose element, r_{ij}, represents the rate of heat transfer between office i and office j per degree difference in temperature.

A temperature equilibrium *within* each room will be reached rather rapidly, while a temperature equilibrium *among* rooms will be reached only slowly, if the r_{ij} are generally large when i and j are offices in the same room, and are close to zero when i and j are offices in different rooms—that is to say, if the matrix R is nearly decomposable. When this is the case, and as long as we are not interested in the rapid fluctuations in temperature among offices in the same room, we can learn all we want to know about the dynamics of this system by placing a single thermometer in each room—it is unnecessary to place a thermometer in each office.

IV. MATHEMATICAL ANALYSIS

In this section, we shall make precise the meaning of propositions stated at the end of Section II, and provide their proofs for the case where the roots of P^* are all distinct.

Every matrix with distinct roots is similar to a diagonal matrix whose nonzero elements are those roots. Hence, there exist nonsingular matrices Z and Z^* such that

$$PZ = Z\Lambda \, , \tag{4.1}$$

$$P^*Z^* = Z^*\Lambda^* \, , \tag{4.2}$$

where Λ and Λ^* are diagonal matrices whose nonzero elements are roots of P and P^*, respectively. Since Z and Z^* are defined only up to a scalar factor and permutations, we select Z^* so that the $\lambda^*_{i_I}$ appear in order of magnitude for each I.

From the argument leading to (2.6), it is clear that the λ_i's are functions of ε. Let us take a particular value of δ, say δ_0, and choose a value of ε, ε_0, which satisfies (2.6). Then, we can define

$$\delta_i(\varepsilon_0) = \lambda_i(\varepsilon_0) - \lambda_i^* \, , \qquad |\delta_i(\varepsilon_0)| < \delta_0 \; ; \tag{4.3}$$

$$v_i = \frac{\delta_i(\varepsilon_0)}{\delta_0} \, , \qquad |v_i| < 1 \; ; \tag{4.4}$$

and a diagonal matrix whose elements are v_i's, i.e.,

$$V = \begin{Vmatrix} v_1 & & & & \\ & \ddots & & & \\ & & v_i & & \\ & & & \ddots & \\ & & & & v_n \end{Vmatrix} . \tag{4.5}$$

We can then write

$$\Lambda = \Lambda^* + \delta_0 V \,. \tag{4.6}$$

Substitution of (2.3) and (4.6) with these choices of ε and δ into (4.1) yields

$$(P^* + \varepsilon_0 C)Z = Z(\Lambda^* + \delta_0 V) \tag{4.7}$$

and

$$P^*Z - Z\Lambda^* = \delta_0 ZV - \varepsilon_0 CZ \,. \tag{4.8}$$

As $\delta_0 \to 0$, and hence $\varepsilon_0 \to 0$, the Z's remaining bounded, the right hand side of (4.8) approaches a matrix whose elements are all zero. Comparison of the left hand side of (4.8) with (4.2) indicates that, if z_{ij} and $\overset{*}{z}_{ij}$ are elements of Z and Z^*, we must have a relation

$$\lim_{\delta_0 \to 0} z_{ij} = c\overset{*}{z}_{ij} \tag{4.9}$$

for all i and j, where c is some constant. Since c is arbitrary, we let $c = 1$. Thus, we can state:

THEOREM 4.1: *There is a way of selecting the matrices Z such that, for an arbitrary positive real number ζ, there exists ε_0 such that, for $\varepsilon < \varepsilon_0$,*

$$\max_{i,j} |z_{ij} - \overset{*}{z}_{ij}| < \zeta \,. \tag{4.10}$$

Let us take a value of ε, ε_1, that satisfies the condition (4.10). Corresponding to this ε_1, we can define $\lambda_i(\varepsilon_1)$, $i = 1,\ldots,n$. These values can then be inserted in (4.1) to yield a specific Z. We then define, using this Z and the Z^* given by (4.2), a new set of values

$$\zeta_{ij} = z_{ij} - \overset{*}{z}_{ij} \,. \tag{4.11}$$

Because of the way in which the ζ_{ij}'s are constructed, we are assured that $|\zeta_{ij}| < \zeta$ for all i and j. Let us further define

$$u_{ij} = \frac{\zeta_{ij}}{\zeta} \,. \tag{4.12}$$

We note that $|u_{ij}| < 1$. We can then write

$$Z = Z^* + \zeta U \tag{4.13}$$

where U is the matrix whose elements are the u_{ij}'s. We know that

$$x(t) = x(0)P^t \,; \qquad x^*(t) = x^*(0)P^{*^t} \,. \tag{4.14}$$

Consider next vectors $y(t)$ and $y^*(t)$ defined by

(4.15a) $$y(t) = x(t)Z^{-1}$$

(4.15b) $$y^*(t) = x^*Z^{*^{-1}}$$

Substituting (4.15) into (4.14), we obtain:

(4.16a) $$y(t) = x(0)(Z^{-1}Z)P^tZ^{-1} = y(0)(ZPZ^{-1})^t = y(0)\Lambda^t$$

(4.16b) $$y^*(t) = x^*(0)(Z^{*^{-1}}Z^*)P^{*^t}Z^{*^{-1}} = y^*(0)(Z^*P^*Z^{*^{-1}})^t = y^*(0)\Lambda^{*^t} .$$

The inverse transformations of (4.15), when the results of (4.16) are substituted into them, yield:

(4.17a) $$x(t) = y(0)\Lambda^tZ \; ;$$

(4.17b) $$x^*(t) = y^*(0)\Lambda^{*^t}Z^* .$$

Let us now look at elements of (4.17) more closely. They have the form

(4.18) $$x_j(t) = \sum_{i=1}^{n} z_{ij}\, \lambda_i^t y_i(0) .$$

It is obvious, from the structure of the decomposable matrix p^*, that

$$z^*_{i_Ij_J} = 0 \qquad \text{for } I \neq J .$$

This, together with (4.13), implies that

(4.19) $$z_{i_Ij_J} = \zeta u_{i_Ij_J} \qquad \text{for } I \neq J .$$

Hence, we can divide the right hand side of (4.18) into five sets of terms according to the scheme:

(4.20) $$x_{j_J}(t) = \zeta u_{1_1j_J}\lambda^t_{1_1}y_{1_1}(0) + z_{1_Jj_J}\lambda^t_{1_J}y_{1_J}(0)$$

$$+ \zeta \sum_{\substack{I=2\\I\neq J}}^{N} u_{1_Ij_J}\lambda^t_{1_I}y_{1_I}(0) + \sum_{i_J=2}^{n_J} z_{i_Jj_J}\lambda^t_{i_J}y_{i_J}(0) + \zeta \sum_{\substack{I=1\\I\neq J}}^{N}\sum_{i_I=2}^{n_I} u_{i_Ij_J}\lambda^t_{i_I}y_{i_I}(0) .$$

In the special case where $J = 1$, the first term is absent. In order to discuss the meaning and implications of (4.20), let us give names to each term on the right hand side of (4.20) as follows:

(4.21) $$x_{j_J}(t) = \zeta S_j^{(1)} + S_j^{(2)} + \zeta S_j^{(3)} + S_j^{(4)} + \zeta S_j^{(5)} .$$

For almost all choices of $y(0)$, each of the five terms on the right side of (4.21) will be nonzero at $t = 0$. We limit ourselves to this case, which is the general one. The following propositions are now self evident, and we state them as a theorem:

THEOREM 4.2. PART (1): *Since $\lambda_{1_J} > \lambda_{j_J}, j = 2,\ldots,n$, for any real positive number η_0 there exists an integer T_0 such that, for $t > T_0$,*

$$\frac{|S_j^{(4)}|}{|S_j^{(2)}|} < \eta_0 . \tag{4.22}$$

For a given $T_1 > T_0$ and arbitrary positive real number η_1, there exists a number ζ_1, and hence a number ε_1 by Theorem 4.1, such that, for $t < T_1$ and $\varepsilon < \varepsilon_1$,

$$\frac{|\zeta(S_j^{(1)} + S_j^{(3)} + S_j^{(5)})|}{|S_j^{(2)} + S_j^{(4)}|} < \eta_1 . \tag{4.23}$$

Theorem 4.2, Part 1, states that, for a sufficiently small ε, the system characterized by a nearly decomposable matrix P behaves in a manner similar to the behavior of the completely decomposable system P^* for small t. This is even clearer when we express $x^*(t)$ as

$$x^*_{i_J}(t) = z^*_{1_J j_J} \lambda^{*t}_{1_J} y^*_{1_J}(0) + \sum_{i=2}^{n} z^*_{i_J j_J} \lambda^{*t}_{i_J} y^*_{i_J}(0) \tag{4.24}$$

and compare (4.24) with (4.20), remembering that

$$z_{i_j} \to z^*_{i_j}, \quad \lambda_i \to \lambda^*_i \quad \text{as} \quad \varepsilon \to 0 .$$

THEOREM 4.2 PART (2): *Given ε_1 satisfying condition (4.23), for an arbitrary positive real number η_2, there exists a number $T_2 > T_1$ such that, for $t > T_2$,*

$$\frac{|S_j^{(4)} + \zeta S_j^{(5)}|}{|\zeta S_j^{(1)} + S_j^{(2)} + \zeta S_j^{(3)}|} < \eta_2 \tag{4.25}$$

and, for any positive real number η_3, there exists a number $T_3 > T_2$ such that, for $t > T_3$,

$$\frac{|S_j^{(2)} + \zeta S_j^{(3)} + S_j^{(4)} + \zeta S_j^{(5)}|}{\zeta |S_j^{(1)}|} < \eta_3 . \tag{4.26}$$

These two inequalities are direct consequences of the fact that we have arranged the index of roots in such a way that $\lambda_{1_I} > \lambda_{i_I}$ for $i - 1,\ldots,n$, $\lambda_{1_I} > \lambda_{1_J}$ for $I < J$.

We may summarize the above propositions by saying that the dynamic behavior of the system represented by the nearly decomposable matrix P can be analyzed in the following four stages: (1) $t < T_0$, where S_2 and S_4 dominate the rest of the terms in the summation (4.20); (2) $T_0 < t < T_1$, where S_2 dominates all the rest; (3) $t > T_2 > T_1$ where S_1, S_2, and S_3 together dominate S^4 and S^5; and (4) $t > T_3 > T_2$, where S_1 finally dominates all the rest.

If $|\lambda_{1_1}| \leqslant 1$ so that the system as a whole is stable, we may use the terminology: stage (1) is the short-run dynamics; stage (2), the short-run equilibrium; stage (3), the long-run dynamics; stage (4), the long-run equilibrium. Note that the terms S_1, S_2, and S_3 involve only the aggregate variables $y_{1_I}(0)$, $I = 1,\ldots,N$

Thus we conclude: In the short-run, or for stages (1) and (2), we may treat our system as though it consists of N independent subsystems; in the long-run, i.e., for stages (3) and (4), we may look at our system as a set of relations among N aggregative variables, the y_{1_I}'s, ignoring the relations within each of the subsystems.

Finally, it is perfectly clear how our argument above can be extended to cover the special case where P^* is stochastic. If P^* is stochastic, the largest roots of all P_I^*'s are unity, and this violates the condition for the existence of the matrix Z^*. However, each submatrix, P_I^*, will have a similar matrix, Λ_I^*. Then, we can define Z_I^* such that

$$P_I^* Z_I^* = Z_I^* \Lambda_I^* . \tag{4.27}$$

Let us now construct, for each Z_I^* and Λ_I^*, an $n \times n$ matrix appropriately bordered with zeros. We shall designate these bordered matrices by the same symbols as are employed for the corresponding $n_I \times n_I$ matrices. We then define

$$Z^* = \sum_{I=1}^{N} Z_I^* ; \quad \Lambda^* = \sum_{I=1}^{N} \Lambda_I^* .$$

Although the bordered Z_I^*'s are singular, Z^* defined above is not singular, and we can define Z^{*-1} to be the inverse of Z^*. When Z^*, Λ^*, Z^{*-1} thus defined are inserted into equation (4.2) and the following equations, the argument can proceed in the same manner as above.

V. A SPECIAL CASE: STOCHASTIC MATRICES

The proof of the basic theorem presented in the preceding section has the advantage that it is straightforward and fairly general. In studying this problem, however, we have found it rather difficult to appreciate the implications of the mathematical results adequately, and we feel that another, somewhat more specialized, but substantially equivalent way of stating our theorems is very helpful. At least, it enables us to follow the dynamic process of the system in more detail. In the present section, we shall state these alternative theorems, leaving their proofs to the Appendix. Having given the general proof in the preceding section, the sole purpose of stating the alternative theorems is to provide for the reader some aid which we ourselves have found useful in getting further insight into the nature of the problem. This being the case, we shall restrict ourselves to the simplest case of the stochastic matrix, and sacrifice mathematical rigor whenever it interferes with the simplicity of our presentation.

Let us restate our systems:

$$x(t+1) = x(t)P\,, \tag{5.1a}$$

$$x^*(t+1) = x^*(t)P^*\,. \tag{5.1b}$$

These relations are identical to equations (2.4) and (2.2) except that now x, x^*, and P, P^* are restricted to probability vectors and stochastic matrices, respectively. We assume that the matrix C in (2.3) has the necessary property to keep both P and P^* stochastic. Thus, we may think of the system as having n possible states, the subscript running over these states; $x_i(t)$ is the unconditional probability that the system is in the ith state in period t; P_{ij} is the conditional probability that the system is in the jth state in period $(t+1)$, given that the system is in state i in period t. We note that the relations (2.8) among the roots of P hold for sufficiently small ε.

We wish to express $x(t)$ and $x^*(t)$ in terms of the roots of the respective matrices. In Section IV we have done so by means of the theorem asserting the existence of a similar diagonal matrix. We shall proceed in a somewhat different manner in this section, as follows: We rewrite (5.1a) and (5.1b) as

$$x(t) = x(0)P^t\,, \tag{5.2a}$$

$$x^*(t) = x^*(0)P^{*^t}\,. \tag{5.2b}$$

Now, for any nonsingular $n \times n$ matrix A whose roots, $k_1,\ldots,k_n$, are distinct, there exists a unique set of n matrices, $\alpha^{(1)},\ldots,\alpha^{(n)}$ with the following characteristics[6]:

(i) $\alpha^{(\varrho)} \cdot \alpha^{(\varrho)} = \alpha^{(\varrho)}\,,\ \varrho = 1,\ldots,n\,.$ (idempotency),

(ii) $\alpha^{(\varrho)} \cdot \alpha^{(\sigma)} = 0\,;\quad \varrho \neq \sigma\,;\quad \varrho, \sigma = 1,\ldots,n$ (orthogonality),

(iii) $$\sum_{\varrho=1}^{n} \alpha^{(\varrho)} = I\,,$$

(iv) $$\sum_{\varrho=1}^{n} k_\varrho \alpha^{(\varrho)} = A\,,$$

where 0 in (ii) is an $n \times n$ matrix whose elements are all zero, and I in (iii) is $n \times n$ identity matrix. It is easy to see that, from these properties, it follows that

(v) $$A^t = \sum_{\varrho=1}^{n} k_\varrho^t \alpha^{(\varrho)}\,.$$

[6] See, for instance, J. H. M. Wedderburn, *Lectures on Matrices*, 1934, pp. 25ff.

Using this representation, we can express P^t thus:

$$P^t = \sum_{\varrho=1}^{n} \lambda_\varrho^t \pi^{(\varrho)} \tag{5.3}$$

where the $\pi^{(\varrho)}$'s are matrices associated with P that satisfy the conditions (i) to (iv) above. Remembering the classification of roots described by (2.8), we divide the terms in the right hand side of (5.3) into three parts:

$$P^t = \pi^{(1_1)} + \sum_{I=2}^{N} \lambda_{1_I}^t \pi^{(1_I)} + \sum_{I=1}^{N} \sum_{\varrho=2}^{n_I} \lambda_{\varrho_I}^t \pi^{(\varrho_I)} . \tag{5.4}$$

We cannot expand P^* directly into idempotent matrices as above because the N largest roots of P^* are all unity. However, any non-decomposable submatrix P_I^* of P^* can be so expanded, and we may write

$$P_I^{*t} = \pi^{*(1_I)} + \sum_{\varrho_I=2}^{n_I} \lambda_{\varrho_I}^{*t} \pi^{*(\varrho_I)} \qquad \text{for all } I . \tag{5.5}$$

As in the argument we used at the end of Section IV, let us construct $n \times n$ matrices by bordering those in (5.5) with the appropriate number of rows and columns of zeros, and designate these by the same symbols as those used for the $n_I \times n_I$ matrices in (5.5). Then

$$P^* = \sum_{I=1}^{N} P_I^* = \sum_{I=1}^{N} \pi^{*(1_I)} + \sum_{I=1}^{N} \sum_{\varrho_I=2}^{n_I} \lambda_{\varrho_I}^* \pi^{*(\varrho_I)} \tag{5.6}$$

and for the tth power of P^*

$$P^{*t} = \sum_{I=1}^{N} \pi^{*(1_I)} + \sum_{I=1}^{N} \sum_{\varrho_I=2}^{n_I} \lambda_{\varrho_I}^{*t} \pi^{*(\varrho_I)} . \tag{5.7}$$

When we compare equations (5.4) and (5.7) with equations (4.20) and (4.24), we see that they are analogous expressions, but they also have some differences. Equation (4.20) was very convenient for obtaining information on the variations in the relative influences of various λ's as the size of ε varied. Equation (5.4) gives clearer indications of the characteristics of the time path of x, as we shall show presently.

We first note that, since the $\lambda_{1_I}^*$'s are unity and the λ_{1_I}'s are very close to unity for all I, the first summation term on the right hand side of equation (5.7) and the first and second summation terms of equation (5.4) remain almost unchanged for a relatively small t. This means that, for x to behave very much like x^* for small t as indicated by Theorem 4.2, Part 1, $\pi^{(\varrho_I)}$ must approach $\pi^{*(\varrho_I)}$ for $\varrho = 2,\ldots,n$ and $I = 1,\ldots,N$, as ε goes to zero. Furthermore, if x is to exhibit the behavior described by Part 2 of Theorem 4.2 when t becomes so large that the $\lambda^t_{1_I}$'s are no longer nearly unity, the elements of $\pi^{(1_I)}$, $I = 1,\ldots,N$, must be functions of j, J, and I, but independent of i.

Before we proceed to state our basic propositions as theorems, we need a few additional definitions, which we list below:

$P^{(t)}_{ij}$: elements of the matrix P^t, i.e., the tth power of the matrix P;

$P^{*(t)}_{ij}$: elements of the matrix P^{*t};

$\bar{x}^*$: equilibrium value of x^*;

$$\bar{x}^*_{i|I} = \frac{\bar{x}^*_{i_I}}{\sum_{i_I=1}^{n_I} \bar{x}^*_{i_I}}, \qquad I = 1,\ldots,N.$$

Note that the vector $[\bar{x}^*_{i|I}]$, $i = 1,\ldots,n_I$, is the characteristic vector of P^*_I associated with the root of unity.

$$\pi^{(1_l)}_{IJ} = \sum_{i_I=1}^{n_I} \sum_{j_J=1}^{n_J} \bar{x}^*_{i_I|I}\, \pi^{(1_l)}_{i_I j_J} \tag{5.8}$$

for $l = 1,\ldots,N$, $I = 1,\ldots,N$, and $J = 1,\ldots,N$.

$$P_{IJ} = \sum_{l=1}^{N} \lambda_{1_l} \pi^{(1_l)}_{IJ}. \tag{5.9}$$

The subscript of λ and superscript of π are written 1_l instead of the usual 1_I to avoid confusion.

In terms of these definitions, the following three theorems are proved in the Appendix.

THEOREM 5.1: *For an arbitrary positive real number ξ_2 there exists a number ε_2 such that for $\varepsilon < \varepsilon_2$,*

$$\max_{i,j} |\pi^{(\varrho_l)}_{ij} - \pi^{*(\varrho_l)}_{ij}| < \xi_2$$

for $\varrho_l = 2,\ldots,n_l$, *and* $l = 1,\ldots,N$.

THEOREM 5.2: *For an arbitrary positive real number ω there exists a number ε_ω such that for $\varepsilon < \varepsilon_\omega$*

$$\max_{i,j} |\pi^{(1_l)}_{i_I j_J} - \bar{x}^*_{j|J}\, \pi^{(1_l)}_{IJ}| < \omega$$

for $l = 1,\ldots,N$, $I = 1,\ldots,N$, $J = 1,\ldots,N$.

THEOREM 5.3: *The right hand side of equation* (5.9) *is the idempotent expansion of the matrix* P_{IJ}.

The implications of the above theorems are quite clear. Since the λ_{1_l} are almost unity for $l = 1,\ldots,N$ as indicated in (2.8), for a relatively small t, say $t < T_2$, $\lambda_{1_l}^t$, $l = 1,\ldots,N$, will be very close to unity. Hence the first two terms on the right hand side of equation (5.4) will not change very much, while the first term on the right hand side of equation (5.7) will not change at all. Hence, for $t < T_2$, the time behavior of x and x^* are completely determined by the last terms on the right hand side of equation (5.4) and (5.7), respectively. But, Theorem 5.1 asserts that the π's appearing in the last term of equation (5.4) can be made as close as we please to the corresponding π^*'s in equation (5.7), by taking ε sufficiently small. We may recall that $\lambda_{i} \to \lambda_{i}^*$ as $\varepsilon \to 0$. Hence, for $t < T_2$ the time path of x must be very close to the time path of x^*. Note that T_2 can be made as large as we please by taking ε sufficiently small.

Since the $\lambda_{i_l}^*$ are independent of ε, and for $i_l = 2,\ldots,n_l$ less than unity as is indicated in (2.7), for any positive real ξ_1 we can define T_1^* such that for $t > T_1^*$ the absolute value of the last summation term on the right hand side of (5.7) is less than ξ_1. T_1^* is independent of ε. On the other hand, (2.8) and Theorem 5.1 insure not only that for any positive real ξ_1 there exists T_1 such that for $t > T_1$ the absolute value of the last summation term on the right hand side of (5.4) is less than ξ_1, but that $T_1 \to T_1^*$ for the same ξ_1 as $\varepsilon \to 0$. That is, for any positive real number ξ_1, there exist T_1^* and T_1 such that

$$(5.10) \qquad \left|\sum_{l=1}^{N} \sum_{\varrho_l=2}^{n_l} \lambda^{*t}_{\varrho_l} \pi^{*(\varrho_l)}\right| < \xi_1 \qquad \text{for } t > T_1^*,$$

$$(5.11) \qquad \left|\sum_{l=1}^{N} \sum_{\varrho_l=2}^{n_l} \lambda^{t}_{\varrho} \pi^{(\varrho_l)}\right| < \xi_1 \qquad \text{for } t > T_1 \text{ and } T_1 \to T_1^* \text{ as } \varepsilon \to 0\,.$$

Since T_2 can be made as large as we please by taking ε sufficiently small while T_1^* is independent of ε, let us take ε such that T_2 is very much larger than T_1. Provided that ε is not identically zero so that none of λ_{1_l} except λ_1 is identically unity, the second summation term on the right hand side of equation (5.4) will eventually become negligible as t becomes indefinitely large. Let us define T_3, corresponding to an arbitrary positive real number ξ_3, such that for $t > T_3$

$$(5.12) \qquad \max_{i,j} \left|\sum_{l=2}^{N} \lambda_{1_l}^t \pi_{ij}^{(1_l)}\right| < \xi_3\,.$$

T_3 also increases without limit as $\varepsilon \to 0$.

We show the relations among the various T's schematically below:

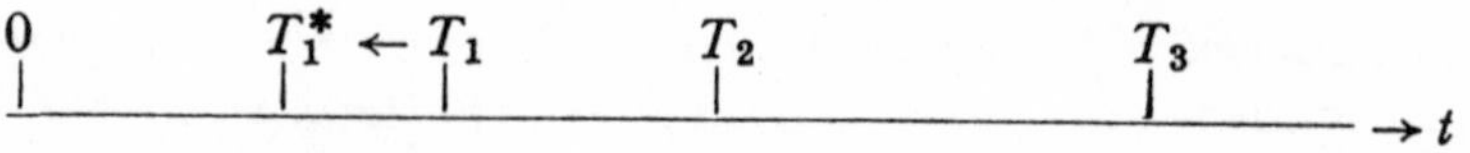

For $T_2 < t < T_3$, corresponding to the period which we called the long run dynamics in Section IV, the last summation term on the right hand side of equation (5.4) has very little influence on the time path of x. The path is determined by the first and second summation terms on the right hand side of equation (5.4). But, Theorem 5.2 asserts that the elements of $\pi^{(1_l)}$, $l = 1,\ldots,N$, are functions only of j, I, J, and independent of i. That is, for any I, J, and l, $[\pi_{i_I 1_J}^{(1_l)}, \ldots, \pi_{i_I j_J}^{(1_l)}, \ldots, \pi_{i_I n_J}^{(1_l)}]$, are proportional to the characteristic vector of P_J^* associated with the root of unity, and are the same for $i_I = 1,\ldots,n_I$. Hence, $[x_{1_I},\ldots,x_{i_I},\ldots,x_{n_I}]$ will move, for the period $T_2 < t < T_3$, keeping a roughly constant proportionality relationship among individual elements for a given I. This permits us, following the Hicks-Lange condition, to replace the n-dimensional vector by an N-dimensional vector, and the $n \times n$ matrix P by an $N \times N$ matrix $||P_{IJ}||$.

The usefulness of Theorem 5.3 will become apparent in the next section when we shall discuss the application of our theorems to the problems of inverting nearly decomposable matrices. Here we merely note that, since (1) $\pi^*_{i_I}$ has $\bar{x}^*_{1|_I}$ as its rows where its elements are not zero, (2) $\pi^*_{i_I}$ are orthogonal to $\pi^*_{i|_I}$ for $i = 2,\ldots,n$, (3) $\pi_{i_I} \to \pi^*_{i_I}$ for $i_I = 2,\ldots,n_I$, we can express P_{IJ} as

$$P_{IJ} = \sum_{i_I=1}^{n_I} \sum_{j_J=1}^{n_J} \bar{x}^*_{i_I|I} P_{i_I j_J}. \tag{5.13}$$

VI. A NUMERICAL ILLUSTRATION

The above results can be understood more readily with the aid of a simple numerical example. Let us consider a nearly decomposable stochastic matrix

$$P = \begin{Vmatrix} .9700 & .0295 & .0005 & 0 \\ .0200 & .9800 & 0 & 0 \\ 0 & 0 & .9600 & .0400 \\ .0002 & .0002 & .0396 & .9600 \end{Vmatrix} \tag{6.1}$$

and the corresponding completely decomposable matrix

$$P = \begin{Vmatrix} .9700 & .0300 & 0 & 0 \\ .0200 & .9800 & 0 & 0 \\ 0 & 0 & .9600 & .0400 \\ 0 & 0 & .0400 & .9600 \end{Vmatrix} = \begin{Vmatrix} P_1^* & 0 \\ 0 & P_2^* \end{Vmatrix}. \tag{6.2}$$

We can compute $\bar{x}^*_j|_J$:

$$[\bar{x}^*_j|_1] = [.4\ .6]\,, \tag{6.3}$$

$$[\bar{x}^*_j|_2] = [.5\ .5]\,; \tag{6.4}$$

and P_{IJ}:

$$\|P_{IJ}\| = \begin{Vmatrix} .9998 & .0002 \\ .0002 & .9998 \end{Vmatrix}. \tag{6.5}$$

The roots of P and their selected powers are

$\lambda_1 = 1;$

$\lambda_2 = .9996;\quad \lambda_2^{128} = .9511;\quad \lambda_2^{(128)^2} = .001724;$

$\lambda_3 = .952004;\quad \lambda_3^{128} = 1.845 \times 10^{-3};\quad \lambda_3^{(128)^2} = 1.091 \times 10^{-350};$

$\lambda_4 = .9202;\quad \lambda_4^{128} = 2.381 \times 10^{-5};\quad \lambda_4^{(128)^2} = 1.622 \times 10^{-592}.$

The idempotent expansion of P is given by

$$P^t = \pi^{(1)} + \lambda_2^t \pi^{(2)} + \lambda_3^t \pi^{(3)} + \lambda_4^t \pi^{(4)}\,, \tag{6.6}$$

i.e.,

$$P^{(t)} = (1.)^t \begin{Vmatrix} 0.20050125 & 0.29824561 & 0.25062657 & 0.25062657 \\ 0.20050125 & 0.29824561 & 0.25062657 & 0.25062657 \\ 0.20050125 & 0.29824561 & 0.25062657 & 0.25062657 \\ 0.20050125 & 0.29824561 & 0.25062657 & 0.25062657 \end{Vmatrix} \tag{6.7}$$

$$+ (.9996)^t \begin{Vmatrix} .198685261 & .296522699 & -.248356576 & -.250865228 \\ .202740062 & .302574184 & -.253425078 & -.255984927 \\ -.199496221 & -.297732997 & .249370276 & .251889168 \\ -.197501259 & -.294755666 & .246876573 & .249370276 \end{Vmatrix}$$

$$+ (.952004)^t \begin{Vmatrix} .6004874 & -.5952777 & .0019774 & -.0807124 \\ -.4030171 & .3995206 & -.0013271 & .0541701 \\ -.0008141 & .0008070 & -.0000027 & .0001094 \\ .0000403 & -.0000399 & .0000001 & -.0000054 \end{Vmatrix}$$

$$+ (.92019)^t \begin{Vmatrix} .0002636 & -.0007692 & -.0062681 & .0062939 \\ -.0000878 & .0002397 & .0020960 & -.0021003 \\ -.0209766 & .0577601 & .5007744 & -.5017791 \\ .0208776 & -.0569881 & -.4983870 & .4993957 \end{Vmatrix}.$$

From (6.7), we also readily compute P^{128} (the matrix for the "middle-run" dynamic system) and $P^{(128)^2}$, the matrix for the long run:

$$(6.8) \qquad P^{128} = \begin{Vmatrix} .390089 & .579037 & .016631 & .014244 \\ .392503 & .586246 & .011831 & .009419 \\ .009465 & .013138 & .487509 & .489888 \\ .011385 & .015999 & .485107 & .487509 \end{Vmatrix},$$

$$(6.9) \qquad P^{(128)^2} = \begin{Vmatrix} .200776 & .298656 & .250286 & .250282 \\ .200782 & .298664 & .250279 & .250275 \\ .200222 & .297829 & .250973 & .250976 \\ .200225 & .297833 & .250970 & .250973 \end{Vmatrix}.$$

Note that, if we neglect roots smaller than 0.002, we have

$$(6.10) \qquad P^{128} = \pi^{(1)} + \lambda_2^{128}\pi^{(2)},$$

$$(6.11) \qquad P^{(128)^2} = \pi^{(1)}.$$

The reader's attention is called to the behavior of elements of P^t from P^{128} to $P^{(128)^2}$—elements of P_1^t and P_2^t maintain the same proportion over the columns and independently of rows within each submatrix while moving toward the full equilibrium.

It is of some interest to see whether or not our results are useful for inverting the nearly decomposable matrix, P. We know that

$$(6.12) \qquad P^{-1} = \sum_{l=1}^{N} \sum_{\varrho_l=1}^{n_l} \lambda_{\varrho_l}^{-1}\pi^{(\varrho_l)}.$$

This relation is of little use for computational purposes, since the π's are very difficult to compute. But, in the case of nearly decomposable matrices, this leads to a potentially useful approximation. We note that, from Theorem 5.1,

$$(6.13) \qquad P^{-1} \simeq \sum_{l=1}^{N} \lambda_{1_l}^{-1}\pi^{(1_l)} + P^{*^{-1}} - \sum_{I=1}^{N} \pi^{*(1_l)}.$$

Since P^* is completely decomposable, it is much simpler to invert. The $\pi^{*(1_l)}$ are, of course, matrices with identical rows, and their rows are the characteristic vectors of the respective submatrices P_I, $I = 1,\ldots,N$, associated with roots of unity. Hence, our problem reduces to that of computing the first term on the right hand side of (6.13). By Theorem 5.2, we can write

$$(6.14) \qquad \sum_{l=1}^{N} \lambda_{1_l}^{-1}\pi_{ij}^{(1_l)} = \bar{x}^*_{j|J} \sum_{l=1}^{N} \lambda_{1_l}^{-1}\pi_{IJ}^{(1_l)}.$$

But, by Theorem 5.3, we have

$$(6.15) \qquad \sum_{l=1}^{N} \lambda_{1_l}^{-1}\pi_{IJ}^{(1_l)} = P_{IJ}^{(-1)}.$$

Hence,

(6.16)
$$\sum_{l=1}^{N} \lambda_{1_l}^{-1} \pi_{ij}^{(1_l)} = \bar{x}_{j|J}^{*} \, P_{IJ}^{(-1)} .$$

To summarize: in order to obtain p^{-1}, (i) find the inverses of P_I^*; (ii) compute $\bar{x}_{j|J}^*$ and form $\pi^{*(1_l)}$ directly from them; (iii) form the aggregate matrix $||P_{IJ}||$ by (5.13); (iv) invert $||P_{IJ}||$; (v) substitute these results into (6.13) to obtain P^{-1}.

Going back to the numerical example of P and P^* given by (6.1) and (6.2), we readily find

(6.17a)
$$P_1^{*^{-1}} = \begin{Vmatrix} 1.031578947 & -.031578947 \\ -.021032617 & 1.021052620 \end{Vmatrix},$$

(6.17b)
$$P_2^{*^{-1}} = \begin{Vmatrix} 1.043478260 & -.043478260 \\ -.043478260 & 1.043478260 \end{Vmatrix}.$$

$[\bar{x}_{j|J}^*]$ and $||P_{IJ}||$ have already been given by (6.3), (6.4), and (6.5). We also have

(6.18)
$$||P_{IJ}||^{-1} = \begin{Vmatrix} 1.00020008 & -.00020008 \\ -.00020008 & 1.00020008 \end{Vmatrix}.$$

Substituting these results into (6.16), we have

(6.19)
$$\sum_{l=1}^{2} \lambda_{1_l}^{-1} \pi^{(1_l)} = \begin{Vmatrix} .400080032 & .600120048 & -.000100040 & -.000100040 \\ .400080032 & .600120048 & -.000100040 & -.000100040 \\ -.000800320 & -.001200480 & .500100040 & .500100040 \\ -.000800320 & -.001200480 & .500100040 & .500100040 \end{Vmatrix}.$$

Further substitutions into (6.13) yield

(6.20)
$$P^{-1} \simeq \begin{Vmatrix} 1.031658979 & -.034588990 & -.000100040 & -.000100040 \\ -.020972585 & 1.021172668 & -.000100040 & -.000100040 \\ -.000800320 & -.001200480 & 1.043578300 & -.043378220 \\ -.000800320 & -.001200480 & -.043378220 & 1.043578300 \end{Vmatrix}.$$

This result may be compared with the inverse obtained by the perturbation method, which is probably the most efficient way of obtaining the approximate inverse of a matrix of the type treated here.[7]

Let C be defined by

(6.21)
$$P = P^* + \varepsilon C$$

where ε is a small positive number. Let $\hat{C}$ be defined by

(6.22)
$$P^{-1} = P^{*^{-1}} + \varepsilon \hat{C}$$

[7] See, for instance, Courant, R. and D. Hilbert, *Methods of Mathematical Physics*, pp. 42–43 and 343–350.

where ε is the same number as in equation (6.21). Then, we have

$$P \cdot P^{-1} = (P^* + \varepsilon C)(P^{*^{-1}} + \varepsilon \hat{C}) . \tag{6.23}$$

Ignoring the terms in higher powers of ε, we get:

$$\hat{C} = -P^{*^{-1}} C P^{*^{-1}} . \tag{6.24}$$

If, in the numerical example of (6.1) and (6.2), we take ε to be 0.0001, we have

$$C = \begin{Vmatrix} 0 & -5 & 5 & 0 \\ 0 & 0 & 0 & 0 \\ 0 & 0 & 0 & 0 \\ 2 & 2 & -4 & 0 \end{Vmatrix} \tag{6.25}$$

$$\varepsilon \hat{C} = \begin{Vmatrix} -.000011 & .000527 & -.000538 & +.000022 \\ .000000 & -.000011 & +.000011 & .000000 \\ .000009 & .000009 & -.000018 & .000001 \\ .000211 & .000206 & .000436 & .000018 \end{Vmatrix} , \tag{6.26}$$

$$P^{-1} \simeq \begin{Vmatrix} 1.031568 & -.031052 & -.000538 & .000022 \\ -.021053 & 1.021042 & .000011 & .000000 \\ .000009 & .000009 & 1.043460 & -.043477 \\ -.000211 & -.000206 & -.043042 & 1.043460 \end{Vmatrix} . \tag{6.27}$$

The direct multiplication of P^{-1} given by (6.27) with P given by (6.1) shows that the approximate inverse obtained by the perturbation method is accurate to the 6th decimal place. The estimate of the inverse given by (6.20), obtained by the aggregation procedure, has an error of about 0.0001 in each element in the product. This relatively large error is caused by the restriction, implicit in the aggregation procedure, that the matrix elements *within* each subset are replaced by the eigenvectors corresponding to the middle-run equilibrium.

On the other hand, the perturbation method assumes implicitly that there is a zero probability that the system will move more than once from a state belonging to one subset to a state belonging to another subset. Hence, we can conclude that, while the perturbation method gives us a good approximation to the short-run behavior of the system, and hence to P^{-1}, its approximation to the middle-run behavior (and hence to $(P^{-1})^t$ for relatively large t) will be much less good. The aggregation method permits us to study this middle-run behavior, as we have seen earlier in this section.

For those readers who may be interested in the comparison, we give P^{-1} obtained by equating $t = -1$ in equation (6.7):

$$(6.28)\quad P^{-1} = \begin{Vmatrix} 1.0306708 & -.0302846 & -.0026491 & -.0783382 \\ -.0206318 & 1.0209660 & -.0019932 & .0492225 \\ .0440999 & -.1027626 & 1.0505158 & -.0510149 \\ -.0408082 & .1067156 & -.0495267 & 1.0505238 \end{Vmatrix} .$$

VII. SOME CONCLUDING COMMENTS

In the preceding sections, we have analyzed the structure of dynamic systems represented by nearly-decomposable matrices. We have seen that such systems may be viewed as composite systems, constructed by the superposition of: (1) terms representing interactions of the variables within each subsystem; and (2) terms representing interactions among the subsystems. We concluded that, over a relatively short period, the first group of terms dominates the behavior of the system, and hence each subsystem can be studied (approximately) independently of other subsystems. Over a relatively long period of time, on the other hand, the second group of terms dominates the behavior of the system, and the whole system moves, keeping the state of equilibrium within each subsystem—i.e., the variables within each subsystem move roughly proportionately. Hence, the variables within each subsystem can be aggregated into indexes representing the subsystem.

Thus, the system of variables in the case just described can be represented as a two-level hierarchy, with the aggregative variables at the higher level. Now, there is no reason why we need to restrict ourselves to a two-level hierarchy. For, in such a hierarchy, each of the subsystem variables at the lower level might be an aggregate of variables at a still lower level of aggregation. The matrix of a three-level hierarchy, for example, might look something like this:

$$\begin{Vmatrix} P_1 & Q_1 & S_1 & S_2 \\ Q_2 & P_2 & S_3 & S_4 \\ R_1 & R_2 & P_3 & Q_3 \\ R_3 & R_4 & Q_4 & P_4 \end{Vmatrix} .$$

In this matrix, the elements of the submatrices designated as Q's are of the first order of smallness, and the elements of the R's and S's of the second order of smallness. At the first level of aggregation, there will be four aggregative variables corresponding to the four submatrices along the diagonal, respectively. At the second level of aggregation, there will be two aggregative variables, corresponding to the blocks indicated by broken lines.

It is of some interest to consider the implications of our analysis concerning the computation involved in inverting a matrix in this context. To invert a matrix like the one above, we would first invert the matrices P_i, then the two aggregative matrices

$$\begin{Vmatrix} P_1 & Q_1 \\ Q_2 & P_2 \end{Vmatrix} \quad \text{and} \quad \begin{Vmatrix} P_3 & Q_3 \\ Q_4 & P_4 \end{Vmatrix},$$

and finally the second level aggregative matrix.

In ordinary methods of matrix inversion, the number of multiplications increases as the cube of the size of the matrix. On the other hand, under the method of inversion suggested above, if the size of the largest matrix to be inverted at any level of aggregation remains constant as n increases, then the number of matrices to be inverted will increase proportionately with n, their size will not increase, and the total number of multiplications will increase only slightly more than proportionately with n.

It may be objected that decomposable matrices are rare objects, mathematically speaking, and nearly decomposable matrices almost as rare. For if the elements of a matrix are selected in any ordinary way by a random process, the probability that the matrix will be decomposable is zero. There is every reason to believe, however, not only that near-decomposability is a very common characteristic of dynamic systems that exist in the real world, but also that many economists and other social scientists conduct their research as through this were the case. As we have pointed out in the introductory remarks, every time economists construct indices representing groups of variables and construct a theory in terms of such indices, they are implicitly assuming that the economic system they study is constructed in the hierarchical form described above.

It is interesting to note that many recent discussions on the problems of aggregation can be looked at as studies of various aspects of a system like the one analyzed here.

Interest in the aggregation of the static input-output matrices largely stems from the desire to facilitate the inversion of the matrices involved.[8] As we have shown in Section VI, the method suggested by our analysis is not so efficient as the perturbation method, in the sense that the product of the original matrix with its inverse obtained by our method deviates further from

[8] See, for instance, J. B. Balderston and T. M. Whitin, *op. cit.*; O. Morgenstern and Whitin, "Aggregation and Errors in Input-Output Models," Logistics Research Project, George Washington University, cited in F.T. Moore, "A Survey of Current Inter-Industry Models," in *Input-Output Analysis, an Appraisal*, Studies in Income and Wealth, vol. 18, p. 228 (National Bureau of Economic Research). J. C. H. Fei, "A Fundamental Theorem for the Aggregation Problem of Input-Output Analysis," *Econometrica*, 1956, pp. 400–412; S. B. Noble, "Structure and Classification in Resource Flow Models," The George Washington University Logistic Research Project, Serial T-100/59, May 19, 1959; and A. Ghosh, "Input-Output Analysis with Substantially Independent Groups of Industries, *Econometrica*, 1960, pp. 88–96.

the identity matrix than the product of the original matrix with the inverse obtained by the perturbation method. Our analysis provides, however, a better ground for interpreting the approximate result than the mechanical application of the perturbation method. Furthermore, the goodness of the approximation must be judged in terms of the decisions that will be based on the approximation rather than the closeness of the product to the identity matrix, and in this sense, it is by no means clear that the perturbation method is superior to ours.

Some of the recent work of Theil can also be related to our analysis.[9] One of his aggregation problems may be looked at in the following way: Suppose that we have a set of observations over time on the x's, and estimate from these observations the matrix of coefficients P. Suppose further that we classify the x's into a few groups, construct indices representing these groups, consider a new linear system relating these indices, and estimate the new aggregate coefficients from the same set of observations. Theil investigated, among other things, the relations between the micro and macro coefficients then estimated. Theil's results show that the conditions under which there exists a relatively simple relation between micro and macro variables are very severe. Our result suggests that, if the underlying structure generating the x's is nearly decomposable, then, as the x's are aggregated, the unit of time over which observations are made should be changed accordingly. However, a more complete analysis of the relation between our results and those of Theil must be deferred to a future study.

In a paper presented at the December, 1959, meetings of the Econometric Society, F. Fisher explored yet another problem that is closely related to our analysis.[10] The conditions that permit the identification of a structural relationship ordinarily state that a certain set of structural coefficients are identically zero, and the estimation can be carried out on the assumption that there exist no relations among the variables under consideration other than those explicitly stated in the system. Suppose, however, that these conditions are only approximately satisfied. Fisher has shown that, as the approximation of these conditions becomes better and better, the estimates of the structural parameters, obtained by the usual estimation method such as the limited information method or the generalized least squares method, are asymptotically consistent.

In the framework of our analysis, Fisher's problem is analogous to that of specifying the conditions under which one of the subsystems can be treated in isolation from all other parts of the system for the purposes of estimation.

The comparison of our result with that of Fisher immediately raises two

[9] H. Theil, *Linear Aggregation of Economic Relations*, 1954.

[10] F. M. Fisher, *op. cit.*

important questions. The first has already been suggested by Fisher; since his results apply to what he calls block recursive systems, nearly triangular matrices must possess some properties analogous to those we have shown in nearly decomposable matrices. The investigation of these analogous properties would open a way to generalize Goodwin's justification of partial dynamics to the case where the coupling is only "nearly-unilateral," as well as to the case where the whole system is "nearly-block-recursive."[11] The second is that, according to our analysis, even a very weak link will eventually make its influence felt given a long enough period of time. Thus, in interpreting Fisher's result, we must be careful to choose the appropriate period over which the observations are made.

Finally, we note that there are a number of other discussions in the economic literature upon which the notion of nearly-decomposable systems appears to throw some light. We have already pointed out that the argument here may be regarded as a statement of the circumstances under which the Lange-Hicks condition will be satisfied. It can easily be seen from our analysis that if the micro-system is dynamically stable, this will also be true of the aggregated system, since the characteristic roots of the aggregative matrix are also roots of the original matrix. This stability theorem has been proved earlier by Tamotsu Yokoyama.[12] Yokoyama assumes that the Lange-Hicks condition is satisfied, and derives the stability theorem from this assumption.

Samuelson points out that aggregation of commodities can seek its justification in either of two kinds of principles that, at first blush, appear rather antithetical to each other.[13] On the one hand (the Lange-Hicks condition), we can aggregate the parts of a subsystem when these are much more closely linked with each other than they are with the rest of the system. On the other hand, we can aggregate a set of variables if each of them is linked with the remainder of the system in just the same way as are the others. Our analysis of near-decomposability shows that the former condition is really a special case of the latter. For if x_i and x_j are variables belonging to different subsets of a nearly decomposable system, then p_{ij} is very small, but $p_{ij}^{(t)}$, for sufficiently large t, is almost independent of i. That is to say, the linkage between i and j is negligible in the short run, and satisfies the second condition in the middle run for which it is not negligible.

Carnegie Institute of Technology and Massachusetts Institute of Technology

[11] R. M. Goodwin, "Dynamic Coupling with Especial Reference to Markets Having Production Lags," *Econometrica*, 1947, pp. 181–204.

[12] Tamotsu Yokoyama, "A Theory of Composite Commodity," *Osaka Economic Papers*, May, 1952.

[13] P. A. Samuelson, *Foundations of Economic Analysis*, 1948, pp. 144–46.

APPENDIX

PROOF OF THEOREM 5.1:

We note first that the elements of the tth power of a matrix are continuous functions of the elements of the original matrix. Hence, for any positive real number ξ_2' and an arbitrary integer T_2 there exists a number ε_2' such that for $t < T_2$ and $\varepsilon < \varepsilon_2'$

$$\text{(A.1)} \qquad \max_{i,j} |P_{ij}^{[t]} - P_{ij}^{*[t]}| < \xi_2'$$

$P_{ij}^{[t]}$ and $P_{ij}^{*[t]}$ are elements of tth power of matrices P and P^*.

Substituting (5.4) and (5.7) into (A.1), we obtain

$$\text{(A.2)} \quad \max_{i,j} |\sum_{I=1}^{N} \pi_{ij}^{*(1_I)} - \pi_{ij}^{(1_1)} - \sum_{I=2}^{N} \lambda_{1_I}^{t} \pi_{ij}^{(1_I)} + \sum_{I=1}^{N} \sum_{\varrho_I=2}^{n_I} \lambda_{\varrho_I}^{*t} \pi_{ij}^{*(\varrho_I)} - \sum_{I=1}^{N} \sum_{\varrho_I=2}^{n_I} \lambda_{\varrho_I}^{t} \pi_{ij}^{(\varrho_I)}| < \xi_2'.$$

Introducing for convenience

$$\text{(A.3)} \qquad D_{ij}^{[t]} = \sum_{I=1}^{N} \pi_{ij}^{*(1_I)} - \pi_{ij}^{(1_I)} - \sum_{I=2}^{N} \lambda_{1_I}^{t} \pi_{ij}^{(1_I)},$$

we rewrite (A.2):

$$\text{(A.4)} \quad \max_{i,j} |D_{ij}^{[t]} + \sum_{I=1}^{N} \sum_{\varrho_I=2}^{n_I} (\lambda_{\varrho_I}^{*t} - \lambda_{\varrho_I}^{t}) \pi_{ij}^{(\varrho_I)} + \sum_{I=1}^{N} \sum_{\varrho_I=2}^{n_I} \lambda_{\varrho_I}^{*t} (\pi_{ij}^{*(\varrho_I)} - \pi_{ij}^{(\varrho_I)})| < \xi_2'.$$

By (2.6), $(\lambda_{\varrho_I}^{*t} - \lambda_{\varrho_I}^{t}) \to 0$ as $\varepsilon \to 0$. Hence, for any positive real ξ_2, we can choose a new ε_2'' so that for $\varepsilon < \varepsilon_2''$,

$$\text{(A.5)} \qquad \max |D_{ij}^{[t]} + \sum_{I=1}^{N} \sum_{\varrho_I=2}^{n_I} \lambda_{\varrho_I}^{*(t)} (\pi_{ij}^{*(\varrho_I)} - \pi_{ij}^{(\varrho_I)})| < \xi_2'.$$

But, since λ^* are all distinct for $i_I \geqslant 2$, and $D_{ij}^{[t]}$ becomes independent of t as $\lambda_{1I}^{t} \to 1$ for all I, this inequality can hold for all $t \leqslant T_0$ only if the coefficients of λ^* become vanishingly small; hence, for any positive real number ξ_2, we can choose a value of ε, ε_2 so that for $\varepsilon < \varepsilon_2$,

$$\text{(A.6)} \qquad \max_{i\,j} |\pi_{ij}^{*(\varrho_I)} - \pi_{ij}^{(\varrho_I)}| < \xi_2$$

for $\varrho_I = 2, \ldots, n_I$ and $I = 1, \ldots, N$.

PROOF OF THEOREM 5.2:

As indicated in the text and in the above proof of Theorem 5.1, we know that (1) as $\varepsilon \to 0$, $T_1 \to T_1^*$, (2) T_2 can be made as large as we please for a given ξ_2 by taking small enough ε, and (3) T_1^* is independent of ε. Hence, by taking ε sufficiently small, we can make T_2 very much larger than T_1 for a given set of ξ_1 and ξ_2. Then, for $T_1 < t < T_2$, we have

$$\text{(A.7)} \quad |P_{i_I j_J}^{[t]} - \bar{x}_{j_J|J}^{*} \Delta_{IJ}| = |(P_{i_I j_J}^{[t]} - P_{i_I j_J}^{*[t]}) + (P_{i_I j_J}^{*[t]} - \bar{x}_{j_J|J}^{*} \Delta_{IJ})| \leqslant \xi_2' + \xi_1$$

for $i_I = 1,\ldots,n_I$, $j_J = 1,\ldots,n_J$, $I, J = 1,\ldots,N$, and where Δ_{IJ} is Kronecker's delta.

Let us now consider $P^{[t]}_{ij}$ for a large enough t so that it can be expressed in the following scheme:

(A.8)
$$P^{[t]}_{ij} = \sum_k \sum_m P^{[t_1]}_{ik} P^{[t_2]}_{km} P^{[t_3]}_{mj}$$

where $t = t_1+t_2+t_3$, and

$$T_1 < t_1 < T_2\,,$$
$$T_1 < t_3 < T_2\,,$$
$$T_1 < t_1 + t_3 < T_2\,,$$
$$T_2 < t_2\,.$$

Then, conditions (5.11) and (A.7) assures us that, for any real positive number ω_0, there exists a value of ε, ε_ω, such that for $\varepsilon < \varepsilon_\omega$, we have

(A.9)
$$\sum_{l=1}^{N} \lambda_{1_l} \pi^{(1_l)}_{ij} = \sum_k \sum_m [\tilde{x}^*_{K|K} \, \Delta_{IK}][\sum_{l=1}^{N} \lambda^{t_2}_{1_l} \pi^{(1_l)}_{km}][\tilde{x}^*_{j|L} \, \Delta_{MJ}] + \omega_{ij}$$
$$\max_{ij} |\omega_{ij}| < \omega_0$$

where the usual 1_I, the subscript of λ and the superscript of π_{ij}, is replaced by 1_l in order to avoid the confusion with the identification of a block of rows and columns of P in this context.

(A.9) becomes, after a rearrangement of terms,

(A.10)
$$\sum_{l=1}^{N} \lambda^t_{1_l} \pi^{(1_l)}_{ij} = \sum_{l=1}^{N} \lambda^{t_2}_{1_l} x^*_{j|J} \, [\sum_{i'_I=1}^{n_I} \tilde{x}^*_{i'_I|I} \sum_{j'_J=1}^{n_J} \pi^{(1_l)}_{i'_I j'_J}] + \omega_{ij}$$
$$\max_{ij} |\omega_{ij}| < \omega_0\,.$$

For this to hold for all permissible values of t_2, we must have

(A.11)
$$\lambda^{(t_1+t_3)}_{1_l} \pi^{(1_l)}_{ij} = x^*_{j|J} \sum_{i_I=1}^{n_I} \tilde{x}^*_{i_I|I} \sum_{j_J=1}^{n_J} \pi^{(1_l)}_{i_I j_J} + \omega_l\,,$$
$$\omega_l \to 0 \text{ as } \omega_0 \to 0,\ l = 1,\ldots,N\,.$$

Comparison of (A.11) with the definition (5.8), remembering that $\lambda^t_1 \to 1$ for $l = 1,\ldots,N$ and for $t < T_2$, and that $t_1 + t_2 < T_2$, yields the result summarized in Theorem 5.2.

PROOF OF THEOREM 5.3:

Let us define

(A.12)
$$\tilde{P}_{ij} = \sum_{l=1}^{N} \lambda_{1_l} \pi^{(1_l)}_{ij}\,.$$

The omission of terms $2_l,\ldots,n_l$ will guarantee that we may write

(A.13)
$$\tilde{P}^{[t]}_{ij} = \tilde{x}^*_{j|J} \sum_{l=1}^{N} \lambda^t_{1_l} \pi^{(1_l)}_{IJ}\,.$$

Suppose that there exists an $N \times N$ nonsingular matrix Q satisfying the condition

(A.14)
$$\tilde{P}_{ij} = \tilde{x}^*_{j|J} Q_{IJ}\,,$$

(A.15)
$$\tilde{P}^{[t]}_{ij} = \tilde{x}^*_{j|J} Q^{[t]}_{IJ}\,,$$

for all t.

Let the idempotent expansion of Q be given by

(A.16) $$Q_{IJ}^{[t]} = \sum_{l=1}^{N} \mu_l^t \phi_{IJ}^{(l)}$$

where μ_l are characteristic roots and $\phi^{(l)}$ are corresponding idempotent matrices. Substituting (A.16) in (A.15) and comparing the result with (A.13), we must have

(A.17) $$\sum_{l=1}^{N} \mu_l^t \phi_{IJ}^{(l)} = \sum_{l=1}^{N} \lambda_{1_l}^t \pi_{IJ}^{(1_l)}$$

for all t. As we shall show presently, this implies that

(A.18) $$\mu_l = \lambda_{1_l} \qquad (l = 1,\ldots,N),$$

(A.19) $$\phi^{(l)} = \pi^{(1_l)} \qquad (l = 1,\ldots,N).$$

These conditions obviously imply that

(A.20) $$[P_{IJ}] = [Q_{IJ}],$$

proving Theorem 5.3.

To justify equation (A.18), we note that $\lambda_{1_1} > \lambda_{1_2} > \ldots > \lambda_{1_N}$.

Let us also assume, without loss of generality, that the subscript of μ is arranged so that $\mu_1 > \mu_2 \ldots > \mu_N$. Dividing both sides of (A.17) by λ_{1_1} and rearranging terms, we have

(A.21) $$\pi_{IJ}^{(1_1)} = \phi_{IJ}^{(1)} \left(\frac{\mu_1}{\lambda_{1_1}}\right)^t + \sum_{l=2}^{N} \pi_{IJ}^{(1_l)} \left(\frac{\lambda_{1_l}}{\lambda_{1_1}}\right)^t + \sum_{l=2}^{N} \phi_{IJ}^{(l)} \left(\frac{\mu_l}{\lambda_{1_1}}\right)^t.$$

Because of the way the matrix Q, and hence μ are defined, $|\mu_l| \leqslant 1$ for $l = 1,\ldots,N$. Hence, as t becomes large, (A.21) may be written as

(A.22) $$\pi_{IJ}^{(1_1)} = \phi_{IJ}^{(1)} \left(\frac{\mu_1}{\lambda_{1_1}}\right)^t + \mu_0$$

where μ_0 is an arbitrarily small real number, since $\pi_{IJ}^{(1_1)}$ and $\phi_{IJ}^{(1)}$ are not zero. For (A.22) to hold for all t, we must have

(A.23) $$\pi_{IJ}^{(1_1)} = \phi_{IJ}^{(1)},$$

(A.24) $$\lambda_{1_1} = \mu_1 .$$

It is clear that this argument can be repeated N times, justifying (A.18) and (A.19).

5

NEAR-DECOMPOSABILITY, PARTITION AND AGGREGATION, AND THE RELEVANCE OF STABILITY DISCUSSIONS*

BY ALBERT ANDO AND FRANKLIN M. FISHER[1]

1. INTRODUCTION

IN RECENT YEARS economists have come to deal with dynamic systems of increasing size and complexity. The difficulty of analyzing such systems, however, appears to increase faster than does our ability to handle them with the aid of high speed computing equipment. As a consequence, it is becoming more and more important to secure information on the nature of those aspects of a system which, when present, enable us to treat a part of it separately from the rest or to deal with the relationship among particular subsystems as though it were independent of the structures within those subsystems. The latter question is that of aggregation, while the former is one whose theoretical importance is difficult to exaggerate; it concerns the conditions under which partial dynamics—or indeed, the dynamics of the economic system as a whole—can be treated without explicit concern for the larger system of socio-physical equations in which a particular structure is embedded. We may refer to this problem as one of partition, and we shall discuss it at length below.

In an earlier paper, [8], Simon and Ando examined the behavior of linear dynamic systems with nearly completely decomposable matrices.[2] They showed that, in the short run, such a system can be treated

* Manuscript received January 10, 1962, revised July 24, 1962.

[1] We are indebted to Robert M. Solow for helpful conversations.

[2] We had better dispose of the terminological problem at the outset. A completely decomposable matrix is a square matrix such that an identical rearrangement of rows and columns leaves a set of square submatrices on the principal diagonal and zeros everywhere else. (Simon and Ando refer to this as "decomposable" without the qualifying adverb, but our present definition corresponds to traditional economic usage.) We shall refer to a completely decomposable matrix which has been placed in the above form as *block diagonal*.

A decomposable matrix (as opposed to a *completely* decomposable one) is a square matrix such that an identical rearrangement of rows and columns leaves a set of square submatrices on the principal diagonal with zeros everywhere *below* (but not necessarily also above) such matrices. We shall refer to a decomposable matrix which has been placed in the above form as *block triangular*.

Near-decomposability and near-complete-decomposability are defined by replacing the zeros in the above definitions by small nonzero numbers.

The relevance of indecomposability for dynamic systems with nonnegative matrices has been examined by Solow, [9].

as though it were in fact completely decomposable (i.e., partitioned) and that, in the middle run, such a system can be treated by replacing each subsystem by a single variable and ignoring the relationships within each subsystem (i.e., aggregated). The theorem is both powerful and interesting, but its usefulness is somewhat limited by the fact that near-complete-decomposability is moderately rare.

At the same time, Fisher, [2], investigated the behavior of the probability limits of simultaneous equation estimators under certain types of specification error. He showed, among other things, that the underlying abstraction involved in using such estimators is the assumption of near-decomposability so that nearly decomposable systems must be assumed to be fairly widespread. Since near-*complete*-decomposability is a special case of near-decomposability, he compared his results with those of Simon and Ando and conjectured that the Simon-Ando theorem could be modified to the case of dynamic systems with nearly decomposable matrices. This paper proves that conjecture and examines some of its simpler implications.[3]

2. STATEMENT AND PROOF OF THE THEOREM

To facilitate our discussion, we shall adapt the notation and proof of Simon and Ando. The reader is referred to their paper for a more detailed treatment.

[3] Experience in oral presentation leads us to emphasize that the principal aim of this paper is to discover the consequences of the approximations generally made in dynamics rather than to aid directly in the partition or aggregation of empirically encountered systems whose coefficient matrices turn out to be of the types here discussed. While such empirical aid is an important secondary object, it is subordinate in the present paper to the more abstract one stated above. We have thus established only existence theorems rather than tests for the "sufficient smallness" of the parameters with which we are concerned.

Fisher also conjectured that a proof of the present theorem exists which makes direct use of his results on specification error and inconsistency and that a very general proposition is true relating the two areas of analysis. While these latter conjectures appear to us to be true, we have not attempted their proof in the present paper since the direct adaptation of the Simon-Ando theorem turns out to be rather straightforward in the present case. The present paper thus leaves Fisher's other conjectures as open questions, although the fact that his first conjecture is here shown to be correct may heuristically strengthen belief in the likelihood of the two more general ones being so.

As in the earlier papers of Simon and Ando [8] and of Fisher [2], we restrict ourselves in this paper to the consideration of linear dynamic systems. Intuitively it seems to us that properties similar to those discussed in this paper are likely to be possessed by nonlinear systems, but this is merely speculation. Of course, our results will apply directly to nonlinear systems in the small. Since this was written, Fisher has extended the results to an important class of nonlinear systems [1] and to models of capital accumulation involving choice [3].

Consider two systems:[4]

$$x(t+1) = Px(t)\,, \tag{1}$$

$$x^*(t+1) = P^*x^*(t)\,, \tag{2}$$

x and x^* are n-dimensional column vectors and P^* is an $n \times n$ decomposable matrix which we take (without loss of generality) in block triangular form:

$$P^* = \begin{bmatrix} P_1^* & G_1^* & & & \\ 0 & P_2^* & G_2^* & & \\ \vdots & \vdots & \vdots & & \\ 0 & \cdot & \cdot & 0 & P_N^* \end{bmatrix}, \tag{3}$$

where P_I^* is a square matrix of order $n_I(I = 1, \cdots, N)$; the zeros represent zero matrices of various sizes; and the G_I^* are matrices with n_I rows and $(N - \sum_{J \leq I} n_J)$ columns, and not all elements zero.[5] We also assume that the P_I^* is itself indecomposable, $I = 1, \cdots, N$.

It is crucial to realize that, while in the Simon-Ando case, the subsystems that are partitioned or aggregated are those corresponding to submatrices P_I^*, in our case, the subsystems are those corresponding to submatrices such as[6]

$$\begin{bmatrix} P_I^* & G_I^* & & & \\ 0 & P_{I+1}^* & G_{I+1}^* & & \\ \vdots & \vdots & \vdots & & \\ 0 & \cdot & \cdot & 0 & P_N^* \end{bmatrix}.$$

P is assumed to be related to P^* by:

[4] An identical development holds for differential equation systems.

[5] Note that this means that the system (1), while nearly decomposable, is not nearly completely decomposable as in Simon-Ando. It is, of course, tempting to ask if it is possible to state a more general theorem covering *both* the nearly completely decomposable systems of Simon and Ando and the nearly decomposable systems that we treat here. The answer is that it is indeed possible, but we have refrained from attempting to do so, because to do so would have made the notation even more cumbersome than it already is (if possible). In addition, we believe that it is difficult to conceive of a linear dynamic system which is not covered either by our theorem or by the Simon-Ando theorem, but for which partition and aggregation are possible. This, however, is an open question.

[6] This statement should be elaborated somewhat. Suppose that we are concerned with the submatrix P^*. The subsystem corresponding to this submatrix is the one exhibited above. The other subsystems with which we are concerned, however, involve matrices P_J^*, $J < I$. It will become clear in our subsequent discussion that the only P_J^*, $J < I$, that are relevant in aggregation are those whose largest roots are greater than the largest of the largest roots of P_K^*, $K \geqq I$.

$$P = P^* + \varepsilon C, \tag{4}$$

where C is an arbitrary $n \times n$ matrix and ε is an arbitrarily small positive scalar. We assume that both P and P^* have no multiple roots[7] so that there exist non-singular matrices, Z and Z^*, such that

$$Z^{-1}PZ = \Lambda \tag{5}$$

and

$$Z^{*-1}P^*Z^* = \Lambda^*, \tag{6}$$

where Λ and Λ^* are diagonal matrices whose diagonal elements are the characteristic roots of P and P^*, respectively.

Since Z and Z^* are defined only up to a scalar multiplication and a permutation and since the latent roots of P^* are precisely those of the $P_I^*(I = 1, \cdots, N)$, we may select Z^* so that the elements of Λ_I^*, say $\lambda_{i_I}^*(i_I = 1, \cdots, n_I)$, corresponding to the I-th submatrix of P^*, appear in order of descending absolute magnitude for all I. Furthermore, we select Z so that $\lim_{\varepsilon \to 0} \Lambda = \Lambda^*$. (Recall that the characteristic roots of any matrix are continuous functions of its elements.)

Since it is not true here (unlike the case of Simon and Ando) that $|\lambda_{1_I}^*| \geqq |\lambda_{1_J}^*|$ whenever $I < J$, we must now adopt a notation which enables us to identify the largest root of any given subsystem. Let

$$|\lambda_{1_{K(I)}}^*| = \max_{J \geqq I} |\lambda_{1_J}^*|, \qquad I = 1, 2, \cdots, N. \tag{7}$$

We shall assume that there are no zero elements in the I-th group of elements of the characteristic vector corresponding to $\lambda_{1_{K(I)}}^*(I = 1, 2, \cdots, N)$.[8]

Let $Z_{i_I j_J}$ be the element of Z in the i-th row of the I-th set of rows and the j-th column of the J-th set of columns and similarly for Z^* and all later matrices. It is obvious that:

$$Z_{i_I j_J}^* = 0, \qquad I > J. \tag{8}$$

In other words, given the numbering convention as to the $\lambda_{i_I}^*$, Z^* turns out to be block triangular with the same arrangement of blocks as P^*.

It is easy to show that for any arbitrary positive real number, ζ,

[7] This assumption can be easily weakened, but to do so would unduly complicate an already burdensome notation. For the present, all that is needed is the similarity of P and P^* to diagonal matrices. See Perlis [6, (170-177)]. Fisher has pointed out that, in view of Perlis [6, (*Theorem* 9-5, 175)], the two proofs given by Simon and Ando hold under identical conditions (although they are separately interesting for other reasons).

[8] Since P^* is not completely decomposable, this merely excludes a case of measure zero. Even this case can be handled, but to do so would be tedious.

there exists an $\varepsilon_0 > 0$ such that, for $\varepsilon < \varepsilon_0$

$$\max_{i,j} | Z_{ij} - Z^*_{ij} | < \zeta \, . \tag{9}$$

Define a new matrix, U, by

$$Z = Z^* + \zeta U \, . \tag{10}$$

It is obvious that (for ε sufficiently small) $| U_{ij} | < 1$.

Further, define new variables, y and y^*, by

$$y(t) = Z^{-1}x(t) \tag{11}$$

and

$$y^*(t) = Z^{*-1}x^*(t) \, . \tag{12}$$

Then we can write

$$x(t) = Z\Lambda^t y(0) \tag{13}$$

and

$$x^*(t) = Z^*\Lambda^{*t}y^*(0) \, . \tag{14}$$

It now follows that any element of the vector $x(t)$ can be expressed as the following sum:

$$\begin{aligned} x_{i_I}(t) = {} & \zeta U_{i_I 1_{K(1)}} \lambda^t_{1_{K(1)}} y_{1_{K(1)}}(0) + Z_{i_I 1_{K(I)}} \lambda^t_{1_{K(I)}} y_{1_{K(I)}}(0) \\ & + \zeta \sum_{\substack{J<I \\ K(J) \neq K(I) \\ K(J) \neq K(1)}} U_{i_I 1_{K(J)}} \lambda^t_{1_{K(J)}} y_{1_{K(J)}}(0) + \sum_{\substack{J \geq I \\ J \neq K(I)}} Z_{i_I 1_J} \lambda^t_{1_J} y_{1_J}(0) \\ & + \sum_{J \geq I} \sum_{j_J=2}^{n_J} Z_{i_I j_J} \lambda^t_{j_J} y_{j_J}(0) + \zeta \sum_{\substack{J<I \\ J \neq K(J)}} U_{i_I 1_J} \lambda^t_{1_J} y_{1_J}(0) \\ & + \zeta \sum_{J<I} \sum_{j_J=2}^{n_J} U_{i_I j_J} \lambda^t_{j_J} y_{j_J}(0) \, . \end{aligned} \tag{15}$$

If $K(1) = K(I)$, the first and the third term are absent (the latter by definition).

It will be highly convenient to give names to the terms on the right hand side of (15) as follows:

$$x_{i_I}(t) = \zeta R^{(1)} + R^{(2)} + \zeta R^{(3)} + R^{(4)} + R^{(5)} + \zeta R^{(6)} + \zeta R^{(7)} \, . \tag{16}$$

Let us examine the meaning of these terms. $R^{(1)}$ represents the influence of the largest root of the whole system; $R^{(2)}$ represents the influence of the largest root of the subsystem under consideration; $R^{(3)}$

represents the influence of those roots (if any) which are the largest roots of subsystems and which are larger than the largest root of the subsystem under consideration, other than those identified in $R^{(1)}$ and $R^{(2)}$; $R^{(4)}$ and $R^{(5)}$ represent the influence of all other roots in the subsystem under consideration; $R^{(6)}$ and $R^{(7)}$ represent the influence of all roots that are not in the subsystem, except those accounted for by terms $R^{(1)}$ and $R^{(3)}$.

In terms of equation (15), we can now state the following theorem, corresponding to *Theorem 4.2* of Simon and Ando:

THEOREM. A. $K(I) \neq K(1)$.

(1) *Partition and Short-Run Behavior. In view of the definition of* $\lambda_{1_{K(I)}}$, *for any real positive number*, η_0, *there exists a positive integer*, $T_0(I, \eta_0)$, *such that for* $t > T_0(I, \eta_0)$

$$\text{(17)} \qquad \frac{|R^{(4)} + R^{(5)}|}{|R^{(2)}|} < \eta_0 , \qquad i_I = 1, \cdots, n_I .$$

Furthermore, for any given integer $T_1 > T_0(I, \eta_0)$ *and any arbitrary real positive number*, η_1, *there exists a number*, $\zeta_1 = \zeta_1(I, \eta_1, T_1) > 0$, *and hence by* (8) *an* $\varepsilon_1 = \varepsilon_1(\zeta_1) > 0$, *such that for* $t < T_1$ *and* $\varepsilon < \varepsilon_1$,

$$\text{(18)} \qquad \frac{|\zeta(R^{(1)} + R^{(3)} + R^{(6)} + R^{(7)})|}{|R^{(2)} + R^{(4)} + R^{(5)}|} < \eta_1 \qquad i_I = 1, \cdots, n_I .$$

(2) *Aggregation and Long-Run Behavior. Given* ε_1 *satisfying* (18), *for any arbitrary positive real number*, η_2, *there exists an integer*, $T_2(I, \varepsilon_1, \eta_2) \geqq T_1$, *such that, for* $t > T_2(I, \varepsilon_1, \eta_2)$

$$\text{(19a)} \qquad \frac{|R^{(4)} + R^{(5)} + \zeta(R^{(6)} + R^{(7)})|}{|\zeta R^{(1)} + R^{(2)} + \zeta R^{(3)}|} < \eta_2 , \qquad i_I = 1, \cdots, n_I ,$$

and for some function $\phi(\varepsilon, t)$:

$$\text{(19b)} \qquad \left| \frac{x_{i_I}(t)}{\phi(\varepsilon, t) R^{(2)}} - 1 \right| < \eta_2 + \mu(\varepsilon)(1 + \eta_2) , \qquad i_I = 1, \cdots, n_I ,$$

where $\lim_{\varepsilon \to 0} \phi(\varepsilon, t)$ *is finite and non-zero, and* $\lim_{\varepsilon \to 0} \mu(\varepsilon) = 0$.

In other words, after $T_2(I, \varepsilon_1, \eta_2)$, the variables in the I-th group of variables remain approximately proportional to their respective $R^{(2)}$ components, the degree of approximation depending on ε.[9] Note that

[9] Unlike the remainder of the theorem, (19b) does not follow immediately from the foregoing and is proved in the Appendix.

Clifford Hildreth and Leonid Hurwicz have suggested that at least Part (A.1) of our theorem can be derived more simply from continuity considerations which do not depend on the linearity of the system. However, the main force of the theorem is clearly in (19b), and this involves an unbounded time interval over which the difference between

(Continued on next page)

for ε sufficiently small, T_1 and $T_2(I, \varepsilon_1, \eta_2)$ can be made to coincide.

Furthermore, given ε_1 *satisfying* (18), *for any arbitrary positive real number,* η_3, *there exists an integer,* $T_3(I, \varepsilon_1, \eta_3) \geqq T_2(I, \varepsilon_1, \eta_2)$ *such that, for* $t > T_3(I, \varepsilon_1, \eta_3)$

$$(20) \quad \frac{|R^{(2)} + \zeta R^{(3)} + R^{(4)} + R^{(5)} + \zeta R^{(6)} + \zeta R^{(7)}|}{|\zeta R^{(1)}|} < \eta_3 , \qquad i_I = 1 \cdots, n_I .$$

Finally, since $T_0(I, \eta_0)$ *does not depend on* ε *but* $T_3(I, \varepsilon_1, \eta_3)$ *does, we may choose an* $\varepsilon_2 = \varepsilon_2(I, \eta_3)$ *such that for* $\varepsilon < \varepsilon_2 \leqq \varepsilon_1$, $T_3(I, \varepsilon_2, \eta_3) > T_0(J, \eta)$ *for all* $J < I$ *where* $\eta = \eta(\eta_3) > 0$ *and thus such that* $T_3(I, \varepsilon_2, \eta_3) > T_2(I, \varepsilon_2, \eta_2)$.

That is, we can make the strong rather than the weak inequality hold by choosing ε so small as to let every $J < I$ reach its own T_0 for an appropriate η depending on η_3, before the I-th group of variables reaches its T_3.[10]

B. $K(I) = K(1)$.

The terms $R^{(1)}$ *and* $R^{(3)}$ *in equation* (15) *are absent. Hence, once* $R^{(2)}$ *dominates* $R^{(4)}$ *and* $R^{(5)}$, *it will dominate the behavior of the entire system, and will continue to do so thereafter.*[11]

$x(t)$ and $x^*(t)$ cannot be bounded. Even so, the approach to the nonlinear case by way of continuity does seem promising. (This has proved to be the case for particular types of systems. See Fisher [1] and [3].)

[10] From now on we drop the arguments in the expressions for the T_j where the context makes it clear what is involved.

[11] More precisely, we may select T_0, T_1, η_0, η_1 and ε_1 in the manner described in the above theorem so that, for $T_0 < t < T_1$,

$$\text{(a)} \qquad \frac{|R^{(4)} + R^{(5)}|}{|R^{(2)}|} < \eta_0$$

and

$$\text{(b)} \qquad \frac{|\zeta(R^{(6)} + R^{(7)})|}{|R^{(2)} + R^{(4)} + R^{(5)}|} < \eta_1 .$$

Since

$$|R^{(2)}| + |R^{(4)} + R^{(5)}| \geqq |R^{(2)} + R^{(4)} + R^{(5)}|$$

(a) and (b) imply

$$\text{(c)} \qquad \frac{|\zeta(R^{(6)} + R^{(7)}|}{|R^{(2)}|} < \eta_1(1 + \eta_0) .$$

Hence

$$\text{(d)} \qquad \frac{|R^{(4)} + R^{(5)} + \zeta(R^{(6)} + R^{(7)})|}{|R^{(2)}|} < \eta_0 + \eta_1(1 + \eta_0) .$$

This relationship holds for $T_0 < t < T_1$. But, because of the absence of $R^{(1)}$ and $R^{(3)}$, it will continue to hold for all $t > T_0$. Hence, when $K(I) = K(1)$, if we choose $\eta_3 = \eta_2 = \eta_0 + \eta_1(1 + \eta_0)$ we may then choose $T_3 = T_2 = T_0$.

Observe that this (or a similar argument for subsystems) implies that further partitioning of a subsystem such as that exhibited on page 55 is interesting only if there is at least one $K(J) \neq K(I)$ for $J > I$, since otherwise $\lambda_{1_{K(I)}}$ will dominate all the other roots of the subsystem from T_0 onward. It follows that it is interesting to partition the entire system into at most as many "nested" subsystems as there is distinct $K(I)$, $I = 1, \cdots, N$.

To see the implications of the theorem more clearly, let us look at the special case of $N = 2$ and $K(2) \neq K(1)$. Our system can be written for simplicity as follows:

$$\begin{pmatrix} x_1(t+1) \\ x_2(t+1) \end{pmatrix} = \begin{pmatrix} P_1 & G \\ E & P_2 \end{pmatrix} \begin{pmatrix} x_1(t) \\ x_2(t) \end{pmatrix}, \qquad E = \varepsilon C_{21} . \tag{21}$$

Part (A.1) of our theorem then asserts that, provided that ε is sufficiently small, there is a time T_1 such that, before T_1, the subsystem of (21)

$$x_2(t+1) = Ex_1(t) + P_2 x_2(t) \tag{21a}$$

behaves almost as if $E = 0$ and thus almost independently of the other part of (21)

$$x_1(t+1) = (P_1 G) \begin{pmatrix} x_1(t) \\ x_2(t) \end{pmatrix} . \tag{21b}$$

In particular, at time T_0 before time T_1, (21a) reaches a neighborhood of its own partial equilibrium formation in the sense that the largest root of P_2 dominates the behavior of (21a). Note that, while T_1 depends crucially on ε, T_0 is independent of ε, so that we may make the period between T_0 and T_1 as long as we please by taking ε sufficiently small. In particular, we may make T_1 sufficiently large, by taking small enough ε, to insure that by $T_2 > T_1$ the largest root of P_1 has also dominated the behavior of (21b). If this is done, we may regard variables in (21a) and variables in (21b) as moving proportionately within each subsystem by T_2. We can then represent the behavior of both subsystems by indices and look at the relation between the two subsystems as the relation between two indices. The existence of T_2 and T_3 asserted by Part (A.2) of our theorem then guarantees that, for a small enough ε, there is a nonzero time period between T_2 and T_3 such that the behavior of the subsystem (21a) reflects the influence both of the largest root of P_2 and that of P_1, before it is finally dominated by the largest root of P_1. Moreover, even after that domination occurs, the elements of x_2 will remain approximately in the relative short-run equilibrium position given by the characteristic vector of P_2 corresponding to the largest root of P_2.

It is interesting and important to note the consequences of restrictions on the smallness of ε. Although our theorem is stated taking ε as entirely arbitrary, in reality, we are likely to be confronted with a situation in which ε is predetermined for us. One of the most relevant cases is the situation in which ε is small enough to insure that the behavior of the I-th group of variables is dominated by the largest root of its own subsystem before the influence of the other roots of the lower-numbered subsystems begins to be felt, but is not small enough to insure that the behavior of lower-numbered groups is dominated by the largest roots of the corresponding subsystems *before* the variables in the I-th group begin to be influenced significantly by such roots. (If this situation obtains, then it is possible that by time T_2, $\zeta R^{(1)}$ has dominated $R^{(2)}$ and $\zeta R^{(3)}$ in our equation (15), making T_2 and T_3 identical.) In this case, however, T_1 and T_2 may be distinct, so that between T_1 and T_2, the influences of non-maximal roots in lower-numbered groups on the behavior of the I-th group can temporarily disturb the partial equilibrium formation of that group. At worst, however, that formation will be regained by the time the largest root of the system as a whole has dominated the I-th group and at best before that time; thus aggregation will at worst be trivially possible and at best quite helpful.

3. DISCUSSION OF THE THEOREM

The importance of this theorem lies in its establishment of plausible sufficient conditions justifying the manner in which nearly all dynamic analysis in the social sciences is carried out.[12] We now examine one example and list others, in which the above theorem provides a guide for the analysis and interpretation of dynamic systems.

Economists are often concerned with the stability properties of the economic system considered in isolation. However, there may be a somewhat uncomfortable feeling that this may not be a meaningful problem since the equations describing the economic system are themselves embedded in a far larger set of equations describing the socio-physical universe. It follows that the movement of the economic variables toward equilibrium may itself disturb variables (such as

[12] As pointed out earlier, this point is reinforced by the parallel theorems of Fisher [2], which show that the same conditions justify the usual procedures of statistical estimation in the social sciences. (We might add that there is clearly no necessary restriction to the social sciences alone.)

tastes or technology) which are assumed by economic theory to be given. Further, noneconomic variables which economic theory admits to be influenced by economic ones may, in turn, influence the latter or the assumed given noneconomic variables and thereby hinder the economic variables from reaching equilibrium. It follows that general equilibrium of the economic variables (which is a partial equilibrium of the larger system) may be unattainable even if it is stable when considered in isolation.

Our theorem suggests a general answer to this problem in the following way.[13] Partition the set of all noneconomic variables into: (1) those variables which economic theory assumes influence economic variables, but are not themselves influenced thereby; (2) those variables which are assumed to be influenced by but which do not influence economic variables; and (3) those variables which are assumed to be unrelated to economic variables. We may disregard the variables in the third category. Thus, we visualize economic theory as assuming that "causal influences"[14] run from the first set to the economic variables to the second set with no feedbacks. The difficulty raised, however, is that there may in fact be weak feedbacks since the assumptions of the theory are at best only good approximations. Our theorem shows that *if these feedbacks are sufficiently weak relative to the direct influences*, that is, if the theoretical assumptions are sufficiently good approximations, there exists a time $T_1 > 0$ such that before T_1 the behavior and stability of the economic system can be analyzed in isolation without regard for the difficulties raised by the presence of such feedbacks. To put it another way, for sufficiently weak feedbacks, our theorem shows that the economic system (if stable in isolation) will in some short run approach its own equilibrium arbitrarily closely (the length of the "short run" depending on the relative strengths of the feedbacks and the direct influences). Since equilibrium can be attained before the very process of such attainment disturbs the equilibrium, it is meaningful to discuss the existence and stability of economic equilibrium in these circumstances.

Furthermore, our theorem asserts that when the time period under consideration is long enough for the influence of other parts of the socio-physical system on the economic system to be necessarily explicitly considered, there will come a time after which the economic system will always be in its own partial equilibrium (if, indeed, transitory outside

[13] The relevance of our theorem to this question was suggested by a remark of W. W. Leontief.

[14] In the sense of Simon [7].

influences ever disturb that equilibrium once it has been reached), that the variables in it will be moving proportionately to one another, and that we can therefore represent the economic system by an index and can consider the influence of other parts of the social system on this index rather than on the economic system in its entire complexity. In the long run, moreover, the asymptotic configuration of the system approximately includes economic equilibrium as a part.

A similar consideration applies to the analogous relationship between the economic system and its subsectors.[15] Moreover, examples of situations in social sciences other than economics where the results of our theorem appear to be useful are reported elsewhere.[16] Finally, Fisher [1] extends the present theorem and that of Simon and Ando to the nonlinear balanced growth model of Solow and Samuelson [10] and Fisher [3] does the same for generalized von Neumann models of growth.

Massachusetts Institute of Technology, U.S.A.

APPENDIX

To establish (19b), we first show the approximate proportionality of the I-th group of components of the characteristic vector of P corresponding to $\lambda_{1_{K(I)}}$ to the corresponding group of components of the characteristic vectors corresponding to $\lambda_{1_{K(J)}}$ for $J < I$ and $K(I) \neq K(J)$. A little manipulation then yields the desired result.

To derive the approximate proportionality just mentioned, it will suffice to consider a two-block system, since we need not require in this Appendix the indecomposability of the P_I^*. Accordingly, let

$$\text{(A.1)} \qquad P(\varepsilon, k) = \left[\begin{array}{c|c} P_1^* + \varepsilon C_1 & kG + \varepsilon C_2 \\ \hline \varepsilon C_3 & P_2^* + \varepsilon C_4 \end{array}\right], \qquad C_3 \neq 0 .$$

Then $P(0, 1) = P^*$ and $P(\varepsilon, 1) = P$ in our old notation. Let $\lambda_1(0, k)$ be the largest characteristic root of P_1^* and $\lambda_2(0, k)$ be the largest characteristic root of P_2^*. By assumption, $|\lambda_1(0, k)| > |\lambda_2(0, k)|$. Let $\lambda_1(\varepsilon, k)$ and $\lambda_2(\varepsilon, k)$ respectively be the roots of $P(\varepsilon, k)$ which approach $\lambda_1(0, k)$ and $\lambda_2(0, k)$ as ε goes to zero and let

$$X^1(\varepsilon, k) = \begin{pmatrix} X_1^1(\varepsilon, k) \\ X_2^1(\varepsilon, k) \end{pmatrix}$$

[15] See, for instance, the system analyzed by Goodwin [5].

[16] Fisher and Ando [4]. This paper also gives such examples for the Simon-Ando Theorem.

and

$$X^2(\varepsilon, k) = \begin{pmatrix} X_1^2(\varepsilon, k) \\ X_2^2(\varepsilon, k) \end{pmatrix}$$

be the corresponding characteristic vectors of $P(\varepsilon, k)$.

LEMMA 1. *For any* k,

$$\lim_{\varepsilon \to 0} \frac{X_{i_2}^1(\varepsilon, 1)}{X_{i_2}^1(\varepsilon, k)} = 1 , \qquad (i_2 = 1, \cdots, n_2) .$$

PROOF. Since $\lambda_1(0, k)$ is a simple root of P_1^*, the matrix $(P_1^* + \varepsilon C_1 - I\lambda_1(\varepsilon, k))$ has rank $n_1 - 1$ for ε sufficiently close to zero. Choose a nonsingular $(n_1 - 1) \times (n_1 - 1)$ submatrix. Consider the remaining column; the element of $X_1^1(\varepsilon, k)$ corresponding to that column cannot be zero (since otherwise the submatrix would be singular). Renumber the variables (and the columns of all appropriate matrices) to make that element the first and impose the normalization requirement:

$$X_{1_1}^1(\varepsilon, k) = 1 . \tag{A.2}$$

Now, in view of the definitions:

$$P(\varepsilon, k)X^1(\varepsilon, k) = \lambda_1(\varepsilon, k)X^1(\varepsilon, k) . \tag{A.3}$$

Consider the nonsingular submatrix of $(P_1^* + \varepsilon C_1 - I\lambda_1(\varepsilon, k))$ already described. Delete the row of $(P_1^* + \varepsilon C_1 - I\lambda_1(\varepsilon, k))$ which does not appear in that matrix and denote the resulting matrix by $Q_1(\varepsilon, k)$. Delete the same row of $kG + \varepsilon C_2$ and denote the resulting matrix by $Q_2(\varepsilon, k)$. Rewrite (A.3), deleting the equation corresponding to that row, and add (A.2), obtaining

$$\left[\begin{array}{c|c} 1\,0\cdots 0 & 0\cdots 0 \\ Q_1(\varepsilon, k) & Q_2(\varepsilon, k) \\ \hline \varepsilon C_3 & P_2 + \varepsilon C_4 - I\lambda_1(\varepsilon, k) \end{array}\right] \begin{bmatrix} X_1^1(\varepsilon, k) \\ \\ X_2^1(\varepsilon, k) \end{bmatrix} = \begin{bmatrix} 1 \\ 0 \\ \vdots \\ 0 \end{bmatrix} . \tag{A.4}$$

Denote the partitioned matrix on the left by

$$A(\varepsilon, k) = \left[\begin{array}{c|c} A_1(\varepsilon, k) & A_2(\varepsilon, k) \\ \hline A_3(\varepsilon, k) & A_4(\varepsilon, k) \end{array}\right]$$

and note that $A_3(\varepsilon, k)$ is independent of k, while $A_1(\varepsilon, k)$ is nonsingular by construction.

Now, in view of the simplifying assumption as to no multiple roots, $A_4(\varepsilon, k)$ and hence $A(\varepsilon, k)$ are nonsingular for ε sufficiently small. Let $B(\varepsilon, k) = A(\varepsilon, k)^{-1}$ and partition $B(\varepsilon, k)$ in the same way as $A(\varepsilon, k)$. From (A.4), $X_2^1(\varepsilon, k)$ is just the first column of $B_3(\varepsilon, k)$. However, it is easy to show that

$$
\begin{aligned}
B_3(\varepsilon, k) &= -[I - A_4(\varepsilon, k)^{-1}A_3(\varepsilon, k)A_1(\varepsilon, k)^{-1}A_2(\varepsilon, k)]^{-1} \\
&\qquad \times [A_4(\varepsilon, k)^{-1}A_3(\varepsilon, k)A_1(\varepsilon, k)^{-1}] \\
&= -\varepsilon[I - \varepsilon A_4(\varepsilon, k)^{-1}C_3A_1(\varepsilon, k)^{-1}A_2(\varepsilon, k)]^{-1} \\
&\qquad \times [A_4(\varepsilon, k)^{-1}C_3A_1(\varepsilon, k)^{-1}] .
\end{aligned} \tag{A.5}
$$

Finally, since $\lambda_1(\varepsilon, k)$ approaches a limit independent of k as ε approaches zero, $A_1(\varepsilon, k)$ and $A_4(\varepsilon, k)$ have the same property. It follows that division of any element in the first column of $B_3(\varepsilon, 1)$ by the corresponding element of the first column of $B_3(\varepsilon, k)$ cancels the leading ε and leaves a fraction whose numerator and denominator both approach a common nonzero limit as ε goes to zero.[17] This proves the lemma.[18]

In far less cumberson fashion, we obtain

LEMMA 2. *For any k,*

$$\lim_{\varepsilon \to 0} \frac{X^2_{i_2}(\varepsilon, k)}{X^2_{i_2}(\varepsilon, 1)} = 1 , \qquad (i_2 = 1, \cdots, n_2) .$$

PROOF. Both the numerator and denominator approach $X^2_{i_2}(0, 1)$. This is nonzero by assumption.

LEMMA 3. *There exists a function, say $\beta(\varepsilon)$, such that*

$$\lim_{\varepsilon \to 0} \frac{X^1_{i_2}(\varepsilon, 0)}{X^2_{i_2}(\varepsilon, 0)\beta(\varepsilon)} = 1 , \qquad (i_2 = 1, \cdots, n_2) .$$

PROOF. This follows directly from the fact that $P(0, 0)$ is *completely* decomposable and the consequences of Simon and Ando [8, (Theorem 5.2)].[19]

Finally, we have

LEMMA 4. *There exists a function, say $\beta(\varepsilon)$, such that*

$$\lim_{\varepsilon \to 0} \frac{X^1_{i_2}(\varepsilon, 1)}{X^2_{i_2}(\varepsilon, 1)\beta(\varepsilon)} = 1 , \qquad (i_2 = 1, \cdots, n_2) .$$

PROOF. Set $k = 0$ in Lemma 1 and Lemma 2. The desired result now follows immediately from the three preceding lemmas. Lemma

[17] The limit is nonzero save on a set of measure zero which we shall forget.

[18] We are indebted to a referee for pointing out a flaw in an earlier proof.

[19] It is worth noting that the use of this lemma implies that the deviations from proportionality in the final result are approximately given by the characteristic vector corresponding to the largest root of the aggregated matrix. See Simon and Ando [8] for details.

4 establishes the approximate proportionality described at the beginning of the Appendix. Now, consider any term in $\zeta R^{(1)}$ or $\zeta R^{(3)}$. Such terms are constant, save for the t-th power of the relevant latent roots. Clearly, however, the constant parts are proportional to the corresponding latent vectors. By Lemma 4, moreover, those constant parts must then be approximately proportional to the constant part of $R^{(2)}$; that is, for any term in $\lambda_{1_{K(J)}}$ appearing in either $R^{(1)}$ or $R^{(3)}$, there exists a function, say $\rho(\varepsilon)$, proportional to the appropriate $\beta(\varepsilon)$ in Lemma 4, such that, as ε approaches zero, the ratio of the term in $\lambda_{1_{K(J)}}$ to $\rho(\varepsilon)R^{(2)}$ approaches $(\lambda_{1_{K(J)}}/\lambda_{1_{K(I)}})^t$. Let us denote the particular $\rho(\varepsilon)$ corresponding to a particular $\lambda_{1_{K(J)}}$ by $\rho(\varepsilon)_{K(J)}$, and choose

(A.6) $$\phi(\varepsilon, t) = 1 + \sum_{\substack{J<I \\ K(J)\neq K(I)}} \rho(\varepsilon)_{K(J)}(\lambda_{1_{K(J)}}/\lambda_{1_{K(I)}})^t .$$

From (A.6) we easily obtain:

LEMMA 5.

$$\lim_{\varepsilon\to 0} \frac{\zeta R^{(1)} + R^{(2)} + \zeta R^{(3)}}{\phi(\varepsilon, t)R^{(2)}} = 1 , \qquad (i_I = 1, \cdots, n_I) .$$

Now let

(A.7) $$\mu(\varepsilon) = \text{lub}\left[\mu : \left| \frac{\zeta R^{(1)} + R^{(2)} + \zeta R^{(3)}}{\phi(\varepsilon, t)R^{(2)}} - 1 \right| < \mu , \quad i_I = 1, \cdots, n_I \right] .$$

By Lemma 5, $\lim_{\varepsilon\to 0} \mu(\varepsilon) = 0$.

We are now ready to derive (19b). Let us shorten the notation slightly by writing

(A.8) $$H = \zeta R^{(1)} + R^{(2)} + \zeta R^{(3)} ;$$

then by (19a), for $t > T_2(I, \varepsilon_1, \eta_2)$,

(A.9) $$| x_{i_I}(t) - H | < \eta_2 | H | , \qquad (i_I = 1, \cdots, n_I) .$$

However, by (A.7)

(A.10) $$\left| \frac{H}{\phi(\varepsilon, t)R^{(2)}} - 1 \right| < \mu(\varepsilon) , \qquad (i_I = 1, \cdots, n_I) .$$

Dividing (A.9) by $|\phi(\varepsilon, t)R^{(2)}|$, adding the result to (A.10), and using the fact that the sum of two absolute values is greater than or equal to the absolute value of the sum, we obtain

(A.11) $$\left| \frac{x_{i_I}(t)}{\phi(\varepsilon, t)R^{(2)}} - 1 \right| < \eta_2 \left| \frac{H}{\phi(\varepsilon, t)R^{(2)}} \right| + \mu(\varepsilon) , \quad (i_I = 1, \cdots, n_I) .$$

However, by (A.10)

$$\left| \frac{H}{\phi(\varepsilon, t)R^{(2)}} \right| < 1 + \mu(\varepsilon) \tag{A.12}$$

and substitution into (A.11) at last yields (19b), as required.

REFERENCES

[1] FISHER, F. M., "Decomposability, Near Decomposability, and Balanced Price Change under Constant Returns to Scale," *Econometrica*, XXXI (January, 1963).

[2] ———, "On the Cost of Approximate Specification in Simultaneous Equation Estimation," *Econometrica*, XXIX (April, 1961), 139-70.

[3] ———, "Properties of the von Neumann Ray in Decomposable and Nearly Decomposable Technologies," (forthcoming).

[4] FISHER, F. M., and A. ANDO, "Two Theorems on *Ceteris Paribus* in the Analysis of Dynamic Systems," *American Political Science Review*, LVI (March, 1962), 108-13.

[5] GOODWIN, R. M., "Dynamical Coupling with Especial Reference to Markets Having Production Lags," *Econometrica*, XV (July, 1947), 181-204.

[6] PERLIS, S., *Theory of Matrices*, (Reading: Addison-Wesley, 1952).

[7] SIMON, H. A., "Causal Ordering and Identifiability," *Studies in Econometric Method*, Cowles Commission Monograph No. 14, ed. Wm. C. Hood and T. C. Koopmans, New York: John Wiley and Sons, 1953), Chapter III; reprinted as Chapter I in H. A. Simon, *Models of Man* (New York: John Wiley and Sons, 1957).

[8] SIMON, H. A. and A. ANDO, "Aggregation of Variables in Dynamic Systems," *Econometrica*, XXIX (April, 1961), 111-38.

[9] SOLOW, R. M., "On the Structure of Linear Models," *Econometrica*, XX (January, 1952), 29-46.

[10] SOLOW, R. M. and SAMUELSON, P. A., "Balanced Growth under Constant Returns to Scale," *Econometrica*, XXI (July, 1953), 412-24.

6

TWO THEOREMS ON *CETERIS PARIBUS* IN THE ANALYSIS OF DYNAMIC SYSTEMS

FRANKLIN M. FISHER AND ALBERT ANDO
Massachusetts Institute of Technology

Analysis of the dynamic properties of two or more interrelated systems is a recurrent problem in social science theory. A particular problem frequently arises (although it often goes unrecognized) in assessing the validity of an analysis of a system, some variables of which are causally related to other variables, which latter, in turn, are either not explicitly taken into account or are assumed constant. Examples are easy to find: economists may study the behavior of a single country's economy with only secondary regard for the rest of the world; studies of group behavior may pay only secondary attention to the other roles played by the group members in other contexts; two more examples are worked out below and others may be found in the works about to be cited. Indeed, in a larger sense, the division of social science itself (or of natural science, for that matter) into separate disciplines is an example, for the variables taken as given by one discipline are the very subject matter of another and *vice versa*. In all these examples, the very real problem is present that if variables taken as given are causally affected by the variables of the system being analyzed, or if variables assumed not to affect that system actually do affect it, the results of the analysis may have little relevance for the study of real problems.

The principal purpose of this paper is to call the attention of social scientists outside the field of mathematical economics to two related theorems in this area that have recently been proved.[1] We shall not attempt a technical discussion of the theorems here but instead give a general description of them in the next section. We then present two illustrative, albeit somewhat simplified, examples of the sort of results that these theorems can be used to obtain in political science.

I

Suppose a number of variables such that at any time, t, the value of each of them is a function of the values of some or all of the same set of variables at some past time t-1.[2] Suppose further that it is possible to collect the variables into subsets such that the variables within each subset are functions only of the past values of variables in the *same* subset, but not of the past values of any variables in any *different* subset.[3] Then the system is said to be *completely decomposable* and it is obvious that it really consists of several independent systems each one of which can be analyzed separately without reference to any of the others. In the examples mentioned above, this would be the case if every country's economy were really closed so that there were no inter-country effects and if every member of a group had no other roles to play outside the

[1] H. A. Simon and A. Ando, "Aggregation of Variables in Dynamic Systems," *Econometrica*, Vol. 29 (April, 1961), pp. 111–138 and A. Ando and F. M. Fisher, "Near-Decomposability, Partition and Aggregation, and the Relevance of Stability Discussions," in detail (forthcoming) present and prove the theorems. The relation of the sort of system involved to ordinary notions of causation is discussed in H. A. Simon, "Causal Ordering and Identifiability," ch. 3 in *Studies in Econometric Method* (W. C. Hood and T. C. Koopmans, eds., New York, 1953; Cowles Commission Monograph No. 14), reprinted as ch. 1 in H. A. Simon, *Models of Man* (New York, 1957); while the bearing of this sort of problem on the estimation of parameters in one of a set of interrelated systems is covered in F. M. Fisher, "On the Cost of Approximate Specification in Simultaneous Equation Estimation." *Econometrica*, Vol. 29 (April 1961), pp. 139–170.

[2] If values in the further past are relevant, a formal redefinition can always be made to eliminate time before $t-1$, without changing anything. Simultaneous dependencies can also be treated, though, for reasons of clarity and intuitive appeal, we restrict ourselves to cases where there is some time lag somewhere in the system. Further, we could consider time as continuous without essential changes. Strictly speaking, however, the theorems under discussion are only known to hold for cases in which the relations involved are linear. Since this was written, the principal results of the theorems have been shown to hold for at least one important class of nonlinear systems in F. M. Fisher, "Decomposability, and Balanced Growth Under Constant Returns to Scale" (forthcoming).

[3] Hereafter, to simplify terminology, by the term "set" instead of "subset," we mean a subset within the set of all variables in the system under consideration.

group or if those other roles had no effect whatsoever on actions within the group.

While the assumption of complete decomposability (or *ceteris paribus*) is often convenient to make, it is seldom likely to be fully satisfied in practice. Thus there *are* some exports and imports affecting every country; there *are* outside roles for group members, and so forth. The question thus naturally arises: What remains of the results of an analysis carried out under an assumption of complete decomposability if the system being studied is in fact embedded in a larger system which is not truly completely decomposable, so that variables assumed to be causally irrelevant do in fact matter? Of course, if the assumption of irrelevance—of complete decomposability—is a very bad one, it is unreasonable to expect much to be left of results obtained under it; but what if variables assumed irrelevant do not in fact matter very much? Is there any sense in which complete decomposability and the great simplification which it permits can be used as a good approximation, so that results obtained under it can be expected to be approximately valid when it is relaxed? This is where the first of our two theorems comes in.

Suppose that our system, instead of being completely decomposable, is in fact only *nearly* completely decomposable. In other words, suppose that the variables within each set do depend on the past values of variables outside that set but that this dependence is small relative to within-set dependencies. In such a case, the Simon-Ando theorem[4] asserts the following: carry out the analysis of the system on the assumption that it is really completely decomposable (*i.e.*, ignore inter-set dependencies altogether). Provided that inter-set dependencies are sufficiently weak relative to intra-set ones, *in the short run* that analysis will remain approximately valid in all respects—that is, the system will behave almost as if it *were* completely decomposable.[5]

Now, if this were all, it would be useful but not very remarkable, for it would merely mean that if neglected influences are sufficiently weak they take a long time to matter much; however, the theorem does not stop here but asserts a far stronger result.

Consider the long-run behavior that the system would exhibit if it were truly completely decomposable. In particular, consider the *relative* behavior of the variables within each set (*i.e.*, consider the long-run behavior of their ratios). Provided again that inter-set dependencies are sufficiently weak relative to intra-set ones, that same relative behavior will show up approximately in the long-run behavior of the true only *nearly* completely decomposable system. It is important to fully grasp this result. It asserts that even when influences which have been neglected have had time to make themselves fully felt, the *relative* behavior of the variables within any set will be approximately the same as would have been the case had those influences never existed, and this despite the fact that the *absolute* behavior of the variables—their levels and rates of change—may be very different indeed. To recapitulate: if a nearly completely decomposable system is analyzed as though it were really completely decomposable, the results obtained will remain approximately valid even in the long run as regards the *relative* behavior of the variables within any one set.[6]

The detailed examples of the next section will make all this clearer; however, let us pause briefly over the examples already cited. In one variant of the international trade case, the Simon-Ando theorem asserts that if a country trades very little with the rest of the world, its short-run production of every commodity will be approximately the same as if it did not trade at all. Further, in the long run, the *ratio* in which it produces any two commodities will also be approximately the same, although the *levels* and *rates of growth* of production may be very different in the two cases. Similarly, in the group behavior case, the Simon-Ando theorem asserts that, if outside roles for group members are relatively unimportant, the short-run behavior of the group will be approximately the same as if those roles did not exist, while in the long run, the *relative* behavior of the group members *vis-à-vis* each other will also be approximately the same, even though the behavior of the group *as a whole*[7] *vis-à-vis* the rest of the world may be quite different.

Unfortunately, however, useful as completely decomposable or nearly completely decomposable systems are, the assumptions inherent in

[4] Simon and Ando, *op. cit.*

[5] Here and later what is meant by "sufficiently weak" depends on what standard of approximation one wishes to impose on the results. The more closely one insists that the behavior of the system must approximate that of the corresponding completely decomposable one, the weaker must "sufficiently weak" be. What the theorem guarantees is that *whatever* standard of approximation is required (so long as it is an approximate and not an exact standard) a non-zero degree of weakness always exists which is sufficient to produce results satisfying that standard.

[6] Even before the full system settles down to its ultimate behavior, variables within any one set will move proportionally, so that inter-set influences can be analyzed as influences among indices, each index representing all variables in a particular subset of the system, rather than as among the individual variables themselves. This point, while a little aside from the main drift of our discussion in the text, is useful and important and will show up in our examples below. It is true of both theorems.

near complete decomposability are grossly unrealistic for many systems which are of great interest to social scientists. We often study systems which we do not believe, even as an approximation, to be causally uninfluenced by outside forces. In many cases, we deal with systems whose variables are believed to be influenced by outside forces but not to influence these outside variables, so that the latter may be taken as givens of the problem. This is the case of causal influences running only one way among sets of variables (although there may be "whorls" of causation within each set). Thus the economist frequently takes tastes or technology as causally influencing the variables he studies but as being causally uninfluenced by them. So too, a sociologist may take the existing means of production as given independently of the variables he studies but as influencing the latter in a significant way.

More formally, this kind of assumption is equivalent to saying that our variables can be collected into sets *numbered* (from 1 to N, say) so that the variables in any given set are functions of their own past values *and* of the past values of the variables in any lower-numbered set but not of the past values of the variables in any higher-numbered one. This sort of system is called *decomposable*. (The reader should go back to the definition of *complete* decomposability to be sure he understands the difference.) Clearly, the dynamic behavior of any set of variables in a decomposable system can be studied, taking the behavior of variables in lower-numbered sets as given and without any regard for higher-numbered sets. (Note, however, that the influence of lower-numbered sets *must* be explicitly recognized.)

Again as in the case of complete decomposability, however, the assumption of decomposability is frequently justified only as a working approximation. Thus tastes and technology are not *really* independent of the workings of the economic system; the means of production are not *really* given independently of sociological factors.[8] The question then arises as before of the validity of results obtained under such assumptions. Indeed, this question is perhaps even more important here than in the completely decomposable case, for we have already pointed out (and the examples just cited illustrate) that the very separation of social science into the social sciences is a use of the assumption of decomposability.

Fortunately, the same things are essentially true here as in the nearly completely decomposable case. For nearly decomposable systems which are not nearly completely decomposable —in other words, for systems in which *one-way* inter-set influences are too large to ignore—the Ando-Fisher theorem[9] yields substantially the same results as the Simon-Ando theorem does for the nearly completely decomposable case. Thus the economist who takes tastes and technology as influencing but uninfluenced by economic variables will find—provided that such an assumption is *nearly* correct—that his results will be approximately valid in all respects in the short run and that even in the long run, when the full effects of feedbacks in the causal structure are felt, the *internal, relative* behavior of the variables he studies will be approximately the same. The importance of this result for the usefulness of intra-disciplinary studies in an interrelated world needs no emphasis.[10]

II

We come now to the application of these theorems to two examples in political science which we shall work out in moderate detail, although without any attempt to argue that these examples are more than illustrations.

First, let us consider an over-simple model of armament races. Suppose that at any time, the stocks of armaments of any country (as measured by the number of units of each type of weapon in its arsenal) are a function of the stocks of armaments of all countries (including itself) at some past date.[11] The influences of such past stocks may be of different kinds. Thus armaments may be higher the higher a prospective enemy's armament stocks; lower the higher the stocks of prospective allies; effects on different weapons may be different; stocks of one

[7] This phrase is not used accidentally. The influence of the outside roles will eventually be on group behavior as a whole rather than on individual behavior within the group (remember that such influences are small relative to within-group forces). See the preceding footnote.

[8] Indeed, it would be odd (although not impossible) for both statements to hold exactly.

[9] Ando and Fisher, *op. cit.*

[10] This is not to deny, of course, the usefulness of inter-disciplinary work. The point is that the results of intra-disciplinary studies need not be vitiated because the real world is not so neatly divided as the academic one.

[11] Again, the use of past time is not a restriction; the past date can be last year or yesterday or an hour ago. Similarly, influences in the further past can be formally subsumed under this model by redefinition. Finally, the formulation includes the case in which it is the *rate of change* rather than the *level* of the armament stocks which are dependent on past armaments. This sort of treatment of arms races originates with L. F. Richardson. See his *Arms and Insecurity* (Chicago, Quadrangle Books, 1960). Of course the stocks of armaments depend on other things such as economic resources; we are trying to keep the example as simple as possible. The functions in question are supposed to represent the strategic choices made by governments.

type of weapon may influence stocks of others positively or negatively; and so forth.

Now suppose that the world is divided into several arms races in such a way that the armaments of a country in any one arms race depend principally on those of the other countries in the same arms race and relatively little on those of countries in other arms races. (This may not be a bad approximation; one might think of the Arabs and Israelis on the one hand and the East-West arms race on the other.) The system is then nearly completely decomposable and the Simon-Ando theorem predicts the following.

From the initiation of the various arms races (since they are at least slightly interdependent they will all begin at least nominally at the same time) until some time thereafter, each arms race will proceed approximately as it would in the absence of the other races. Indeed, this will continue until after the transient effects of different starting stocks of armaments have effectively disappeared. Once this has happened, there will come a time after which the stocks of various weapons for all the countries in each arms race will grow (or shrink or fluctuate) approximately proportionally, so that the influence of any one arms race on any other may be considered as that of an aggregate "country" with one aggregate stock of weapons on another, despite the fact that the influences among the countries and weapons making up the aggregates may be quite varied. Finally, in the long run, the size and rate of growth of every country's armament stocks at any period will be determined by the rate of growth of that arms race which would grow fastest in the absence of the other arms races, but the *relative* sizes of the weapon stocks within any one arms race will remain approximately the same as if no other arms races existed.

Now consider a somewhat different situation in which the world is again divided into arms races and the arms races are numbered such that armament stocks in any given country are functions of past stocks of other countries in the same arms race and of countries in lower-numbered arms races but only slightly of stocks of countries in higher-numbered arms races.[12] (This, too, may be somewhat realistic. On the one hand, the level of Pakistani armaments is affected by United States military aid; on the other hand, the level of United States armaments is hardly affected by Pakistani arms levels.) Then the system is nearly decomposable and the Ando-Fisher theroem yields results similar to those just presented in the nearly completely decomposable case. Perhaps it is worth remarking here that the theorem thus shows that a very rapid long-run rate of arms accumulation in a high-numbered arms race (say India-Pakistan or North and South Vietnam) can force the long-run rate of arms accumulation in a lower-numbered race (say U. S.-U.S.S.R.) to the same level but cannot more than negligibly affect the *relative* positions in the latter race.

For our second example, we turn to the voting strength of political parties. Suppose that there are several political parties and that the number of votes for any one party at a given time is a function of the number of votes for each party at some past time. For convenience, we shall assume a constant total population and that every individual votes for one and only one party. We shall further assume that the effect of past votes on present party strength can be represented for each party by a sum of terms, each term representing the probability of an individual who votes initially for a particular party changing his vote to the party in question, times the number of people voting for the initial party. Of course, individuals who stay in the same party are counted as going from that party to itself. It follows then that if we add the coefficients which give the probabilities of going from a particular party to all parties in existence, the sum must be unity, as every individual must end up somewhere.[13]

Thus, in equation form, let X_{1t} be the number of votes for the first party at time, t, X_{2t} be the number of votes for the second party at the same time, and so forth. We have (where there are n parties):

$$(1)\quad \begin{aligned} X_{1t} &= A_{11}X_{1t-1} + A_{12}X_{2t-1} + \cdots + A_{1n}X_{nt-1} \\ X_{2t} &= A_{21}X_{1t-1} + A_{22}X_{2t-1} + \cdots + A_{2n}X_{nt-1} \\ &\vdots \\ X_{nt} &= A_{n1}X_{1t-1} + A_{n2}X_{2t-1} + \cdots + A_{nn}X_{nt-1} \end{aligned}$$

Here, A_{11} is the probability of an individual voting for party 1 continuing to do so; A_{12} is the probability of an individual voting for party 2 changing to party 1; A_{21} is the probability of an individual voting for party 1 changing to party 2; and so forth. Clearly, all the A's must lie between zero and one, and the sum of the A's in any column must be unity.

[12] They need not be functions of armament stocks in *all* lower-numbered races; one will do. Similarly, not every country in the given arms race need have such links; all that is required is that at least one does, so that the system, while nearly decomposable, is not nearly *completely* decomposable. It is also possible to analyze a case in which a part of a nearly decomposable system happens to be nearly completely decomposable.

[13] A discussion of this general sort of model which aggregates from the individual level is given in T. W. Anderson, "Probability Models for Analyzing Time Changes in Attitudes," Chapter 1 in *Mathematical Thinking in the Social Sciences*, P. F. Lazarsfeld, ed. (Glencoe, 1954). It would be

Now consider any set of parties (a single party can count as a set). Ignore the fact that such a set may gain votes from outside itself and consider only its own internal workings. There will be in the long run a single probability that a randomly chosen individual voting for some party in the set will continue to vote for some party in the set at the next time period (he may move between parties in the set). Equivalently, without ignoring the fact that the set may gain votes from outside, we may consider the long-run probability that one of the people *originally* voting for some party in the set who has remained so voting through some particular time will continue so to vote for yet one more period; this comes to the same thing. (In either definition, we assume that every party in the set begins with a very large number of votes so that a zero vote does not become a problem save for parties which lose all their votes every time period.) We call that long-run probability the *cohesiveness* of the set. Clearly, it must lie between zero and one; the cohesiveness of any single party is the A coefficient in its own row and column (thus, for example, A_{11} is the cohesiveness of the first party taken alone); and the cohesiveness of all parties taken together is unity (since nobody can leave the system as a whole). In general, the cohesiveness of a set lies between the smallest and the largest probability of an individual voting for any given party in the set staying put or changing to another party in the same set (this latter probability is given by the sum of the A's in the column corresponding to the party in question and in the rows corresponding to all parties in the set including the initial one).[14]

Now suppose that the parties can be divided into sets such that the probability of an individual moving between sets is small relative to the probability of his remaining in the same set. Clearly, each set then has cohesiveness close to unity. The system is then nearly completely decomposable and the Simon-Ando theorem yields the following results:

Begin with any distribution of voting chosen at random. In the short run, the voting strength of each party will behave approximately as it would if there were no movements between sets of parties whatsoever. Moreover, there will come a time after which the ratio of the votes for any party to the votes for any other party in the same set will remain approximately constant. Thereafter, each set of parties can be treated as a single party for purposes of analyzing inter-set movements, with the cohesiveness of the set acting as the probability of remaining therein. Finally, even in the long run, the equilibrium distribution of relative voting strength *within* each set of parties will be approximately the same as if there were no inter-set movements, although the absolute number of votes involved may be quite different.

In this example, however, the more interesting case is that of near decomposability. Let us first consider what a truly decomposable system would be. This would occur if the parties could be divided into sets where the sets are numbered (from 1 to N, say) in such a way that nobody voting for a party in any set ever changes to a party in a lower-numbered set but such that there are non-negligible movements into higher numbered sets. Thus anybody in set N stays there; anybody in set $N-1$ either stays there or moves to set N; anybody in set $N-2$ either stays there, moves to set $N-1$, or moves to set N; and so forth. (Note that set N has cohesiveness 1; no other single set has cohesiveness 1, but set N and set $N-1$ together, set N, set $N-1$, and set $N-2$ together, and so forth all have cohesiveness 1). The sets are thus "nested," in the sense that all inter-set movements go toward the center which consists of set N.

Now suppose that all sets begin with a very large number of votes (so that the fact that the lower-numbered sets will eventually lose all their votes is not a difficulty). Consider any set. A time will come such that thereafter the *relative* strength of the parties in that set is determined primarily by their tendency to attract voters from parties in the set with the highest cohesiveness among those sets that are not higher numbered than the set in question. (In the case of set N or of set 1, this is the set in question itself; in any other case, it need not be.) This is a reasonable result, because as time goes on the parties in the sets with the greatest cohesiveness will acquire more and more votes, so that, given the probabilities of

possible to abandon the probability interpretation and to let higher strength in one party lead to lower strength in another, but this would lead to an example without some of the nice features of the present one. It would also be possible to build in other influences on party voting strength. Again, we are striving for an illuminating example rather than for a full-blown "realistic" theory. The assumption that every individual votes for some party is innocuous, since we can count all those not voting for any formal party as voting for a party of their own, the "Non-such" Party.

[14] *Technical footnote.* Precisely, cohesiveness is given by the largest characteristic root of the submatrix of A's corresponding to the parties in the set. See F. M. Fisher, "An Alternate Proof and Extension of Solow's Theorem on Nonnegative Square Matrices," *Econometrica*, Vol. 30 (July, 1962) forthcoming. The fact that the root lies between the largest and smallest column sums is well known—see R. M. Solow, "On the Structure of Linear Models," *Econometrica*, Vol. 21 (January, 1952), pp. 29–46.

any *single* voter moving among the sets, what happens to these sets becomes of increasing importance to all those sets of parties that acquire voters from them.

We now alter the assumptions and suppose that although the dominant inter-set movements are to higher-numbered sets, there are small movements to lower-numbered ones. (This may not be too unrealistic. We might think of set N as the major parties; there may be a far higher tendency to move into or stay in them than there is to move out.) The system is now only nearly decomposable and the Ando-Fisher theorem yields the following results:

Begin with any distribution of voting chosen at random. In the short run, the actual number of votes for each party will behave approximately as it would if the only inter-set movements were to higher-numbered sets. Moreover, there will come a time after which the *relative* distribution of voting among the parties within any set will remain approximately the same as would have been the case in the truly decomposable case earlier described. After this time, inter-set movements can be analyzed without regard for the voting distribution within the various sets. Finally these *relative* intra-set distributions will be approximately maintained even in the long run, although the absolute number of votes eventually cast for the parties in each set will depend almost wholly on the tendency of that set as a whole to gain voters from set N (which by this time is far larger than any other set).

Note that this result implies that an analysis of the *relative* strength of "minor" parties can proceed without explicit account of the tendency of such parties to gain voters from or even to lose voters to major ones, despite the fact that the latter tendency is large. So far as *relative* voting strength is concerned, all that matters are the various tendencies of the minor parties to lose voters to and gain voters from each other (and even some of these may be negligible). Even wide differences in tendencies to lose voters to (or gain them from) major parties need not be explicitly taken into account, provided only that the former tendencies are very strong relative to the latter, a rather surprising result.[15]

[15] We are perhaps making this result sound a bit more paradoxical than it is. Different tendencies to lose voters to major parties do in fact matter and get taken into account in an implicit fashion. Since every party's voters end up *somewhere* (the sum of the A's in any column is one), a minor party with a high propensity to lose voters to major ones will have—*other things being equal*—a lower propensity to retain voters than a minor party with a lower propensity to lose voters to major ones. This will show up in considering their relative strength in isolation; however, it can be nullified by other tendencies if other things are *not* equal.

7

DECOMPOSABILITY, NEAR DECOMPOSABILITY, AND BALANCED PRICE CHANGE UNDER CONSTANT RETURNS TO SCALE

By Franklin M. Fisher[1]

The paper extends the results of the Solow-Samuelson article [**12**], reinterpreting their balanced growth model in terms of prices rather than output and weakening their monotonicity assumption to consider cases in which the production system is decomposable, completely decomposable, or approximates one of these. It is shown, among other things, that results similar to those obtained by Simon and Ando [**11**] and Ando and Fisher [**1**] for linear systems hold for the asymptotic behavior of this sort of nonlinear system of difference equations.

1. Introduction and Interpretation of the Model

Some time ago, Solow and Samuelson [**12**] proved a collection of powerful and interesting theorems about a system of difference equations which they interpreted as describing a rather special closed economy operating under constant returns to scale. Briefly, let $X_i(t)$ be the output of the ith commodity at time t and let this period's outputs be next period's inputs. Then:

$$X_i(t+1) = H^i(X_1(t), X_2(t), \ldots, X_n(t)) \qquad (i = 1, \ldots, n) \tag{1.1}$$

where the H^i are nonnegatively valued functions defined on the nonnegative orthant and are homogeneous of degree one. Solow and Samuelson assume that the H^i are continuous and monotonic increasing functions of each argument so that some of every output will be produced provided that at least one input is positive. They show that under these conditions there exists a unique balanced growth configuration for the system; that configuration is associated with a unique real positive growth rate; finally, that configuration and growth rate are stable in the large, in the sense that no matter where the system starts it approaches that configuration and rate of growth as time goes to infinity.

It happens, however, that the original interpretation of the Solow-Samuelson model in terms of inputs and outputs is not a very interesting one. This is so primarily because the H^i are not production functions in the usual sense.[2] Instead of every output being a function of the inputs specifically used in its production, every output is made a function of the total amount of each input in the economy. In this context, the assumption of monotonicity is very strong, far stronger than the assumption of positive

[1] I am indebted to Albert Ando, Lionel McKenzie, Paul A. Samuelson, and Robert M. Solow for their comments. The usual release is hereby granted.

[2] See Neisser [8] and Solow and Samuelson [**13**].

marginal productivities. Indeed, the only output model which seems at all plausible here is that of one process producing every good jointly.

It has, however, been recognized in the literature[3] that while the output interpretation of the Solow-Samuelson model is not of much interest, the system (1.1) can be given an interesting interpretation in terms of prices. Thus, in a generalized von Neumann model, along any intertemporally efficient path—and perfectly competitive economies will, under appropriate conditions, move along such paths—the price vector of inputs will determine the factor combinations used which (together with the input prices) will determine the price vector of outputs.[4] Thus prices at time $t + 1$ can be thought of as determined by prices at time t; moreover, the functions describing such determination are clearly homogeneous of degree one and at least weakly monotonic in all arguments.

Moreover, it is at least clear what strong monotonicity means in such a model. In general (aside from other cases), it will occur if (even though technical coefficients are variable) some (even if very little) of every input is needed to produce every output. While this is clearly a rather strong assumption (and one which this paper will explicitly weaken), it is not uninteresting.

Since the price interpretation of the Solow-Samuelson model is thus the one of greatest interest to date, it seems appropriate to cast the interpretation of further mathematical work with that model in terms of that interpretation, rather than to continue with Solow and Samuelson's own output interpretation. Accordingly, we shall generally do so in this paper, although the theorems will be stated in purely mathematical terms as they are clearly not limited to any one interpretation.

Let us then begin by recasting the Solow-Samuelson results in terms of prices. Instead of balanced growth rays, we shall speak of balanced price rays, and instead of growth rates, we shall speak of inflation rates. This last usage, however, requires a bit of discussion.

It is obvious that an inflation rate less than unity corresponds to a fall, rather than a rise in prices. Indeed, this is a likely circumstance in the model, for if the output side of a von Neumann economy is growing, the price side will be falling to meet no-profit conditions. Indeed, when the economy is in balanced growth, the price configuration will also be balanced, with the inflation rate the reciprocal of the growth rate. This means, for instance, that when we speak of a sector with a high inflation rate, we shall be speaking of a sector with a low rate of growth of output and a consequently low rate of decline (high rate of rise) of prices—a "bottleneck" sector.

[3] For example, Hicks [**5**, p. 80]; Morishima [**7**, pp. 92–3]. The latter paper is concerned primarily with linear cases.

[4] See Hicks, *loc. cit.*, for a somewhat more extended treatment.

In this interpretation, then, the Solow-Samuelson results show that if every input is required for the production of every output, then there exists a unique balanced price ray and unique associated inflation rate and that such ray and rate are approached asymptotically starting from any initial price vector.

In this paper, we shall consider the behavior of such a system when the strict monotonicity assumption is relaxed in one of several rather special but highly interesting ways. In particular, we shall be concerned with its behavior when the system is decomposable or completely decomposable or approaches one of these cases.[5] In view of the remarks made by Solow and Samuelson [**12**, p. 413n], this is equivalent to a somewhat more general weakening of the monotonicity assumption, since by taking the time unit sufficiently large any *in*decomposable and acyclic system can be considered monotonic. The principal case not covered by this is thus that of a system in which monotonicity depends on the values of the variables (an important exception).[6]

Moreover (returning for a moment to the output interpretation of the model), the results for the decomposable case can easily be used to analyze the case of a constant-returns-to-scale production model with one or more fixed factors, a case considered by Suits [**14**] with rather different (although not formally contradictory) results. A generalization of the price model to the case of rigid prices is also possible.

The results here obtained are also of interest beyond the immediate interpretation, as among them are theorems analogous to those of Simon and Ando [**11**] and Ando and Fisher [**1**] on the behavior of nearly completely decomposable and nearly decomposable linear systems, respectively. We thus show that those theorems are by no means restricted to the special linear case.[7]

[5] Following the terminology of Ando and Fisher [**1**]: a completely decomposable linear system is one whose matrix can be transformed by identical permutations of rows and columns into a matrix with square blocks of elements on the main diagonal and zeros everywhere else (a "block diagonal" matrix); a decomposable linear system (without the qualifying adverb) is one whose matrix can be similarly transformed into a matrix with square blocks of elements on the principal diagonal and zeros *below* these blocks (a "block triangular" matrix); a *nearly* decomposable or *nearly* completely decomposable linear system is one whose matrix satisfies the appropriate above definition with the zeros replaced by very small elements. The precise usage to be employed here for the more general *non*linear case will be given below as will the interpretation in terms of prices.

[6] Since this was written, the paper by Morishima [**6**] has appeared which does offer results on the general case. Indecomposability is assumed for some but not all of the theorems therein.

[7] This was conjectured by Ando and Fisher [**1**]. Unfortunately, the dependence of the proofs on the Solow-Samuelson results is so great that no immediate generalization to other nonlinear systems seems possible. A complete statement of the theorems

Finally, it is of interest to observe that results similar to those of the present paper hold under appropriate conditions for the behavior of the production side of generalized von Neumann models.[8]

2. THE CASES OF COMPLETE AND NEAR COMPLETE DECOMPOSABILITY

We begin with the cases of complete decomposability and near complete decomposability as much the simplest.

It will be convenient to adopt some new notation. Suppose that the column vector of the $X_i(t)$ is partitioned into N disjunct subvectors, $X^1(t), X^2(t), \ldots, X^N(t)$. Group the equations of (1.1) corresponding to each $X^I(t)$ and write them as N vector equations:

$$X^I(t+1) = F^I(X^1(t), X^2(t), \ldots, X^N(t)) \qquad (I = 1, \ldots, N) . \tag{2.1}$$

Let the number of elements in $X^I(t)$ be n_I. Here and in similar cases later, we shall write the jth function of F^I as F^I_J.

Now, drop the monotonicity assumption and suppose that the above partitioning can be accomplished, renumbering the $X_i(t)$, if necessary, in such a way that:

$$\begin{aligned} X^1(t+1) &= F^1(X^1(t), 0, 0, \ldots, 0) \equiv \phi^1(X^1(t)) , \\ X^2(t+1) &= F^2(0, X^2(t), 0, \ldots, 0) \equiv \phi^2(X^2(t)) , \\ &\vdots \\ X^N(t+1) &= F^N(0, 0, \ldots, 0, X^N(t)) \equiv \phi^N(X^N(t)) , \end{aligned} \tag{2.2}$$

identically in the $X^I(t)$. We shall call such a system completely decomposable. In other words, a completely decomposable production system is one in which each set of outputs uses only itself as inputs. We shall assume, for simplicity, that each member function of each ϕ^I is still monotonic increasing in every element of its own special $X^I(t)$ so that every output of a given sector requires inputs of every good in that sector.

It is easy to see what the behavior of such a system must be. Obviously, each ϕ^I is homogeneous of degree one in the elements of its own $X^I(t)$ and the behavior of the other $X^J(t)$ doesn't affect it at all. Each of the N sets of difference equations in (2.2) must thus behave exactly as did the whole set

involved can be found in the two works cited. Fisher and Ando [**4**] give an informal description of those theorems and apply them to two examples in political science. Simon [**10**] discusses (among other things) the relation of such systems to notions of causation, while Fisher [**2**] considers their importance for simultaneous equation estimation with approximate models.

[8] Fisher [**3**].

in (1.1) under strict monotonicity. The economy is really made up of N small sub-economies each of which is independent of all the others and to each of which the Solow-Samuelson analysis applies. Each such sub-economy will thus have its own unique balanced price configuration and inflation rate to which it converges. These inflation rates will in general be different for different sectors, so that the economy as a whole will not achieve balanced inflation. For later simplicity, we shall assume that here and in all subsequent similar cases, there are no two identical such inflation rates.[9]

Now, let $G^I(X^1(t), \ldots, X^N(t); \varepsilon)$ $(I = 1, \ldots, N)$ be a set of price determination functions, continuous and homogeneous of degree one in the elements of all the $X^J(t)$ and monotonic increasing in all those elements for $\varepsilon \neq 0$. Let them be continuous in ε. Finally, let:

$$G^I(0, 0, \ldots, 0, X^I(t), 0, \ldots, 0; \varepsilon) = \phi^I(X^I(t)) \qquad (I = 1, \ldots, N) \tag{2.3A}$$

for all ε, and

$$\lim_{\varepsilon \to 0} G^I(X^1(t), \ldots, X^N(t); \varepsilon) = \phi^I(X^I(t)) \qquad (I = 1, \ldots, N) \tag{2.3B}$$

for all values of the $X^J(t)$. Consider the system:

$$X^I(t + 1) = G^I(X^1(t), \ldots, X^N(t); \varepsilon) \qquad (I = 1, \ldots, N) \tag{2.4}$$

Clearly, as ε approaches zero, this system approaches (2.2). In other words, the economy approaches complete decomposability as, for the production of the outputs of a particular sector, the requirements and usefulness of inputs from outside that sector become less and less. Nevertheless, no matter how small ε is, so long as it is not zero, the system obeys the strict monotonicity requirement and has a unique stable balanced price ray and inflation rate.[10]

As in Solow and Samuelson, let us now normalize the $X^I(t)$ so that the sum of *all* the *original* $X_i(t)$ is unity. We shall write the resulting $X_i(t)$ as V_i and the corresponding $X^I(t)$ as V^I (dropping the time argument for simplicity). Observe that the V^I are nonnegative, and consider the mapping:

$$y^I = \frac{G^I(V^1, \ldots, V^N; \varepsilon)}{\sum_{I=1}^{N} \sum_{j=1}^{n_I} G_j^I(V^1, \ldots, V^N; \varepsilon)} \qquad (I = 1, \ldots, N). \tag{2.5}$$

Clearly, $y^I \geqslant 0$ and $\sum_{I=1}^{N} \sum_{j=1}^{n_I} y_j^I = 1$. By Brouwer's fixed-point theorem,

[9] It would doubtless be possible, though tedious, to drop this assumption. In the linear case it is slightly weaker than the assumption that the relevant matrix has no multiple latent roots.

[10] Throughout, ε need not be thought of as a single parameter in any simple sense. It may be a vector of parameters, or it may be the distance of such a vector from a particular point in the parameter space, and so forth.

(2.5) thus has at least one fixed point, say $V^*(\varepsilon)$. Indeed, for $\varepsilon \neq 0$, Solow and Samuelson's uniqueness proof applies and $V^*(\varepsilon)$ is unique. It is obvious, however, that for $\varepsilon = 0$, there are precisely N such fixed points, say $V^*(0,1), \ldots, V^*(0,N)$ (where the second argument is introduced to avoid ambiguity in superscripts). These points are characterized by the fact that (for $I = 1, \ldots, N$), $V^{*J}(0,I) = 0$ for $J \neq I$, while $V^{*I}(0,I)$ is itself the *unique* fixed point of the mapping:

$$z_i = \frac{\phi_i^I(W^I)}{\sum_{j=1}^{n_I} \phi_j^I(W^I)} \qquad (i = 1, \ldots, n_I) \tag{2.6}$$

where

$$W^I = \frac{V^I}{\sum_{j=1}^{n_I} V_j^I}. \tag{2.7}$$

We prove the following lemma.[11]

LEMMA 2.1: *For any α, $Lim_{\varepsilon \to \alpha} V^*(\varepsilon)$ exists. Moreover, $V^*(\varepsilon)$ is continuous at $\varepsilon = \alpha \neq 0$ and upper semi-continuous at 0. (In other words, the fixed point property is not lost in taking the limit.)*

Proof. We shall prove the lemma for $\alpha \neq 0$ and the upper semi-continuity property at 0 now. The fact that the limit at zero exists will follow in the proof of Theorem 2.1 below.

Take a sequence of values of ε converging to α. Consider the corresponding sequence of the $V^*(\varepsilon)$. Since the simplex is compact, that sequence contains a convergent subsequence. Moreover, it will suffice to show that any such convergent subsequence converges to (the unique) $V^*(\alpha)$ for $\alpha \neq 0$, since if the full sequence did not so converge it would contain an infinite number of points some finite distance from $V^*(\alpha)$ which (again by the compactness of the simplex) would in turn include a convergent subsequence converging to some other point. Finally, since upper semi-continuity at 0 requires only that any convergent subsequence converge to one of the $V^*(0,I)$ $(I = 1,\ldots, N)$, we need only show that the fixed-point property is preserved in taking the limit along any convergent subsequence.

[11] I am indebted to Robert M. Solow for providing the basic structure of the proof and to Ethan Boker and Stephen Goldfeld for discussion of some of the problems involved.

Now, let the column vector of the y^I in (2.5) be denoted by $y = y(V, \varepsilon)$. This function is clearly continuous in all arguments. Hence, as ε goes to α, and $V^*(\varepsilon)$ moves along a convergent subsequence, $\text{Lim}_{\varepsilon\to\alpha} V^*(\varepsilon) = \text{Lim}_{\varepsilon\to\alpha} y(V^*(\varepsilon), \varepsilon) = y\,(\text{Lim}_{\varepsilon\to\alpha} V^*(\varepsilon), \alpha)$. Thus the fixed point property is preserved in the limit and the lemma follows (save for the existence of the limit at 0) by the remarks made at the outset.

Now, let λ_I be the unique balanced inflation rate associated with $V^*(0, I)$ $(I = 1, \ldots, N)$. Let λ_K be the largest of these. Let $\lambda(\varepsilon)$ be the unique balanced inflation rate of the entire system (2.4) for $\varepsilon \neq 0$. We prove:

THEOREM 2.1: *For* $\varepsilon \neq 0$, $\lambda(\varepsilon) > \lambda_K$. *However,* $\text{Lim}_{\varepsilon\to 0}\, \lambda(\varepsilon) = \lambda_K$ *and* $\text{Lim}_{\varepsilon\to 0}\, V^*(\varepsilon) = V^*(0, K)$.

Proof. Since both $V^*(\varepsilon)$ and $V^*(0, K)$ are fixed points of (2.5) for appropriate ε, we have:

$$\lambda(\varepsilon) V_j^{*K}(\varepsilon) = G_j^K(V^{*1}(\varepsilon), \ldots, V^{*K}(\varepsilon), \ldots, V^{*N}(\varepsilon); \varepsilon) \quad (j = 1, \ldots, n_K) \tag{2.8}$$

and

$$\lambda_K V_j^{*K}(0, K) = G_j^K(0, \ldots, 0, V^{*K}(0, K), 0, \ldots, 0; 0) \quad (j = 1, \ldots, n_K). \tag{2.9}$$

By homogeneity, therefore,

$$\lambda(\varepsilon) = G_j^K\left(\frac{V^{*1}(\varepsilon)}{V_j^{*K}(\varepsilon)}, \ldots, \frac{V^{*K}(\varepsilon)}{V_j^{*K}(\varepsilon)}, \ldots, \frac{V^{*N}(\varepsilon)}{V_j^{*K}(\varepsilon)}; \varepsilon\right) \quad (j = 1, \ldots, n_K) \tag{2.10}$$

and

$$\lambda_K = G_j^K\left(0, \ldots, 0, \frac{V^{*K}(0, K)}{V_j^{*K}(0, K)}, 0, \ldots, 0; 0\right) \quad (j = 1, \ldots, n_K)\,. \tag{2.11}$$

Suppose that $\lambda_K \geqslant \lambda(\varepsilon)$ for $\varepsilon \neq 0$. Then, since the other arguments in (2.10) are positive, monotonicity clearly requires that at least one of the elements of $V^{*K}(0, K)/V_j^{*K}(0, K)$ be greater than the corresponding element of $V^{*K}(\varepsilon)/V_j^{*K}(\varepsilon)$ for *every* $j = 1, \ldots, n_K$. This is impossible, however, for if it held for $j = 1, \ldots, n_K - 1$, that would imply that it did not hold for $j = n_K$ as shown in Solow and Samuelson [**13**, p. 416]. Hence, $\lambda(\varepsilon) > \lambda_K$ for $\varepsilon \neq 0$.[12]

Now, it is evident given the normalization of the V^I (and this is pointed out by Solow and Samuelson) that at $V^*(\varepsilon)$ the denominator of the fraction

[12] Note the analogy with the well-known theorem in the linear case that the largest root of a nonnegative matrix is a nondecreasing function of the elements thereof.

on the right hand side of (2.5) is precisely $\lambda(\varepsilon)$. Similarly, it is easy to see that at $V^*(0, I)$ the denominator of the fraction on the right hand side of (2.6) is precisely $\lambda_I (I = 1, \ldots, N)$. However, in view of Lemma 2.1 and the continuity of the G^I in all arguments, the denominator in (2.5) must approach one of the denominators in (2.6) as ε approaches zero ($V^*(\varepsilon)$ moving along a convergent sequence), since $V^{*J}(0, I) = 0$ for $J \neq I$. Thus $\lambda(\varepsilon)$ must approach one of the λ_I. In view of the inequality already established, however, this can only be λ_K. The remainder of the theorem now follows immediately.

In other words, in the long run, an indecomposable system will always have an inflation rate higher than the highest inflation rate of any corresponding completely decomposable system. Moreover, for the system very close to complete decomposability, the balanced inflation rate and price configuration, respectively, will be very close to the largest balanced inflation rate of any sector in the corresponding completely decomposable system and its associated balanced price configuration. Note that the latter price configuration has zero as the price of any good not in the sector that has the highest inflation rate, i.e., the worst bottleneck sector.

A much stronger result than this is available, however. It is:

THEOREM 2.2:

$$\lim_{\varepsilon \to 0} \frac{V_j^{*I}(\varepsilon)}{\sum_{j=1}^{n_I} V_j^{*I}(\varepsilon)} = \frac{V_j^{*I}(0,I)}{\sum_{j=1}^{n_I} V_j^{*I}(0,I)} \qquad (I = 1, \ldots, N)\ (j = 1, \ldots, n_I)\,.$$

Proof. If $I = K$, the result follows immediately from Theorem 2.1; if $I \neq K$, however, the theorem is not at all trivial.

Let

$$W^{*I}(\varepsilon) = \frac{V^{*I}(\varepsilon)}{\sum_{j=1}^{n_I} V_j^{*I}(\varepsilon)} \qquad (I = 1, \ldots, N)\,.$$

Then:

$$\text{(2.12)}\quad \lim_{\varepsilon \to 0} W_j^{*I}(\varepsilon) = \lim_{\varepsilon \to 0} \frac{G_j^I(V^{*1}(\varepsilon), \ldots, V^{*I}(\varepsilon), \ldots, V^{*N}(\varepsilon); \varepsilon)}{\sum_{j=1}^{n_I} G_j^I(V^{*1}(\varepsilon), \ldots, V^{*I}(\varepsilon), \ldots, V^{*N}(\varepsilon); \varepsilon)}\,.$$

We prove:

LEMMA 2.2:

$$\lim_{\varepsilon\to 0} \frac{G_j^I(V^{*1}(\varepsilon), \ldots, V^{*I}(\varepsilon), \ldots, V^{*N}(\varepsilon); \varepsilon)}{\sum_{j=1}^{n_I} G_j^I(V^{*1}(\varepsilon), \ldots, V^{*I}(\varepsilon), \ldots, V^{*N}(\varepsilon); \varepsilon)}$$

$$= \lim_{\varepsilon\to 0} \frac{G_j^I(0, \ldots, 0, V^{*I}(\varepsilon), 0, \ldots, 0; \varepsilon)}{\sum_{j=1}^{n_I} G_j^I(0, \ldots, 0, V^{*I}(\varepsilon), 0, \ldots, 0; \varepsilon)}.[13]$$

Proof. The result is trivial if $I = K$ but not otherwise, since then $V^{*I}(\varepsilon)$ approaches zero. For simplicity, it will suffice to consider a system with only two sectors and $K = 1$. We shall thus derive the desired result for the second sector.

For any $V = (V^1 \quad V^2)$ in the simplex, we have:

$$\lim_{\varepsilon\to 0} \left| \frac{G_j^2(0, V^2; \varepsilon)}{G_j^2(V^1, V^2; \varepsilon)} - \frac{\sum_{j=1}^{n_2} G_j^2(0, V^2; \varepsilon)}{\sum_{j=1}^{n_2} G_j^2(V^1, V^2; \varepsilon)} \right| = 0 \tag{2.13}$$

for any $j = 1, \ldots, n_2$. This is so because if $V^2 \neq 0$, both ratios approach unity, while if $V^2 = 0$, both ratios are zero for all nonzero ε. Further, since the simplex is a compact set, the limit in (2.13) is approached uniformly. Thus, for any scalar $\eta > 0$, there exists an $\varepsilon_1 > 0$, such that $0 < |\varepsilon| < \varepsilon_1$ implies

$$\left| \frac{G_j^2(0, V^{*2}(\varepsilon); \varepsilon)}{G_j^2(V^{*1}(\varepsilon), V^{*2}(\varepsilon); \varepsilon)} - \frac{\sum_{j=1}^{n_2} G_j^2(0, V^{*2}(\varepsilon); \varepsilon)}{\sum_{j=1}^{n_2} G_j^2(V^{*1}(\varepsilon), V^{*2}(\varepsilon); \varepsilon)} \right| < \eta . \tag{2.14}$$

However, this implies

$$\left| \frac{G_j^2(0, V^{*2}(\varepsilon); \varepsilon)}{\sum_{j=1}^{n_2} G_j^2(0, V^{*2}(\varepsilon); \varepsilon)} - \frac{G_j^2(V^{*1}(\varepsilon), V^{*2}(\varepsilon); \varepsilon)}{\sum_{j=1}^{n_2} G_j^2(V^{*1}(\varepsilon), V^{*2}(\varepsilon); \varepsilon)} \right| \tag{2.15}$$

$$< \eta \left(\frac{G_j^2(V^{*1}(\varepsilon), V^{*2}(\varepsilon); \varepsilon)}{\sum_{j=1}^{n_2} G_j^2(0, V^{*2}(\varepsilon); \varepsilon)} \right) \equiv \eta D(\varepsilon), \text{ say.}$$

[13] I am indebted to Lionel McKenzie for pointing out that this proposition certainly requires proof and to Peter A. Diamond for discussion of the present demonstration.

But $D(\varepsilon)$ is bounded as ε goes to zero, for, since $G_j^2(V^{*1}(\varepsilon), V^{*2}(\varepsilon); \varepsilon) = \lambda(\varepsilon) V_j^{*2}(\varepsilon)$, dividing both numerator and denominator of $D(\varepsilon)$ by $V_j^{*2}(\varepsilon)$ yields by homogeneity:

$$D(\varepsilon) = \frac{\lambda(\varepsilon)}{\sum_{j=1}^{n_2} G_j^2\left(0, \frac{V^{*2}(\varepsilon)}{V_j^{*2}(\varepsilon)}; \varepsilon\right)}, \tag{2.16}$$

and the numerator approaches λ_K by Theorem 2.1, while the denominator is clearly bounded away from zero by the monotonicity assumption. Since η can be chosen arbitrarily small, the desired result is now immediate.

Returning now to the proof of the theorem, we have:

$$\begin{aligned}
\lim_{\varepsilon \to 0} W_j^{*I}(\varepsilon) &= \lim_{\varepsilon \to 0} \frac{G_j^I(0, \ldots, 0, V^{*I}(\varepsilon), 0, \ldots, 0; \varepsilon)}{\sum_{j=1}^{n_I} G_j^I(0, \ldots, 0, V^{*I}(\varepsilon), 0, \ldots, 0; \varepsilon)} \\
&= \lim_{\varepsilon \to 0} \frac{\left(\frac{1}{\sum_{j=1}^{n_I} V_j^{*I}(\varepsilon)}\right)\left(G_j^I(0, \ldots, 0, V^{*I}(\varepsilon), 0, \ldots, 0; \varepsilon)\right)}{\left(\frac{1}{\sum_{j=1}^{n_I} V_j^{*I}(\varepsilon)}\right)\left(\sum_{j=1}^{n_I} G_j^I(0, \ldots, 0, V^{*I}(\varepsilon), 0, \ldots, 0; \varepsilon)\right)} \\
&= \lim_{\varepsilon \to 0} \frac{G_j^I(0, \ldots, 0, W^{*I}(\varepsilon), 0, \ldots, 0; \varepsilon)}{\sum_{j=1}^{n_I} G_j^I(0, \ldots, 0, W^{*I}(\varepsilon), 0, \ldots, 0; \varepsilon)} \\
&= \frac{\phi_j^I(\lim_{\varepsilon \to 0} W^{*I}(\varepsilon))}{\sum_{j=1}^{n_I} \phi_j^I(\lim_{\varepsilon \to 0} W^{*I}(\varepsilon))} \qquad (I = 1, \ldots, N; j = 1, \ldots, n_I).
\end{aligned} \tag{2.17}$$

As $W^{*I}(\varepsilon)$, and therefore its limit, is in the simplex, we have shown that $\lim_{\varepsilon \to 0} W^{*I}(\varepsilon)$ is a fixed point of (2.6). However, that mapping has only one fixed point, by Solow and Samuelson's uniqueness theorem, namely, $V^{*I}(0, I)$; and the theorem is proved.

This result is the extension of the major long-run result of Simon and Ando

[11].[14] It states that, provided the system is sufficiently close to complete decomposability, the long-run internal price structure of each sector (i.e., the *relative* prices of the different goods therein) will be approximately the same as in the corresponding completely decomposable system, although the price levels and the rate of inflation will generally be greater, possibly considerably so, the latter rate being above that of the greatest bottleneck sector in the limiting case.[15]

3. THE DECOMPOSABLE CASE

We turn now to the cases of decomposability and near decomposability. Our task is somewhat harder here, for we must first examine the behavior of decomposable systems themselves, and the Solow-Samuelson results are not as immediately applicable to this case as they were to the case of completely decomposable systems. Accordingly, we devote this section to theorems on the behavior of decomposable constant-returns-to-scale systems leaving the case of near decomposability (which will then be easy) to a later section.

Return to our rewriting of the original system (2.1). Suppose that, instead of (2.2), the partitioning of the orginal $X_i(t)$ can be accomplished (renumbering the $X_i(t)$, if necessary) in such a way that:

$$\begin{aligned} X^1(t+1) &= F^1(X^1(t), 0, \ldots, 0) \equiv \psi^1(X^1(t))\,, \\ X^2(t+1) &= F^2(X^1(t), X^2(t), 0, \ldots, 0) \equiv \psi^2(X^1(t), X^2(t))\,, \\ X^3(t+1) &= F^3(X^1(t), X^2(t), X^3(t), 0, \ldots, 0) \equiv \psi^3(X^1(t), X^2(t), X^3(t))\,, \\ &\;\;\vdots \\ X^N(t+1) &= F^N(X^1(t), \ldots, X^N(t)) \equiv \psi^N(X^1(t), \ldots, X^N(t))\,, \end{aligned} \tag{3.1}$$

[14] The extension of their short-run results (that in the short run a nearly completely decomposable system will behave approximately like the corresponding completely decomposable one) to the present case (and indeed to all well-behaved cases) is easily accomplished by considerations of continuity. The extension of their middle-run results (that each sector in a nearly completely decomposable system will eventually adjust to the long-run inflation rate keeping its internal structure approximately unchanged) does not appear easy to accomplish since it seems to require explicit solution of the difference equation system (1.1) in the general, nonlinear case. Heuristically, however, it seems almost certain to hold in view of Theorem 2.2 and the remarks just given as to short-run behavior.

[15] As in all such cases, the meaning of "sufficiently close" depends on the meaning of "approximately the same." Naturally, the closer one insists that the approximation be, the closer must the system be to complete decomposability to satisfy that standard. What the theorem asserts is the existence of a sufficient nonzero degree of closeness for *any* nonzero degree of approximation.

identically in the $X^I(t)$. We shall call such a system decomposable. In other words, a decomposable production system is a hierarchic one in which every sector uses and requires as inputs only its own outputs and the outputs of lower-numbered sectors but not the outputs of higher-numbered ones. (In the next section, we shall see that the first sector can now consist of fixed price commodities.) For simplicity, we shall assume that each member function of each of the ψ^I is monotonically increasing in each of its arguments so that every output of every not-higher-numbered sector really is required as an input to every output of a given sector.[16]

Now, clearly, if, for any I, it just happens to be the case that all $X^J(t)$ start off equal to zero for all $J < I$ (i.e., all external inputs to sector I are free goods) nothing that happens to the Ith sector can ever make them non-zero. It follows that every sector has at least one balanced price configuration and inflation rate, the one it would have if the system were *completely* decomposable. It will be convenient to refer to this inflation rate for the Ith sectors as its "internal" inflation rate and to continue to denote it by λ_I $(I = 1, \ldots, N)$.

It will further be convenient to distinguish between single sectors and what we shall term "subsystems." Whereas the Ith sector consists of just $X^I(t)$ and the associated Ith set of equations in (3.1), we shall define the Ith subsystem as the variables $X^1(t), \ldots, X^I(t)$ and the associated I sets of equations in (3.1) $(I = 1, \ldots, N)$. Note that the first subsystem is identical with the first sector; such an identity does not hold for any other subsystem; the Nth subsystem is identical with the full system (3.1); and, finally, every subsystem other than the first is itself decomposable.

[16] By lengthening the time period, this can be seen to be implied by the weaker assumption that, for all $I = 1, \ldots, N$, Ψ^I is monotonically nondecreasing in all arguments and monotonically increasing in all the elements of $X^I(t)$ and that, for $I = 2, \ldots, N$, at least one Ψ_j^I $(j = 1, \ldots, n_I)$ is monotonically increasing in at least one element of $X^{I-1}(t)$. Other cases can be similarly devised. In general, these are the cases in which every output of a not-higher numbered sector is at least *indirectly* required as an input for every output of a given sector.

Thus the decomposable cases ruled out by the assumption in the text are those of complete decomposability; of systems whose first S sectors form a completely decomposable system but such that inputs from the first S sectors are used in higher-numbered sectors in such a way that the system as a whole is not completely decomposable; of systems in which the first group of sectors provides inputs for two or more later groups of sectors which do not provide inputs for each other; and of combinations of the last two cases in which the stream of production forks and later comes together again. We are thus dealing directly in this section only with strictly hierarchical production systems; however, it is not hard to see that the results of this section can be combined with those for the completely decomposable case to yield an analysis for each of the cases just mentioned. Such a treatment, however, would be extremely tedious, and the results would not be sufficiently different (qualitatively) from those of the present section to warrant undertaking it.

Finally, we shall call ϱ a balanced inflation rate for the Ith subsystem if and only if there is some configuration of the variables of that subsystem such that if it is ever attained it is repeated in all subsequent periods, every variable being multiplied by ϱ each period. We shall denote by $V^*(\varrho, I)$ the corresponding balanced price configuration with its elements normalized to add to unity, *the sum being taken over the variables of the I-th subsystem only* ($I = 1, \ldots, N$). Note that we have already observed that λ_I is always a balanced inflation rate for the Ith subsystem with $V^{*J}(\lambda_I, I) = 0$ for $J < I$.

We prove:[17]

THEOREM 3.1: *For any $I = 1, \ldots, N$:*

(A) ϱ is a balanced inflation rate for the I-th subsystem if and only if either (1) $\varrho = \lambda_I$ or (2) ϱ is a balanced inflation rate for the $(I - 1)$-st subsystem and $\varrho > \lambda_I$.

(B) If ϱ is a balanced inflation rate for the I-th subsystem, then $\varrho = \lambda_J$ for some $J \leqslant I$, and $V^*(\varrho, I)$ is unique.

(C) Let $\lambda_{K(I)} = \max_{J \leq I} \lambda_J$. (In other words, the $K(I)$-th sector is that sector supplying inputs to the I-th sector—including the I-th sector itself—with the largest internal inflation rate.) Then the I-th subsystem has at most $(I - K(I) + 1)$ balanced inflation rates among which is $\lambda_{K(I)}$.

Proof. (A) For the first subsystem the theorem is trivial since we know from Solow and Samuelson that there is a unique balanced inflation rate for the first sector and that this is λ_1. For $I > 1$, $\varrho \neq \lambda_I$ cannot be a balanced inflation rate for the Ith subsystem unless it is one for the $(I - 1)$-st subsystem, for, since λ_I is unique, $V^{*J}(\varrho, I)$ cannot be zero for all $J < I$. Since we already know that λ_I is a balanced inflation rate for the Ith subsystem, it remains to be proved only that if ϱ is a balanced inflation rate for the $(I - 1)$-st subsystem it is one for the Ith subsystem also if and only if $\varrho > \lambda_I$.

It will suffice to consider the case of $I = 2$, since we shall not need to use the monotonicity properties of the internal structure of the $(I - 1)$-st subsystem in the proof and can thus consider that subsystem as a single sector for present purposes. (In any case, the detailed proof for $I > 2$ involves only more writing and not any essential difference.)

[17] Nikaidô [9] (which came to my attention shortly after this paper was written) obtains results which are similar to those of this section for the special case in which the range of problems he considers can be made to coincide with those treated in the present paper. This is the case if the effects of input prices from lower-numbered sectors on the output prices of a given sector are purely additive to the effects of the prices of the given sector's own commodities.

Let π be a nonnegative scalar parameter and normalize the variables of the second sector by requiring that their sum be unity. Denote the resulting normalized vector by W. Let ϱ be a balanced inflation rate for the first subsystem and consider the continuous mapping:

$$z = \frac{\psi^2(\pi V^{*1}(\varrho, 1), W)}{\sum_{j=1}^{n_2} \psi_j^2(\pi V^{*1}(\varrho, 1), W)}. \tag{3.2}$$

Clearly, z lies in the simplex and the mapping therefore has at least one fixed point by Brouwer's fixed-point theorem. That point clearly depends on π, and we shall thus write it as $W^*(\pi)$. Further, the denominator of the fraction on the right hand side of (3.2) gives the amount by which $W^*(\pi)$ will be multiplied in one period. This also depends on π, and we shall write it as $\mu(\pi)$. Clearly, $\mu(\pi) = \varrho$ is equivalent to ϱ being a balanced inflation rate for the second subsystem.

We prove the following lemma:

LEMMA 3.1: *(i) $\mu(\pi)$ and $W^*(\pi)$ are single-valued and continuous functions of π_0.*
(ii) $\mu(\pi)$ is monotonically increasing in π.

Proof. We first prove (ii) assuming (i). Let $\pi_1 > \pi_2$ and consider $W^*(\pi_1)$ and $W^*(\pi_2)$. If these are equal then $\mu(\pi_1) > \mu(\pi_2)$ by the monotonicity of the original system. If not, choose h such that:

$$\frac{W_h^*(\pi_2)}{W_h^*(\pi_1)} = \max \frac{W_j^*(\pi_2)}{W_j^*(\pi_1)} \qquad (j = 1, \ldots, n_2). \tag{3.3}$$

Observe that in view of the normalization of the $W^*(\pi_i)$, this must be greater than unity. From this definition, however,

$$\frac{W_j^*(\pi_1)}{W_h^*(\pi_1)} = \frac{W_j^*(\pi_1)}{W_h^*(\pi_2)} \frac{W_h^*(\pi_2)}{W_h^*(\pi_1)} \geqslant \frac{W_j^*(\pi_1)}{W_h^*(\pi_2)} \frac{W_j^*(\pi_2)}{W_j^*(\pi_1)} = \frac{W_j^*(\pi_2)}{W_h^*(\pi_2)} \quad (j=1,\ldots,n_2) \tag{3.4}$$

with the strict inequality holding at least once. However, we then have by the monotonicity of the original system:

$$\mu(\pi_1) = \psi_h^2\left(\frac{\pi_1 V^{*1}(\varrho, 1)}{W_h^*(\pi_1)}, \frac{W^*(\pi_1)}{W_h^*(\pi_1)}\right) > \psi_h^2\left(\frac{\pi_2 V^{*1}(\varrho, 1)}{W_h^*(\pi_2)}, \frac{W^*(\pi_2)}{W_h^*(\pi_2)}\right) = \mu(\pi_2). \tag{3.5}$$

To see the uniqueness of $\mu(\pi)$ for a given π, observe that nonuniqueness would require nonuniqueness of $W^*(\pi)$. The argument just given, however, could then be used to show that each of two $\mu(\pi)$ was strictly greater than the other. Hence, $\mu(\pi)$ is unique. Since this is the case, $W^*(\pi)$ must also be unique since otherwise the identical argument could be used to show that $\mu(\pi)$ is greater than itself.

As for continuity, that of $W^*(\pi)$ follows from the proof of Lemma 2.1 and the fact that $W^*(\pi)$ is a single-valued function of π. Further, since $\mu(\pi)$ equals the denominator on the right hand side of (3.2) and that denominator is continuous in its arguments, $\mu(\pi)$ must be continuous in π, given the continuity of $W^*(\pi)$.

We return now to the main proof of Theorem 3.1. Let $\pi = 0$, then clearly $\mu(\pi) = \lambda_2$. By Lemma 3.1, however, $\mu(\pi)$ is a continuous and monotonically increasing function of π. Hence, there exists a $\pi > 0$ such that $\mu(\pi) = \varrho$ if and only if $\varrho > \lambda_2$.[18] This, by our earlier remarks, completes the proof of part (A) of the theorem.

(B) This part of the theorem follows immediately from part (A), Lemma 3.1, and the fact that the first subsystem has a unique balanced inflation rate, λ_1, and unique $V^*(\lambda_1, 1)$, by Solow and Samuelson.

(C) This follows immediately from the preceding two parts of the theorem, and the proof is complete.[19]

In other words, the first sector taken alone has only one mode of balanced inflation; the first and second taken together have one mode of balanced inflation with the first sector having only free goods and one more if the first sector's internal inflation rate is greater than that of the second sector; the first three sectors have one mode of balanced inflation with the first two sectors having only free goods and one for each of the preceding subsystem's modes (if any) with a higher rate of inflation than the third sector's internal one, and so forth. In general, any sector is capable of balanced inflation at its own internal inflation rate and along the corresponding ray; it is also

18 Remember that we are assuming no multiple internal inflation rates, for simplicity. However, note that $\mu(\pi) = \lambda_2$ if and only if $\pi = 0$ so that balanced inflation is impossible if $\lambda_1 = \lambda_2$ unless all prices in the first sector are zero.

19 Let $A \geqslant 0$ be a decomposable but not completely decomposable matrix with square matrices A^{II} on the diagonal $(I = 1, \ldots, N)$ and zero matrices above the diagonal. Let λ_I denote the Frobenius root of A^{II}. Finally, if for some I and J, such that $J \neq I$, $\lambda_J = \lambda_I$, agree to assign any latent vector corresponding to such a multiple root to λ_I if the first nonzero element in that vector occurs in the Ith group of elements and to λ_J if the first nonzero element occurs in the Jth group of elements. (This is reasonable, since if $J > I$ and the first nonzero element in the latent vector occurs in the Jth group of elements, the vector will be unaffected by changes in A^{II}.) Then Theorem 3.1 yields the following result:

Corollary to Theorem 3.1: A latent root of A, say ϱ, is associated with a nonnegative characteristic vector if and only if for some $I = 1, \ldots, N$, $\varrho = \lambda_I > \lambda_J$ for all $J = I + 1, \ldots, N$.

capable of balanced inflation at a rate equal to the internal inflation rate of any of its supplying sectors, provided that such a supplying sector does not also supply another supplier of the given sector (including the given sector itself) which has a higher internal rate of inflation than does the original supplying sector. Complicated as this sounds, it makes good economic sense, for the contribution to costs of the prices of a relatively quickly growing input sector that has relatively quickly declining prices will eventually become negligible relative to that of a relatively quickly growing one with relatively slowly declining prices. That this is generally so, we prove in the next theorem.

THEOREM 3.2: *For all $I = 1, \ldots, N$, define $K(I)$ as in Theorem 3.1. Let there be at least one initial non-free good in the first sector.*[20] *Then, as time grows without limit, the variables of the I-th subsystem approach the configuration $V^*(\lambda_{K(I)}, I)$ and the inflation rate $\lambda_{K(I)}$.*

In other words, every sector eventually approaches the unique balanced inflation ray and rate corresponding to that one of its (nonzero) supplying sectors (including itself) which is the biggest bottleneck.

Proof. The proof is by induction. The theorem is clearly true for $I = 1$, by Solow and Samuelson's stability proof. It will therefore suffice to show that it is true for I if it is true for $I - 1$. There are three cases to be considered:

(A) $K(I) = I$. Here it will suffice to consider a two-sector system because we shall not need the properties of the internal structure of the sectors up through $I - 1$ in the proof and can thus lump them all together.

By the "normalized distance" between two points, we shall mean the distance between the two points where the rays through the origin and the given points cut the simplex.

By the induction hypothesis, the first sector ultimately grows at the rate λ_1; further, since in the case under consideration $K(2) = 2$, $\lambda_1 < \lambda_2$, the internal inflation rate of the second sector. However, it is obvious that, in view of the monotonicity property, the variables of the second sector must always be at least as large in any time period with a nonzero first sector as they would be in isolation. It follows that

$$(3.5) \qquad \lim_{t\to\infty} \frac{X^2(t)}{\lambda_2^t} \neq 0\,; \qquad \lim_{t\to\infty} \frac{X^1(t)}{\lambda_2^t} = \lim_{t\to\infty} V^{*1}(\lambda_1, 1)(\lambda_1^t/\lambda_2^t) = 0\,.$$

[20] It should be evident why this is a necessary condition if the theorem is to hold for all $I = 1, \ldots, N$. If the first initial nonzero price occurs in the Jth sector, a similar result holds, because we may simply forget about sectors $1, \ldots, J - 1$ whose prices will forever be zero.

Now define new variables $Z^1(t)$, $Z^2(t)$, as:

$$Z^J(t) = X^J(t)/\lambda_2^t \qquad (J = 1, 2). \tag{3.6}$$

Then:

$$\begin{aligned} Z^1(t+1) &= (1/\lambda_2)\ \psi^1(Z^1(t))\,, \\ Z^2(t+1) &= (1/\lambda_2)\ \psi^2(Z^1(t), Z^2(t))\,. \end{aligned} \tag{3.7}$$

Fix an initial time, T_0, and a time interval, $T_1 - T_0 > 0$. Fix $Z^2(T_0)$. In view of the continuity of the ψ^J and the fact that the simplex is a compact set, for any $\eta > 0$, there exists an $\varepsilon > 0$ such that if the normalized distance of a point $(Z^1(T_0), Z^2(T_0))$ from the point $(0, Z^2(T_0))$ is less than ε, the normalized distance between the corresponding later points at time T_1 will be less than η, *where* ε *is independent of* $Z^2(T_0)$.

Furthermore, in view of Solow and Samuelson's stability theorem, it is likewise true that for any $\eta > 0$, there exists a time interval $T_1 - T_0 > 0$ independent of $Z^2(T_0)$, so large that for any point $(0, Z^2(T_0))$ the normalized distance between the corresponding point $(0, Z^2(T_1))$ and the point $V^*(\lambda_2, 2)$ is less than η.

Now choose any $\eta_0 > 0$. Choose an $\eta_1 < \eta_0$ but greater than zero. By the remarks just made, there exists a time interval $T_1 - T_0 > 0$ such that for any point $(0, Z^2(T_0))$, the normalized distance between the corresponding point $(0, Z^2(T_1))$ and $V^*(\lambda_2, 2)$ is less than η_1. Choose $\eta_2 = \eta_0 - \eta_1$. As already observed, there exists an $\varepsilon > 0$ so small that if the normalized distance of a point $(Z^1(T_0), Z^2(T_0))$ from the point $(0, Z^2(T_0))$ is less than ε, the normalized distance between the corresponding points at time T_1 will be less than η_2. In view of (3.5) and (3.6), however, we may choose T_0 so large that for $t \geqslant T_0$ the normalized distance between $(Z^1(t), Z^2(t))$ and $(0, Z^2(t))$ is less than ε. It follows immediately that the normalized distance between $(Z^1(T_1), Z^2(T_1))$ and $V^*(\lambda_2, 2)$ is less than η_0.

Finally, for any time period $T_0 + \theta$, where $\theta > 0$, the normalized distance between $(Z^1(T_0 + \theta), Z^2(T_0 + \theta))$ and $(0, Z^2(T_0 + \theta))$ will be less than ε, and the uniform continuity and convergence properties mentioned above show that the normalized distance between $(Z^1(T_1 + \theta), Z^2(T_1 + \theta))$ and $V^*(\lambda_2, 2)$ will be less than η_0. We have thus shown that for arbitrary $\eta_0 > 0$, there exists a time period $T_1 > 0$, so large that $t \geqslant T_1$ implies that the normalized distance between $(Z^1(t), Z^2(t))$ and $V^*(\lambda_2, 2)$ is less than η_0. However, if this is true of the $Z^J(t)$, it is clearly true of the $X^J(t)$ and the desired result is immediate.

(B) $K(I) = 1$. Here it will again suffice to consider a two-sector system. By hypothesis, the theorem is true of the first sector, and it is easy to show that Solow and Samuelson's original stability proof [**12**, pp. 419–21] applies to the second sector, considering only the functions $\psi^2(X^1(t), X^2(t))$.

(C) $1 < K(I) < I$. Here it suffices to consider a three-sector system: the first sector consisting of the original sectors $1, \ldots, K(I) - 1$; the second of the original sectors $K(I), \ldots, I - 1$; and the third being the original Ith sector. By hypothesis, the theorem is true of the $(I - 1)$-st subsystem and an argument similar to that given in Case A above shows that the behavior of the Ith subsystem approaches that of the same subsystem with the first sector set equal to zero. By Case B above, however, the theorem is true of the latter subsystem; hence an argument similar to that of Case A establishes that it must be true of the actual Ith subsystem also.

These cases being exhaustive, the proof of the theorem is complete, by the remarks given at the outset.

4. APPLICATIONS TO CASES OF NON-PRODUCED FACTORS AND OF RIGID PRICES

Turning back for a moment to the original Solow-Samuelson output interpretation of the model, we may use these results to relax the assumption of constant returns to scale. Suppose that there are some factors of production (such as land) available in constant amount each time period but not themselves produced. (Further generalizations to cases of exhaustible raw materials can be made along similar lines.) Suppose further that constant returns to scale prevail in the production of all other goods in the sense that multiplying *all* factors including the fixed ones by a scalar, λ, would multiply all outputs of produced commodities by λ. Then, since some factors are fixed, the outputs of produced commodities will not be homogeneous in variable factors taken alone and there will be less than constant returns to scale. (Indeed, the existence of this case is probably the most cogent argument against assuming constant returns.)

This situation can be easily analyzed in terms of the results of the last section. The economy described can be looked on as a decomposable one with two sectors. The first of these consists of the fixed factors which reproduce themselves every time period without using the variable factors as inputs. Clearly, this sector has an internal growth rate equal to unity. The second sector consists of the produced commodities which use both themselves and the fixed factors as inputs. Our theorems then yield the following result:

If with all fixed factors zero, the balanced growth rate of the produced commodity sector would be greater than unity (i.e., *balanced* growth *rather than balanced* decay *or stationarity*), *then the actual behavior of that sector will approach that same balanced growth rate and configuration regardless of the level of the fixed factors. If the internal growth rate of the produced commodity sector is unity then balanced growth will not be achieved with nonzero fixed factors, although nonbalanced growth will occur.*[21] *If that internal growth rate is less than unity, then (and then only) a stationary state will be approached.*[22]

This result is in strong contrast to that of Suits [**14**, p. 501], who apparently showed that a Solow-Samuelson economy characterized by constant returns to scale up to the point where a fixed factor is fully employed must approach a stationary state. The source of this clear conflict lies in Suits' interpretation of his theorems, rather than in the theorems themselves, and may be explained as follows.[23]

Suits terms a vector function $H(X)$ "homogeneous of order at most n'" if for any vector X and any scalar $a \geqslant 0$, there exists a function $\phi(a, X) = n$ such that $H(aX) = a^n H(X)$ and $\text{Sup}\, \phi(a, X) = n'$. His proof of stationarity is for functions of order at most $n' < 1$ (although some of his other results are not so limited). However, it is clear that the case of a constant returns Solow-Samuelson production system with fixed factors is *not* this case, even with all fixed factors fully employed from the outset, because, taking ever larger values for the variable inputs, it is clear that as the contribution of the fixed factors becomes negligible, the functions involved approach homogeneity of the ordinary kind of order one in those inputs. Hence, this is a case of homogeneity (in Suits' sense) of order at most 1, and Suits' stationarity theorem does not apply.

The culprit in Suits' interpretation is clearly his failure to realize the full implications of the strong monotonicity assumption. Indeed, another way of showing the inapplicability of his stationarity theorem to the present case is to observe that under strong monotonicity the produced commodity sector cannot grow more slowly than it could with zero fixed factors.[24]

Returning to the more interesting price interpretation, a similar application of our results can be made to the case where the prices of one or more factors which are directly or indirectly[25] required for the production of every good are fixed (for whatever reason). (Generalization to the case of some prescribed time paths is also possible.) We may take the prices of all such factors as comprising the variables of the first sector (or first J sectors), and our theorems yield the following results.

If, with all such rigid prices zero, the balanced inflation rate of the remainder of the system (or any part thereof) would be greater than unity (i.e., balanced

[21] See footnote 18 above.

[22] Provided that there is at least one nonzero fixed factor. Obviously, if the internal growth rate in question is less than unity and all fixed factors are zero, balanced decay will eventually result.

[23] In the following paragraph only we use Suits' notation rather than our own.

[24] Cf. Theorems 2.1 above and 5.1 below.

[25] See footnote 16 above.

inflation rather than balanced deflation), then with nonzero rigid prices, the same inflation with the same relative prices will ultimately take place. If with all such rigid prices zero, the prices of the remainder of the system would ultimately fall, then with such prices nonzero, the prices of the remainder of the system will ultimately be constant. Finally, if with all such prices zero the prices of the remainder of the system would ultimately be constant, then with such prices nonzero the prices of the remainder of the system will ultimately grow, but such growth will not be balanced.

In short, rigid prices for such strategic factors cannot halt an inflation which would take place if the factors in question were all free, but they will halt a deflation and can destabilize a system of otherwise stable prices.[26]

5. THE NEARLY DECOMPOSABLE CASE

We are now in position to dispose rather briefly of the nearly decomposable case, since the desired results follow almost immediately from the same or similar arguments employed in the earlier sections. Indeed, as might be expected, the results here exactly parallel those already obtained for the nearly completely decomposable case. Accordingly, turn back to (2.3) and alter the definition of the $G^I(X^1(t), \ldots, X^N(t); \varepsilon)$ by requiring:

$$G^I(X^1(t),\ldots,X^I(t),0,\ldots,0;\varepsilon) = \psi^I(X^1(t),\ldots,X^I(t)) \qquad (I=1,\ldots,N) \tag{5.1A}$$

for all ε, and

$$\lim_{\varepsilon\to 0} G^I(X^1(t),\ldots,X^N(t);\varepsilon) = \psi^I(X^1(t),\ldots,X^I(t)) \qquad (I=1,\ldots,N) \tag{5.1B}$$

for all values of the $X^J(t)$. We retain all the other properties of the G^I. Consider the system:

$$X^I(t+1) = G^I(X^1(t), \ldots, X^N(t); \varepsilon) \qquad (I = 1,\ldots, N)\,. \tag{5.2}$$

Clearly, as ε approaches zero, this system approaches (3.1). In other words, the economy approaches decomposability as the importance to and requirements for the output of a particular sector of inputs from higher numbered sectors become less and less.

Once more consider the mapping (2.5) and the fixed points thereof. As in Section 2, let $V^*(\varepsilon)$ denote the unique fixed point of that mapping and $\lambda(\varepsilon)$ its associated inflation rate for $\varepsilon \neq 0$. Then Lemma 2.1 still holds and an

[26] Of course, this says absolutely nothing about effective demand or any such issue. Prices fall in this model because the economy is productive. Note also that such price rigidity, while failing to halt an inflation of the type described, might very well halt an inflation otherwise brought about by a rise in the prices of the factors in question.

argument similar to that of Theorem 2.1 yields (where the notation not just explained is that of the previous section):

THEOREM 5.1: *For* $\varepsilon \neq 0$, $\lambda(\varepsilon) > \lambda_{K(N)}$. *However,* $\mathrm{Lim}_{\varepsilon \to 0}\, \lambda(\varepsilon) = \lambda_{K(N)}$ *and* $\mathrm{Lim}_{\varepsilon \to 0}\, V^*(\varepsilon) = V^*(\lambda_{K(N)}, N)$.

In other words, in the long run, an indecomposable system will always have a rate of inflation higher than the highest internal rate of inflation of any sector in the corresponding decomposable system. For the system very close to decomposability, however, the balanced inflation rate and price configuration will be respectively very close to the balanced inflation rate and price configuration of the subsystem of the decomposable system which is the full decomposable system itself. Note that the latter price configuration has zero prices for the outputs of sectors not receiving inputs from sector $K(N)$, i.e., sectors with lower numbers in the chain of production than the sector which is the biggest bottleneck.

For later purposes, observe that the last statement of the theorem can be considered as a purely mathematical result about certain fixed point relationships.

It is now easy to prove our final theorem. Parallel to Theorem 2.2, we have:

THEOREM 5.2: *For all* $J \leqslant I$,

$$\lim_{\varepsilon \to 0} \frac{V_j^{*J}(\varepsilon)}{\sum_{J \leq I} \sum_{j=1}^{n_J} V_j^{*J}(\varepsilon)} = \frac{V_j^{*J}(\lambda_{K(I)}, I)}{\sum_{J \leq I} \sum_{j=1}^{n_J} V_j^{*J}(\lambda_{K(I)}, I)}$$

and

$$\lim_{\varepsilon \to 0} \frac{V_j^{*I}(\varepsilon)}{\sum_{j=1}^{n_I} V_j^{*I}(\varepsilon)} = \frac{V_j^{*I}(\lambda_{K(I)}, I)}{\sum_{j=1}^{n_I} V_j^{*I}(\lambda_{K(I)}, I)} \qquad (I = 1, \ldots, N;\ j = 1, \ldots, n_I)\,.$$

Proof. The second statement follows immediately from the first which remains to be proved. Further, for $I \geqslant K(N)$ the result is an immediate consequence of Theorem 5.1. We must therefore prove it for the case $I < K(N)$.

Analogous to the proof of Theorem 2.2, let $W^*(\varepsilon, I)$ be the vector whose elements are the fraction whose limit is being taken in the first statement of the theorem. $W^*(\varepsilon, I)$ is thus the vector of the elements of the Ith subsystem at $V^*(\varepsilon)$, normalized to lie in the simplex. An argument similar to that of the proof of Theorem 2.2. shows that as ε approaches zero, $W^*(\varepsilon, I)$ approaches one of the $V^*(\lambda_J, I)$. However, as that argument also shows that the same limit would be approached with $X^J(t) = 0$ for all $J > I$, and as this is the limit of the balanced growth configuration of a nearly decomposable system consisting of only the first I sectors of the original one, Theorem 5.1 yields immediately the fact that the limit involved can only be $V^*(\lambda_{K(I)}, I)$, and the theorem is proved.

This result is the extension of the major long-run result of Ando and Fisher [1][27] It states that, provided the system is sufficiently close to decomposability, the long-run internal price structure of each *subsystem* as well as of each sector (i.e., the relative prices of the different goods therein) will be approximately the same as in the corresponding decomposable system, although the levels and rate of change of the prices will generally be greater, possibly considerably so.[28] It follows here, as in the nearly completely decomposable case that the internal price structure of any sector or subsystem can be analyzed on the approximate assumption of decomposability without losing the relevance of the analysis.

Massachusetts Institute of Technology

REFERENCES

[1] Ando, A., and F. M. Fisher: "Near Decomposability, Partition and Aggregation, and the Relevance of Stability Discussions," *International Economic Review*, Vol. 4, No. 1, January, 1963, pp. 53–67.

[2] Fisher, F. M.: "On the Cost of Approximate Specification in Simultaneous Equation Estimation," *Econometrica*, Vol. 29, No. 2 (April, 1961), pp. 139–70.

[3] ———: "Properties of the Von Neumann Ray in Decomposable and Nearly Decomposable Technologies" (forthcoming).

[4] Fisher, F. M., and A. Ando: "Two Theorems on *Ceteris Paribus* in the Analysis of Dynamic Systems," *American Political Science Review*, Vol. LVI, No. 1 (March, 1962), pp. 108–13.

[5] Hicks, J. R.: "The Story of a Mare's Nest," *Review of Economic Studies*, Vol. XXVIII(2) (February, 1961), pp. 77–88.

[6] Morishima, M.: "Generalizations of the Frobenius-Wielandt Theorems for Non-Negative Square Matrices," *Journal of the London Mathematical Society*, Vol. 36 (1961), pp. 211–20.

[7] ———: "Proof of a Turnpike Theorem: the 'No Joint Production Case'," *Review of Economic Studies*, Vol. XXVIII (2) (February, 1961), pp. 89–97.

[8] Neisser, H. P.: "Balanced Growth Under Constant Returns to Scale: Some Comments," *Econometrica*, Vol. XXII, No. 4 (October, 1954), pp. 502–3.

[27] The analogous remarks to those of footnote 14, above, apply here.

[28] See footnote 15, above.

[9] Nikaidô, H.: "Balanced Growth in a Generalized Nonlinear Leontief System with Autonomous Factors," The Institute of Social and Economic Research, Osaka University, Discussion Paper No. 24 (July, 1961).

[10] Simon, H. A.: "Causal Ordering and Identifiability," Chapter 3 in *Studies in Econometric Method* (W. C. Hood and T. C. Koopmans, eds.), New York: John Wiley and Sons, 1953 (Cowles Commission Monograph No. 14); reprinted as Chapter 1 in H. A. Simon, *Models of Man*, New York: John Wiley and Sons, 1957.

[11] Simon, H. A., and A. Ando: "Aggregation of Variables in Dynamic Systems," *Econometrica*, Vol. 29, No. 2 (April, 1961), pp. 111–38.

[12] Solow, R. M., and P. A. Samuelson: "Balanced Growth under Constant Returns to Scale," *Econometrica*, Vol. 21, No. 3 (July, 1953), pp. 412–24.

[13] ———: "A Brief Comment," *Econometrica*, Vol. XXII, No. 4 (October, 1954), p. 504.

[14] Suits, D. B.: "Dynamic Growth Under Diminishing Returns to Scale," *Econometrica*, Vol. 22, No. 4 (October, 1954), pp. 496–501.

8

PROPERTIES OF THE VON NEUMANN RAY IN DECOMPOSABLE AND NEARLY DECOMPOSABLE TECHNOLOGIES

By Franklin M. Fisher*

Massachusetts Institute of Technology

1. Introduction

In a recent paper, Furuya and Inada [5] cast considerable light on the relations between the Turnpike Theorem for the maximal balanced growth path in generalized von Neumann models[1] and the stability properties of the similar path in the deterministic model of Solow and Samuelson [11]. Briefly, they showed that — under certain assumptions — the von Neumann ray is stable in the large in the sense that every nonterminating intertemporally efficient path converges to it. They further showed that every such path is uniquely determined by its initial input vector. Thus, considering only nonterminating intertemporally efficient paths, the generalized von Neumann model behaves quite similarly to the Solow-Samuelson constant returns model — as had been conjectured by the latter authors [12].

The resemblance between the two models is further heightened by Furuya and Inada's "primitivity" assumption that any nonzero initial input vector can eventually yield a strictly positive output vector after some fixed number of periods. This corresponds almost precisely to the Solow-Samuelson "monotonicity" assumption that every output is increased by increasing <u>any</u> input. I recently [4] extended the Solow-Samuelson model, reinterpreting it in terms of prices in the von Neumann model of production, by removing that assumption and examining cases in which the production structure was decomposable or completely decomposable or approached one of these cases. The present paper proves parallel results for the generalized von Neumann model

---

*I am greatly indebted to Robert M. Solow for his comments and criticism. I am solely responsible for remaining errors.

[1]Von Neumann [8]. The Turnpike Theorem was conjectured by Dorfman, Samuelson, and Solow [2, pp. 326-345], and proofs for different cases have been given by Morishima [7], Radner [9], and McKenzie [6].

in similar technologies and thus extends the Furuya-Inada stability results as well as the Turnpike Theorem to an important class of technological cases. In view of the price interpretation of the Solow-Samuelson model, [4], this paper is in a sense concerned with the dual system to that of my previous one.

2. Notation and Basic Assumptions

We follow Furuya and Inada in the basic outline of the model, adapting their notation where necessary.

A production process which transforms an initial vector of inputs, a, into a vector of outputs, b, one period later is denoted by $(a, b) \in T$. Thus, T is the set of technological possibilities constant over time. Both a and b are n-component vectors of amounts of the same commodities. Where it is necessary to distinguish between different time periods, a process during the tth production period will be denoted by $(a^{(t-1)}, b^{(t)})$.

The following assumptions will be made throughout and will apply to any production set defined.[2]

Assumption 2.1 (Nonnegativity): If $(a, b) \in T$, then $a \geqq 0$ and $b \geqq 0$.[3] For any $a \geqq 0$, there exists $b \geqq 0$ such that $(a, b) \in T$.

Thus any nonnegative n-component vector can serve as the input into a production process (which may perhaps only use up inputs without producing any positive output).

Assumption 2.2 (Impossibility of the Land of Cockaigne): If $(0, b) \in T$, then $b = 0$.

Thus it requires some positive input to produce a positive output.

Assumption 2.3 (Positive Homogeneity): If $(a, b) \in T$, then for any scalar $\pi \geq 0$, $(\pi a, \pi b) \in T$.

In other words, there are constant returns to scale.

Assumption 2.4 (Superadditivity): If $(a, b) \in T$ and $(\tilde{a}, \tilde{b}) \in T$, then for any scalars $\pi_1 \geq 0$, $\pi_2 \geq 0$, such that $\pi_1 + \pi_2 = 1$, there exists a process $(\pi_1 a + \pi_2 \tilde{a}, b^*) \in T$ such that $b^* \geqq \pi_1 b + \pi_2 \tilde{b}$.

---

[2]Occasionally, this will be true as a consequence of the same assumptions being made on another production set so that they need not always be made directly. Where this is important, it will be discussed. These assumptions are essentially identical with those made by Furuya and Inada [5, pp. 96-97]. The definitions below are also theirs.

[3]We follow the usual conventions for vector inequalities. Thus, if x and y are two n-component vectors, $x = y$ means $x_i = y_i$ $(i = 1, \ldots, n)$; $x \geqq y$ means $x_i \geq y_i$ $(i = 1, \ldots, n)$; $x \geq y$ means $x \geqq y$ but $x \neq y$.

This is essentially a weak convexity assumption. It will be strengthened later.

Assumption 2.5 (Closedness): T is a closed set in 2n-dimensional Euclidean space.

This assumption asserts a form of continuity of the technology. The following definitions will be useful:

Definition 2.1: For $a \geq 0$, define λ by

$$\lambda = \min \left\{ \frac{b_j}{a_j} \mid a_j \neq 0 \right\}.$$

We shall call λ so defined the growth factor of the process $(a, b) \in T$.

Definition 2.2: A time sequence of successive possible transformations $(a^{(t-1)}, b^{(t)})$ $(t = 1, \ldots, m)$ is called a feasible path of order m if and only if every member of the sequence is in T and $a^{(t)} = b^{(t)}$ $(t = 1, \ldots, m - 1)$. For convenience, such a path will generally be denoted by $(a^{(0)}, b^{(m)}) \in T^{(m)}$.

Definition 2.3: A balanced growth path is a feasible path in which $b^{(t)} = \lambda a^{(t-1)}$ holds in every time period.

Definition 2.4: T is said to be strongly superadditive if and only if, for any two independent vectors a and $\tilde{a}$ and any two scalars $\pi_1 > 0$ and $\pi_2 > 0$, $(a, b) \in T$ and $(\tilde{a}, \tilde{b}) \in T$ imply the existence of a process $(\pi_1 a + \pi_2 \tilde{a}, b^*) \in T$ such that $b^* \geq \pi_1 b + \pi_2 \tilde{b}$.[4]

Strong superadditivity is essentially a requirement of strict convexity.

Definition 2.5: A feasible path $(a^{(0)}, b^{(m)}) \in T^{(m)}$ is called intertemporally efficient of order m (for brevity, efficient of order m) if and only if there is no feasible path $(a^{(0)}, \tilde{b}^{(m)}) \in T^{(m)}$ such that $\tilde{b}^{(m)} \geq b^{(m)}$.

Definition 2.6: Let $\{a^{(t)}\}$ $(t = 0, 1, 2, \ldots,$ ad inf.) be a feasible path extending infinitely. Such a path is called an intertemporally efficient path of infinite order if and only if, for any m, the finite path consisting of the first m + 1 terms of the sequence is intertemporally efficient of order m.

Definition 2.7: T is said to be primitive if and only if there is a

[4]This is stated somewhat differently from Furuya and Inada's definition [5, p. 99), to bring out the relation to Assumption 2.4, but is obviously equivalent to it in the presence of Assumptions 2.3 and 2.4.

finite number s such that $(a^{(0)}, b^{(s)}) \in T^{(s)}$ and $b^{(s)} > 0$ for any $a^{(0)} \geq 0$.

If T is primitive, then some of every output can be produced after at most s periods provided that there is some nonzero initial amount of any input. Furuya and Inada assume primitivity; as already remarked, this is quite similar to the Solow-Samuelson monotonicity assumption.[5]

Furuya and Inada show that Assumptions 2.1-2.5 imply the existence of a maximal growth factor, which, thenceforth assuming primitivity, is associated with a balanced growth path. For obvious reasons, we shall refer to such a path as a von Neumann ray. Furuya and Inada show that if T is primitive and strongly superadditive, that ray is unique, and intertemporally efficient paths of infinite order converge relatively to it.[6] They also show that the von Neumann path is intertemporally efficient of any order and that if T is primitive and strongly superadditive, any intertemporally efficient path of infinite order is uniquely determined by its initial input vector.

3. Complete and Near Complete Decomposability

Suppose that T is not primitive, but that the commodities can be grouped into sectors, such that the outputs of each sector can be produced only from inputs of that sector. Formally, we adopt the following notation:

Partition a and b into $(a^1\ a^2 \ldots a^N)$ and $(b^1\ b^2 \ldots b^N)$, respectively. For such a partitioning, let T^1 be the set of all (a^1, b^1) such that $(a^1\ 0 \ldots 0,\ b^1\ 0 \ldots 0) \in T$; let T^2 be the set of all (a^2, b^2) such that $(0\ a^2\ 0 \ldots 0,\ 0\ b^2\ 0 \ldots 0) \in T$, and so forth. Let the number of elements in a^I (and also in b^I) be n_I.

Definition 3.1: A production set T is called completely decomposable if and only if there is a partitioning such that $(a, b) \in T$ if and only if $(a^I, b^I) \in T^I$ $(I = 1, \ldots, N > 1)$.

For convenience, we shall assume that if this is the case, each of the T^I is primitive $(I = 1, \ldots, N)$. Obviously, each of the T^I satisfies Assumptions 2.1-2.5. It is evident that if T is completely decomposable, it is made up of a number of subtechnologies, which have nothing to do with each other. In this case, the economy is nothing more than a collection of subeconomies, each one of which behaves like an indecomposable economy in its own right. Thus, each T^I will have its own maximum growth

---

[5] As, indeed, Furuya and Inada point out [5, p. 99, n. 7].

[6] Actually, Furuya and Inada's Relative Stability Theorem [5, Theorem 4, p. 102] is wrong as stated in assuming only uniqueness of the von Neumann ray and not strong superadditivity. See Fisher [3] for the correct result.

factor which will be associated with at least one balanced growth path. If each T^I is strongly superadditive, then that path will be unique and will have the Turnpike and Furuya-Inada Relative Stability properties, and so forth.

It will be convenient in such a case to denote the maximum growth factor for processes in T^I by λ_I; to assume hereafter (save where explicitly noted) that the λ_I are distinct $(I = 1, \ldots, N)$; and to let $\lambda_K = \max_I \lambda_I$. Further, consider the set (possibly consisting of only one member) of processes in T^I associated with λ_I.[7] For any such process, normalize the inputs so that they sum to unity. Denote the set of all such normalized input vectors by $V^{*I}(0, I)$. Finally, consider the set of all n-component partitioned vectors whose Jth set of components is zero for all J, $J \neq I$, and whose Ith set is a vector in $V^{*I}(0, I)$; denote that set by $V^*(0, I)$.[8]

We now consider cases of systems that lie very close to complete decomposability, that is, systems in which inputs from outside a given sector have a very low (but positive) marginal productivity in that sector. More precisely, we shall consider a sequence of systems which approaches complete decomposability as a limit.

Thus let $\varepsilon \geq 0$ be a scalar parameter.[9] Let $T(\varepsilon)$ be a variable production set. We shall assume:

Assumption 3.1: $T(\varepsilon)$ is primitive for $\varepsilon \neq 0$ and completely decomposable for $\varepsilon = 0$. Further, if $(a, b) \in T(0)$, then $(a, b) \in T(\varepsilon)$ for all ε.

Now denote by $F(a, \varepsilon)$ the (generally not single-valued) correspondence which assigns to a and ε the set of all b such that $(a, b) \in T(\varepsilon)$. We assume:

Assumption 3.2: $F(a, \varepsilon)$ is upper semicontinuous in ε at $\varepsilon = 0$.

In other words, the limiting completely decomposable technology forms part of all other primitive technologies considered and forms a limit for such technologies, in the sense that as ε goes to zero, holding inputs fixed and letting outputs approach a limit, the limiting output can be produced from the fixed inputs with the completely decomposable technology. The nature of the limit is clarified by:

Lemma 3.1: For any $a \geqq 0$ and any scalar $\eta > 0$, there exists an $\varepsilon^* > 0$ such that for $\varepsilon < \varepsilon^*$, if $(a, b) \in T(\varepsilon)$, there exists a

---

[7] Note that since the T^I are all assumed primitive, all such processes give balanced growth paths by Furuya and Inada [5, Theorem 1, p. 99].

[8] The reason for the first argument will appear shortly.

[9] This is merely the simplest case. There is no reason why ε cannot be a vector of parameters.

$\tilde{b}$ such that $(a, \tilde{b}) \in T(0)$ and $d(b, \tilde{b}) \equiv \max_j | b_j - \tilde{b}_j | < \eta$.

Proof: Fix a and choose an infinite sequence of ε's approaching 0. If the lemma is false, it is possible to find an infinite sequence of $b(\varepsilon)$ such that $(a, b(\varepsilon)) \in T(\varepsilon)$ and the sequence is bounded away from any $\tilde{b}$ such that $(a, \tilde{b}) \in T(0)$. However, Assumptions 2.2 and 2.5 clearly imply that such a sequence lies in a compact set and must therefore contain a convergent subsequence. Such a subsequence, however, cannot converge to any member of $F(a, 0)$, which violates Assumption 3.2.

We further assume for the remainder of this section:

Assumption 3.3 (Free Disposal): For any ε, if $(a, b) \in T(\varepsilon)$ and $\tilde{a} \geq a$, then $(\tilde{a}, b) \in T(\varepsilon)$.[10]

We prove:

Lemma 3.2: For any ε, $(a, b) \in T(\varepsilon)$, and scalar $\eta > 0$, there exists a scalar $\delta > 0$ such that $d(a, \tilde{a}) < \delta$ implies $(\tilde{a}, \tilde{b}) \in T(\varepsilon)$ and $d(b, \tilde{b}) < \eta$.

Proof: Consider any $(a, b) \in T(\varepsilon)$. For any $\eta > 0$, choose a scalar π such that $0 < \pi < 1$ and $d(b, \pi b) < \eta$. By Assumption 2.3, $(\pi a, \pi b) \in T(\varepsilon)$. Now choose a scalar $\delta > 0$ such that $d(a, \tilde{a}) < \delta$ implies $\tilde{a} \geq \pi a$. By Assumption 3.3, $(\tilde{a}, \pi b) \in T(\varepsilon)$, and the lemma is proved.

Now, for any nonzero ε, there is a maximum growth factor for processes in $T(\varepsilon)$. Denote that growth factor by $\lambda(\varepsilon)$. Associated with $\lambda(\varepsilon)$ will be one or more balanced growth processes. For each of these processes, normalize the input vector by requiring it to lie in the simplex, and denote by $V^*(\varepsilon)$ the mapping of ε into the normalized input vectors so constructed.

We prove:

Theorem 3.1:

(1) For any $\varepsilon \neq 0$, $\lambda(\varepsilon) \geq \lambda_K$. However,

(2) $\lim_{\varepsilon \to 0} \lambda(\varepsilon) = \lambda_K$

(3) Take any sequence of values of ε converging to zero and any corresponding sequence of elements of $V^*(\varepsilon)$ which approaches a limit. That limit will be a member of $V^*(0, K)$.

(4) If $V^*(0, K)$ has only one member, then as ε goes to zero, the limit of every sequence of elements of $V^*(\varepsilon)$ exists and is

---

[10] This statement cannot quite be derived from superadditivity by taking $(a, b) \in T(\varepsilon)$ and $(\tilde{a} - a, 0) \in T(\varepsilon)$ (which itself involves free disposal of inputs) to imply $(\tilde{a}, b^*) \in T(\varepsilon)$ and $b^* = b$ because of the possibility either that $(\tilde{a} - a, \tilde{b}) \in T(\varepsilon)$ implies $\tilde{b} \geq 0$, or that $b^* \geq b + \tilde{b} \geqq b$ as a matter of necessity, or both.

that member. (Note that it is not required that $V^*(\varepsilon)$ be single-valued.)

Proof: (1) is trivial in view of the definition of $\lambda(\varepsilon)$ as maximal and Assumption 3.1.[11]

To prove the remaining statements, take any sequence of values of ε converging to zero and choose a sequence of $Z(\varepsilon) \in V^*(\varepsilon)$ converging to a limit, say $Z(0)$. Since the simplex is compact, ε^* in Lemma 3.1 may be chosen independently of the input vector for all points in the simplex; hence, for ε sufficiently small, there exists a $W(\varepsilon)$ such that $(Z(\varepsilon), W(\varepsilon)) \in T(0)$ and $d(W(\varepsilon), \lambda(\varepsilon)Z(\varepsilon)) < \eta$, where η can be made arbitrarily small.

On the other hand, it is easy to use Lemma 3.2 to show that $W(\varepsilon)$ gets arbitrarily close to some $W(0)$ as $Z(\varepsilon)$ goes to $Z(0)$ where $(Z(0), W(0)) \in T(0)$.

It follows that $\lambda(\varepsilon)$ approaches $\sum_{j=1}^{n} W(0)_j$, since $Z(\varepsilon)$ lies in the simplex, and processes associated with $\lambda(\varepsilon)$ are balanced for $\varepsilon \neq 0$. However, this is clearly then the growth factor of $(Z(0), W(0)) \in T(0)$, and in view of (1) and the definition of λ_K, this growth factor can only be λ_K. Statements (2) and (3) are now immediate.

To see (4), it suffices to observe that for any sequence of members of $V^*(\varepsilon)$, all members of such a sequence lie in the simplex, which is compact. It therefore suffices to show that every convergent subsequence of such a sequence approaches the stated limit,[12] but this has already been established, and the theorem is proved.

Thus, in technologies very close to complete decomposability, the maximal growth rate is above but very close to the maximal growth rate of the limiting completely decomposable technology, and the configuration of the system along any von Neumann ray is very close to some similar configuration of the completely decomposable technology, the latter configuration having 0 for all goods not in the fastest-growing sector. However, the continuity of the system is even stronger than this, as will be seen below.

Definition 3.2: For any ε, a feasible path $(a^{(0)}, b^{(m)}) \in T^{(m)}(\varepsilon)$ will be called weakly efficient of order m if and only if there is no other feasible path $(a^{(0)}, \tilde{b}^{(m)}) \in T(\varepsilon)$ such that for all I for which $a^{(0)I} \neq 0$, $\tilde{b}^{(m)I} > b^{(m)I}$. (A path $(a^{(0)I}, b^{(m)I}) \in T^{(m)I}$

---

[11] Remark 3.1: If, for some $\varepsilon \neq 0$, $V^*(\varepsilon)$ is single-valued and $V^{*I}(\varepsilon) \neq 0$ for some $I \neq K$ (where, as before, the superscript indicates the corresponding set of components), then for that ε, $\lambda(\varepsilon) > \lambda_K$.

[12] See Fisher [4, Lemma 2.1] for the proof of this.

will be called weakly efficient of order m if and only if $(0 \ldots 0\ a^{(0)I}\ 0 \ldots 0,\ 0 \ldots 0\ b^{(m)I} 0 \ldots 0) \in T^{(m)}(0)$ is weakly efficient of order m as just defined.)

Note that every efficient balanced-growth path of order m is weakly efficient of that order, although this need not be true of nonbalanced efficient paths.

Definition 3.3: Let $\{a^{(t)}\}$ ($t = 0, 1, \ldots$, ad inf.) be a feasible path extending infinitely. Such a path will be called weakly efficient of infinite order if and only if the path consisting of the first m + 1 terms of the sequence is weakly efficient of order m for all m.

Now, denote by $G(a, \varepsilon, m)$ the correspondence which assigns to a, ε, and m the set of all $b^{(m)}$ such that $(a, b^{(m)}) \in T^{(m)}(\varepsilon)$ is a weakly efficient path of order m.

Lemma 3.3: $G(a, \varepsilon, m)$ is upper semicontinuous in ε at $\varepsilon = 0$. Further, for any scalar $\eta > 0$ and any $a \geqq 0$ and any m, there exists an $\varepsilon^* > 0$ such that for $\varepsilon < \varepsilon^*$, if $b \in G(a, \varepsilon, m)$, there exists a $\tilde{b} \in G(a, 0, m)$ such that $d(b, \tilde{b}) < \eta$.

Proof: Take a sequence of ε's converging to 0 and a corresponding sequence of $b^{(m)}(\varepsilon) \in G(a, \varepsilon, m)$ converging to a limit, say $b^{(m)}(0)$. It is obvious that Assumption 3.2 implies that $(a, b^{(m)}(0)) \in T^{(m)}(0)$. Now, suppose that $b^{(m)}(0) \notin G(a, 0, m)$. Then there exists $(a, \bar{b}^{(m)}) \in T^{(m)}(0)$ such that for all I for which $a^I \neq 0$, $\bar{b}^{(m)I} > b^{(m)I}(0)$. However, by Assumption 3.1, $(a, \bar{b}^{(m)}) \in T^{(m)}(\varepsilon)$ for all ε. Thus we can take ε so small that for all I for which $a^I \neq 0$, $\bar{b}^{(m)I} > b^{(m)I}(\varepsilon)$ so that $\bar{b}^{(m)}(\varepsilon)$ is not in $G(a, \varepsilon, m)$, contrary to assumption. The final assertion of the lemma now follows as in Lemma 3.1.

Lemma 3.4: $G(0 \ldots 0\ a^I\ 0 \ldots 0,\ 0,\ m)$ is upper semicontinuous in a^I ($I = 1, \ldots, N$) provided that a^I does not approach 0.

Proof: Take a sequence of a^I's approaching a nonzero limit, say $\bar{a}^I$. Take a corresponding sequence of $b^{(m)}$'s such that $b^{(m)} \in G(0 \ldots 0\ a^I\ 0 \ldots 0,\ 0,\ m)$. Suppose the latter sequence approaches a limit, say $\bar{b}^{(m)}$, not in $G(0 \ldots 0\ \bar{a}^I\ 0 \ldots 0, 0, m)$. Then there exists a $\tilde{b}^{(m)}$ such that $(\bar{a}^I, \tilde{b}^{(m)I}) \in T^I$ and $\tilde{b}^{(m)I} > \bar{b}^{(m)I}$. However, an obvious extension of Lemma 3.2 shows that for a^I sufficiently close to $\bar{a}^I$ there exists a $\hat{b}^{(m)}$ such that $(a^I, \hat{b}^{(m)I}) \in T^I$ and $\hat{b}^{(m)}$ is arbitrarily close to $\tilde{b}^{(m)}$. It follows that by taking a^I sufficiently close to $\bar{a}^I$, there exists $(a^I, \hat{b}^{(m)I}) \in T^I$ such that $\hat{b}^{(m)I} > b^{(m)I}$ so that $b^{(m)}$ is not a member of $G(0 \ldots 0\ a^I\ 0 \ldots 0,\ 0,\ m)$, contrary to assumption.

Lemma 3.5: For any $I = 1, \ldots, N$, suppose that T^I is strongly superadditive. Suppose further that for some $a^{(0)I}$ in the simplex, there exists a finite $s > 0$ such that for any $m \geq s$ there is a path $(a^{(0)I}, b^{(m)I}) \in T^{(m)I}$ which is efficient of order m and $b^{(m)I} = \lambda^{(m)} a^{(0)I}$ for some scalar $\lambda^{(m)}$. Then $a^{(0)I}$ is the unique member of $V^{*I}(0, I)$.

Proof: Since any efficient path of order m must have as its first steps an efficient path of order $m - 1$, if the lemma were false there would exist an efficient path of infinite order which failed to converge relatively to the unique member of $V^{*I}(0, I)$. Since T^I is strongly superadditive, this would contradict Furuya and Inada's Relative Stability Theorem.[13]

We now assume for the remainder of this section:

Assumption 3.4 (Redundancy of Inefficiently Employed Inputs): For all $I = 1, \ldots, N$, if $(a^{(0)I}, b^{(m)I}) \in T^{(m)I}$ is not efficient of order m, then there exists an $\bar{a}^{(0)I} \leq a^{(0)I}$ such that $(\bar{a}^{(0)I}, b^{(m)I}) \in T^{(m)I}$.

Thus, if production is not efficient, there is at least one input which is redundant. (I have been unable to derive this proposition from the other assumptions of the model, although its converse is clearly true and it does follow for all paths which are not at least weakly efficient of order m.)

Lemma 3.6: For any $I = 1, \ldots, N$, let s^I be the s in Definition 2.7 when T is replaced by T^I. Then, for any $m \geq s^I$, $(a^{(0)I}, b^{(m)I}) \in T^{(m)I}$ is a weakly efficient path of order m if and only if it is an efficient path of order m.

Proof: That such a path is weakly efficient if it is efficient is obvious; it remains to prove the reverse implication.

Suppose that $(a^{(0)I}, b^{(m)I})$ is weakly efficient of order m but not efficient of order m. Then, by Assumption 3.4, there exists an $\bar{a}^{(0)I} \leq a^{(0)I}$ such that $(\bar{a}^{(0)I}, b^{(m)I}) \in T^{(m)I}$. Consider $\tilde{a}^{(0)I} = (a^{(0)I} - \bar{a}^{(0)I}) \geq 0$. Since T^I is primitive and $m \geq s^I$, there exists $(\tilde{a}^{(0)I}, \tilde{b}^{(m)I}) \in T^{(m)I}$ and $\tilde{b}^{(m)I} > 0$. By superadditivity, therefore, there exists a process $(a^{(0)I}, \hat{b}^{(m)I}) \in T^{(m)I}$ such that $\hat{b}^{(m)I} \geqq b^{(m)I} + \tilde{b}^{(m)I} > b^{(m)I}$ contradicting the assumption that $(a^{(0)I}, b^{(m)I})$ is weakly efficient of order m, and the lemma is proved.

We can now prove:

Theorem 3.2: For any $I = 1, \ldots, N$, let T^I be strongly superadditive. Consider any sequence of ε's approaching zero and any corresponding sequence of $a(\varepsilon) \in V^*(\varepsilon)$ for which, for all positive ε in some neighborhood of zero, $a^I(\varepsilon) \neq 0$ for some I. Let

---

[13] [5, Theorem 4, p. 102]. See Fisher [3].

$$W(\varepsilon, I) = \frac{a^I(\varepsilon)}{\sum_{j=1}^{n_I} a_j^I(\varepsilon)} .$$

Then for that I, $\lim_{\varepsilon \to 0} W(\varepsilon, I)$ exists and is the unique member of $V^{*I}(0, I)$.[14]

The result is trivial for $I = K$ in view of Theorem 3.1; it is not trivial for $I \neq K$.

Proof: Since $W(\varepsilon, I)$ lies in the simplex, it suffices to show that the theorem is true for any convergent subsequence of the $W(\varepsilon, I)$.[15] We may thus assume the existence of the limit for the remainder of the proof.

Let $H(a, \varepsilon, m, I)$ be the correspondence which assigns to a, ε, m, and I the set of all

$$\frac{b^I}{\sum_{j=1}^{n_I} b_j^I}$$

where $b^I \neq 0$ and $b \in G(a, \varepsilon, m)$. Note that for any scalar $\pi > 0$, $H(\pi a, \varepsilon, m, I) = H(a, \varepsilon, m, I)$. Note further that since by Furuya and Inada [5, Theorem 3, p. 101] any balanced growth path associated with $\lambda(\varepsilon)$ is efficient of any order m, $W(\varepsilon, I) \in H(a(\varepsilon), \varepsilon, m, I)$, for ε sufficiently close to zero.

Now Lemma 3.3 and an argument essentially that used in the proof of Fisher [4, Lemma 2.2] shows that as ε approaches zero, $W(\varepsilon, I)$ approaches a member of $H(a(\varepsilon), 0, m, I) = H(0 \ldots 0\ a^I(\varepsilon)\ 0 \ldots 0, 0, m, I) = H(0 \ldots 0\ W(\varepsilon, I)\ 0 \ldots 0, 0, m, I)$; furthermore, Lemma 3.4 now yields the result that $\lim_{\varepsilon \to 0} W(\varepsilon, I) \in H(0 \ldots 0 \lim_{\varepsilon \to 0} W(\varepsilon, I)\ 0 \ldots 0, 0, m, I)$. Hence, for any $m > 0$, there exists a path $(\lim_{\varepsilon \to 0} W(\varepsilon, I), b^{(m)I}) \in T^{(m)I}$ which is weakly efficient of order m and such that $b^{(m)I} = \lambda^{(m)} \lim_{\varepsilon \to 0} W(\varepsilon, I)$ for some scalar $\lambda^{(m)}$. By Lemma 3.6, however, for $m \geq s^I$, any such path is efficient of order m, and application of Lemma 3.5 yields the theorem by the remarks given at the outset.

---

[14] Note that it is not required that $T(\varepsilon)$ be strongly superadditive.

[15] See Fisher [4, Lemma 2.1 p. 72].

Theorem 3.2 extends the major long-run result of Simon and Ando [10] and parallels the similar result of Fisher [4, Theorem 2.2]. It states that in systems sufficiently close to complete decomposability, the internal composition of outputs in each nonzero sector along any von Neumann ray will be approximately the same as the similar composition of outputs along that sector's own von Neumann ray when the technology is in fact completely decomposable, despite the fact that the level and rate of growth of the entire sector will in general be quite different.

4. The Decomposable Case

We turn now to the perhaps more interesting case of decomposability rather than complete decomposability. This is the case in which there is a natural ordering of sectors such that inputs from higher-numbered sectors have zero marginal productivity in the production of outputs in lower-numbered sectors, but not the reverse. Note that this may include the case in which inputs from lower-numbered sectors are required in order to produce any nonzero outputs in higher-numbered ones.

As in the last section, let us partition a and b into N sectors; we shall continue to use the notation T^I as in that section. Let $S^1 = T^1$; let S^2 be the set of all $(a^1 a^2, b^1 b^2)$ such that $(a^1 a^2 0 \ldots 0, b^1 b^2 b^3 \ldots b^N) \in T$ for some b; let S^3 be the set of all $(a^1 a^2 a^3, b^1 b^2 b^3)$ such that $(a^1 a^2 a^3 0 \ldots 0, b^1 b^2 b^3 b^4 \ldots b^N) \in T$ for some b; and so forth, until $S^N = T$. We define:

Definition 4.1: T will be called decomposable if and only if $(a, b) \in T$ implies $(a^1 \ldots a^I, b^1 \ldots b^I) \in S^I$ for all $I = 1, \ldots, N$.

Note that for all $I = 2, \ldots, N$, S^I is also decomposable. We shall refer to the S^I as subsystems, reserving the term sectors for the T^I, as before. Observe that every S^I satisfies Assumptions 2.1-2.5. We shall later in effect continue to assume that T^1 is primitive but shall drop that assumption for all $T^I (I = 2, \ldots, N)$. Note that complete decomposability is a special case.

We shall continue to denote the maximal growth rate for processes in T^I by λ_I. Note, however, that while $\lambda_1 > 0$ is reasonable, it is by no means necessary that $\lambda_I > 0$ for $I = 2, \ldots N$, since it is entirely possible that outside inputs are required for production, so that for $I = 2, \ldots, N$, T^I may consist only of processes $(a^I, 0)$. We drop the assumption that the λ_I are distinct save where explicitly reinstated and shall refer to them as the internal growth rates of the N sectors.

Denote the maximal growth rate for processes in S^I by ρ_I. Clearly, $\rho_1 = \lambda_1$. We prove:

Theorem 4.1: For all $I = 2, \ldots, N$:

(1) If $\rho_{I-1} \leq \lambda_I$, then $\rho_I = \lambda_I$.

(2) If $\rho_{I-1} \geq \lambda_I$, then $\rho_I = \rho_{I-1}$.
(3) Let $\lambda_{K(I)} = \max_{J \leq I} \lambda_J$. Then $\rho_I = \lambda_{K(I)}$.

Proof: The last statement of the theorem obviously follows from repeated application of the first two and the fact that $\rho_1 = \lambda_1$. It will thus suffice to prove the first two statements. Furthermore, it will suffice to consider only the case in which I = 2, assuming $\rho_1 > 0$. (The proof for I > 2 is no different but involves a more cumbersome notation.)

Let $(\bar{a}^1, \bar{b}^1) \in S^1$ be a (not necessarily unique) process associated with ρ_1.

If $\rho_1 \leq \lambda_2$, then $\rho_2 = \lambda_2$. This follows because no process in S^2 with $a^1 \geq 0$ can have a growth rate greater than ρ_1, and because for any process $(a^2, b^2) \in T^2$ there is a process $(0\ a^2, 0\ b^2) \in S^2$, so that ρ_2 cannot be less than λ_2.

On the other hand, if $\rho_1 \geq \lambda_2$, then $\rho_2 \geq \rho_1$ since there is a process $(\bar{a}^1 0, \bar{b}^1 b^2) \in S^2$ with growth rate ρ_1. However, since, by the remarks already made, no process in S^2 can have a growth rate greater than the larger of ρ_1 and λ_2, $\rho_2 = \rho_1$, the theorem is proved.

Note that Theorem 4.1 leaves open the question of whether when $\rho_{I-1} > \lambda_I$ there exists a process in S^I with growth rate $\rho_I = \rho_{I-1}$ and $b^I \geq 0$. Clearly, there will exist such a process if, with the (I - 1)st subsystem growing at rate ρ_{I-1} and zero inputs from the Ith sector, positive outputs can be produced in the Ith sector as a by-product; however, this is a rather unusual situation.[16] A more reasonable possibility is that with the (I - 1)st subsystem growing at rate ρ_{I-1} and with some positive inputs from the Ith sector, the latter sector can grow at least at that rate.

On the other hand, the possibility that in such a situation the Ith sector can grow at a rate greater than ρ_{I-1} is a difficult one with which to deal.[17] In this case (which includes the case of zero input and nonzero output in the Ith sector as a limit), the goods of the Ith sector turn out to be free ones in the von Neumann

---

[16] Although it is by no means an impossible one. Suppose, for example, that I = 2 and the first sector consists of the labor force and the agricultural products needed to sustain it. It is certainly possible to have labor producing other goods while reproducing itself but not very plausible that it should do so with no outside inputs.

[17] Note that the difficulty arises only when all goods in the Ith sector grow at least at some greater rate. This possibility is what will be assumed away below. There is no problem in the entirely likely case that some (but not all) goods in the Ith sector can grow at a rate faster than ρ_{I-1} in such a situation.

price system developed below, and our results below will not apply to them. However, it is clear that if, in such a situation, the Ith sector can grow at a rate above ρ_{I-1}, then for any $\varepsilon > 0$ there exists an m sufficiently large that the growth rate in the Ith sector over any set of m consecutive periods cannot exceed $(\rho_{I-1} + \varepsilon)^m$. We can therefore interpret our results below as applying to very long production periods, but this is somewhat artificial. Thus while such considerations may help to make the assumption about to be stated more palatable, they should not disguise the fact that it is a rather strong one. We make it for the remainder of this section.

Assumption 4.1: If $\rho_{I-1} \geq \lambda_I$ and $(\bar{a}^1 \ldots \bar{a}^I, \bar{b}^1 \ldots \bar{b}^I) \in S^I$ is a process associated with $\rho_I = \rho_{I-1}$, then

$$\min \left\{ \frac{\bar{b}^I_j}{\bar{a}^I_j} \;\middle|\; \bar{a}^I_j \neq 0 \right\} \leq \rho_I$$

$(j = 1, \ldots, n_I)$, $(I = 1, \ldots, N)$.

We now define:

Definition 4.2: T will be said to be conditionally primitive if and only if $\lambda_I > 0$ implies T^I primitive $(I = 1, \ldots, N)$.

Note that if every T^I is primitive, then T is conditionally primitive, but not the reverse.

Definition 4.3: T will be said to be conditionally strongly superadditive if and only if, for all $I = 1, \ldots, N$, $\lambda_I > 0$ implies that T^I is strongly superadditive.

Note that if T is conditionally strongly superadditive, then so also is every S^I $(I = 1, \ldots,$ and $N)$.

Definition 4.4: T will be said to be von Neumann primitive if and only if, for every $I = 2, \ldots, N$ for which $\rho_{I-1} > \lambda_I$, there exists a finite s such that if $(\bar{a}^{(0)1} \ldots \bar{a}^{(0)I-1})$ is any input vector to a process in S^{I-1} associated with ρ_{I-1}, and $a^{(0)I} \geq 0$, there is a process $(\bar{a}^{(0)1} \ldots \bar{a}^{(0)I-1}\, a^{(0)I}, \bar{b}^{(s)1} \ldots \bar{b}^{(s)I-1}\, b^{(s)I}) \in S^{(s)I}$ such that $\bar{b}^{(s)J} \geqq \rho^s_{I-1}\, \bar{a}^{(0)J}$ for all $J = 1, \ldots, I-1$ and $b^{(s)I} > 0$.

Note, as before, that if every T^I is primitive, then T is von Neumann primitive, but not the reverse.

Definition 4.5: For every $I = 2, \ldots, N$ for which $\rho_{I-1} > \lambda_I$, let $(\bar{a}^1, \ldots, \bar{a}^{I-1})$ be any input vector to a process in S^{I-1} associated with ρ_{I-1}. Further, let a^I and $\tilde{a}^I$ be independent vectors such that $(\bar{a}^1, \ldots, \bar{a}^{I-1}, a^I, b^1, \ldots, b^I) \in S^I$ and $(\bar{a}^1, \ldots, \bar{a}^{I-1}, \tilde{a}^I, \tilde{b}^1, \ldots, \tilde{b}^I) \in S^I$, with $b^J \geqq \rho_{I-1}\, \bar{a}^J \leqq b^J$ for

$J = 1, \ldots, I-1$. Then, T is said to be <u>von Neumann strongly superadditive</u> if and only if, for every such I and for any two scalars $\pi_1 > 0$ and $\pi_2 > 0$, there exists a process $((\pi_1 + \pi_2)\overline{a}^1 \ldots (\pi_1 + \pi_2)\overline{a}^{I-1}\ \pi_1 a^I + \pi_2 \tilde{a}^I,\ b^{*1} \ldots b^{*I}) \in S^I$ such that $b^{*J} \geqq \pi_1 b^J + \pi_2 \tilde{b}^J$ for $J = 1, \ldots, I$ and $b^{*I} \geq \pi_1 b^I + \pi_2 \tilde{b}^I$.

As before, note that if T is von Neumann strongly superadditive, then so is very S^I $(I = 1, \ldots, N)$.

The assumptions of conditional and von Neumann strong superadditivity essentially assume strong superadditivity for special processes in T (the extra outputs occurring in the logical sector) but not for all processes. In effect, the assumptions of conditional and von Neumann primitivity and conditional and von Neumann strong superadditivity are rather weak, since they merely require certain properties to hold in certain sectors for certain configurations of inputs, rather than requiring them more generally. Note, for example, that the readily interpretable assumptions that every T^I is primitive and every S^I strongly superadditive imply, respectively, conditional and von Neumann primitivity and conditional and von Neumann strong superadditivity. Such assumptions are far stronger than necessary for our purposes, however. It is possible to proceed without this type of assumption, but the analysis becomes a great deal more complicated without yielding much of interest in that case.[18]

From now on, it will be convenient to agree in otherwise ambiguous cases that when the symbols $(\overline{a}^1 \ldots \overline{a}^I)$ are used to represent the inputs to a process in S^I associated with ρ_I, $\overline{a}^J$ shall be taken as being nonzero $(J = 1, \ldots, I)$ unless the Jth sector has zero inputs for <u>all</u> processes in S^I associated with ρ_I. (It will be evident by superadditivity that there is no difficulty in doing this.) This convention will not extend to other symbols representing the inputs to such a process.

<u>Theorem 4.2</u>: If

(1) $\lambda_1 > 0$,

(2) T is conditionally primitive, and

(3) T is von Neumann primitive,

then

(A) for all $I = 1, \ldots, N$, any process in S^I associated with ρ_I is a balanced growth process.

If, in addition,

(4) the λ_I are distinct,

(5) T is conditionally strongly superadditive,

(6) T is von Neumann strongly superadditive,

then

(B) for all $I = 1, \ldots, N$, if $(\overline{a}^1 \ldots \overline{a}^I)$ is the input to a proc-

---

[18] For example, the system can branch into separate systems which must be analyzed jointly. Cf. Fisher [4].

ess in S^I associated with ρ_I and so is $(a^1 \ldots a^I)$, then, for some set of scalars $\pi_J \geq 0$, $a^J = \pi_J \bar{a}^J$ $(J = 1, \ldots, I)$. Note that if $\bar{a}^J = 0$, then $a^J = 0$ but that $a^J = 0$ is possible even if $\bar{a}^J \neq 0$.

Proof:

(A) Since T is conditionally primitive and $\lambda_1 > 0$, $T^1 = S^1$ is primitive. The desired result thus holds for I = 1 by Furuya and Inada's Theorem 1.[19] It will thus suffice to show that it is true for I if it is true for I - 1.

To see this, suppose that $\lambda_I > \rho_{I-1}$, then $\rho_I = \lambda_I$ and any process in S^I associated with ρ_I has zero for the first I - 1 sectors. Furuya and Inada's Theorem 1 then yields the desired result, since λ_I must be greater than zero, and thus T^I must be primitive since T is conditionally primitive. On the other hand, if $\rho_{I-1} > \lambda_I$, any process in S^I associated with ρ_I must have its first I - 1 sectors forming a similarly associated process in S^{I-1}. By Assumption 4.1, the Ith sector cannot grow faster than ρ_{I-1}, so that either both inputs and outputs in the Ith sector are zero or else the desired result again follows from the proof of Furuya and Inada's Theorem 1, this time because T is von Neumann primitive. Finally, if $\rho_{I-1} = \lambda_I$, one or the other of the above analyses applies to every process in S^I associated with ρ_I.

(B) As before, since $\lambda_1 > 0$ and T is conditionally strongly superadditive, the desired result follows for T^1 by Furuya and Inada's Corollary.[20] It will thus suffice again to show that the desired result holds for I if it holds for I - 1.

To see this, observe that if $\lambda_I > \rho_{I-1}$, $\rho_I = \lambda_I$, any process in S^I associated with ρ_I is a process in T^I, and T^I is strongly superadditive since T is conditionally strongly superadditive. The desired result thus follows from Furuya and Inada's Corollary. On the other hand, if $\rho_{I-1} > \lambda_I$, the desired result follows from the proof of that corollary, the assumption that it is true for I - 1, and the fact that T is von Neumann strongly superadditive. Finally, the case in which $\rho_{I-1} = \lambda_I$ is ruled out by the assumption that the λ_I are distinct and the third statement of Theorem 4.1 above. This completes the proof.[21]

---

[19] [5, p. 99].

[20] Loc. cit.

[21] Note that since T is superadditive, the assertion that the process associated with ρ_I is itself unique (as opposed to its intrasectoral configurations) cannot be generally maintained, since, for example, if $\rho_1 > \lambda_2$ and there exists a process $(\bar{a}^1 \bar{a}^2, \bar{b}^1 \bar{b}^2) \in S^2$ associated with $\rho_2 = \rho_1$, then there also exists a process $(\bar{a}^1 0, \bar{b}^1 0) \in S^2$ by the definition of decomposability and Assumption 4.1, so that for any scalar $\pi > 0$, $(\pi\bar{a}^1 \bar{a}^2, \pi\bar{b}^1 \tilde{b}^2) \in S^2$ and $\tilde{b}^2 \geqq \bar{b}^2$ (in view of (A), $\tilde{b}^2 = \bar{b}^2$).

The assumption that the λ_I are distinct is a bit stronger than necessary; this is also true in later theorems.

We are now ready to discuss prices, interest rates, and profits.

Theorem 4.3: If
(1) $\lambda_1 > 0$,
(2) T is conditionally primitive,
(3) T is von Neumann primitive,
then
(A) there exists a price vector, $\overline{p} = (\overline{p}^1 \ldots \overline{p}^N)$, such that for every $I = 1, \ldots, N$,

$$\sum_{J=1}^{I} \left[\overline{p}^J\right]' \overline{b}^J = \rho_I \sum_{J=1}^{I} \left[\overline{p}^J\right]' \overline{a}^J$$ [22]

for any process $(\overline{a}^1 \ldots \overline{a}^I, \overline{b}^1 \ldots \overline{b}^I) \in S^I$ associated with ρ_I and

$$\sum_{J=1}^{I} \left[\overline{p}^J\right]' b^J \leq \rho_I \sum_{J=1}^{I} \left[\overline{p}^J\right]' a^J$$

for all processes in S^I.[23]

Furthermore, if in addition,
(4) the λ_I are all distinct,
(5) T is conditionally strongly superadditive,
(6) T is von Neumann strongly superadditive,
then
(B)
$$\sum_{J=1}^{I} \left[\overline{p}^J\right]' b^J < \rho_I \sum_{J=1}^{I} \left[\overline{p}^J\right]' a^J$$

for any process in S^I for which there is no set of nonnegative scalars π_J $(J = 1, \ldots, I)$ such that $a^J = \pi_J \overline{a}^J$ where $(\overline{a}^1 \ldots \overline{a}^I)$ is the input vector to some process in S^I associated with ρ_I.

Proof:
(A) Following the structure of the proof of the first part of

---

[22]For convenience, we have been writing all vectors as rows. It is to be understood, however, that they are actually columns, so that the products in the text are defined scalar products. To avoid confusion, we write $[p]'$ instead of p' to represent the transpose of p.

[23]Note that the same $\overline{p}$ serves for all S^I.

Furuya and Inada's Theorem 2,[24] define C(I) as the closure of the convex hull of the set $\{(b^1 - \rho_I a^1, \ldots, b^I - \rho_I a^I); (a^1 \ldots a^I, b^1 \ldots b^I) \in S^I\}$. Clearly, C(I) is a closed convex cone; we begin by showing that it contains no vector $v \geq 0$.

In the first place, since $\lambda_1 > 0$ and T is conditionally primitive, T^1 is primitive, and Furuya and Inada's proof applied to C(1) shows that the latter cone contains no such vector. It will therefore suffice to show that C(I) contains no vector $v \geq 0$ if C(I - 1) does not.

To see this, observe that in view of Theorem 4.1, $\rho_I \geq \rho_{I-1}$. Since, by assumption, C(I - 1) contains no vector greater than or equal to zero, C(I) can only contain such a vector if the first I - 1 sets of components thereof are all zero. There are two cases to consider.

First, if $\lambda_I > \rho_{I-1}$, and $v = (v^1 \ldots v^I) \geqq 0 \in C(I)$, $a^J = 0$ for all J = 1, ..., I - 1. However, since $\lambda_I > 0$ in this case, and T is conditionally primitive, T^I is primitive, and Furuya and Inada's proof shows that $v^I = 0$, whence $v = 0$.

Second, if $\lambda_I \leq \rho_{I-1}$, $v^J = 0$ for all J = 1, ..., I - 1 is possible either for all $a^J = 0$ (J = 1, ..., I - 1) or for $(a^1 \ldots a^{I-1}, b^1 \ldots b^{I-1}) \in S^{I-1}$, a process associated with ρ_{I-1}. In the former case, the preceding analysis applies, while in the latter case, the fact that T is von Neumann primitive combines easily with the Furuya and Inada proof to yield the result that $v^I = 0$, as before.

Thus C(I) contains no vector greater than zero. It follows immediately that there is a nonempty set of vectors, say P(I), such that $p(I) = (p(I)^1 \ldots p(I)^I) \in P(I)$ if and only if

$$p(I) > 0,$$

$$\sum_{J=1}^{I} \left[p(I)^J\right]' \bar{b}^J = \rho_I \sum_{J=1}^{I} \left[p(I)^J\right]' \bar{a}^J,$$

and

$$\sum_{J=1}^{I} \left[p(I)^J\right]' b^J \leqq \rho_I \sum_{J=1}^{I} \left[p(I)^J\right]' a^J$$

for any process in S^I.[25]

It thus remains to show that there exists a $\bar{p} \in P(N)$ whose first set of components lies in P(1), whose first two sets lie in P(2), and so forth. We shall do this by construction.

First consider P(2). Suppose that $\rho_1 = \rho_2$; then, since every

---

[24][5, pp. 100-101].

[25]See Furuya and Inada [5, p. 101]. The statement there given on the analogous point is too strong; for the correct statement, see Fisher [3].

vector in C(1) is part of a vector in C(2) and the latter vector has its second group of components nonnegative, it is obvious that any vector in P(2) has its first set of components belonging to P(1). Similarly, let the H_1th sector be the lowest-numbered sector (if one exists) for which $\lambda_{H_1} = \rho_{H_1} > \rho_1 = \lambda_1$. By similar reasoning, every vector in $P(H_1 - 1)$ has its first set of components in P(1), its first two sets in P(2), and so forth. If $\rho_N = \rho_1$, the desired result is immediate. We may thus go directly to the consideration of $P(H_1)$ on the assumption that H_1 exists.

Consider any vector in $P(H_1)$, say $p(H_1)$, and any vector in $P(H_1 - 1)$, say $p(H_1 - 1)$. Since $\rho_{H_1 - 1} < \rho_{H_1}$, $p(H_1 - 1) > 0$, and

$$\sum_{J=1}^{H_1 - 1} \left[p(H_1 - 1)^J\right]' b^J \leq \rho_{H_1 - 1} \sum_{J=1}^{H_1 - 1} \left[p(H_1 - 1)^J\right]' a^J$$

for all processes in $S^{H_1 - 1}$, it follows that

$$\sum_{J=1}^{H_1 - 1} \left[p(H_1 - 1)^J\right]' b^J < \rho_{H_1} \sum_{J=1}^{H_1 - 1} \left[p(H_1 - 1)^J\right]' a^J$$

for all such processes. Hence, since any process in S^{H_1} has its first $H_1 - 1$ sectors a process in $S^{H_1 - 1}$, there clearly exists a scalar $\alpha_1 > 0$ so large that for any process in S^{H_1},

$$\sum_{J=1}^{H_1 - 1} \left[\alpha_1 p(H_1 - 1)^J\right]' b^J + \left[p(H_1)^{H_1}\right]' b^{H_1}$$

$$- \rho_{H_1} \left(\sum_{J=1}^{H_1 - 1} \left[\alpha_1 p(H_1 - 1)^J\right]' a^J + \left[p(H_1)^{H_1}\right]' a^{H_1} \right)$$

$$\leq \sum_{J=1}^{H_1} \left[p(H_1)^J\right]' b^J - \rho_{H_1} \sum_{J=1}^{H_1} \left[p(H_1)^J\right]' a^J \leq 0$$

the equalities all holding if the process is associated with ρ_{H_1}.[26] Thus there is an $\alpha_1 > 0$ such that for any vector in $P(H_1)$, and any vector in $P(H_1 - 1)$, replacing the first $H_1 - 1$ sets of compo-

---

[26]Note that for such a process, the first $H_1 - 1$ sectors have zero for all outputs and inputs. That the statement holds for all processes in S^{H_1} with the same α_1 follows from Assumptions 2.2 and 2.5 and the fact that it obviously suffices to take the inputs in the simplex.

nents of the vector in $P(H_1)$ by α_1 times the vector in $P(H_1 - 1)$ gives another vector in $P(H_1)$ whose first $H_1 - 1$ sets of components lie in $P(H_1 - 1)$.[27]

We now continue. Suppose that $\rho_{H_1} + 1 = \rho_{H_1}$. Then, as before, any vector in $P(H_1 + 1)$ has a vector in $P(H_1)$ as its first H_1 sets of components. If its first $H_1 - 1$ sets do not form a vector in $P(H_1 - 1)$, we may obviously substitute for them a vector which is in $P(H_1 - 1)$, obtaining another vector in $P(H_1 + 1)$ which has a vector in $P(J)(J = 1, \ldots, H_1 + 1)$ as its first J sets of components. We may continue in this way until either $P(N)$ is reached — in which case the desired result has been obtained — or until we reach some sector, say H_2, such that $\lambda_{H_2} = \rho_{H_2} > \rho_{H_1} = \lambda_{H_1}$. In this case, as before, we can find an $\alpha_2 > 0$ sufficiently large that for any vector in $P(H_2)$, and any vector in $P(H_2 - 1)$, substituting α_2 times the vector in $P(H_2 - 1)$ for the first $H_2 - 1$ sets of components of the vector in $P(H_2)$ in question yields another vector in $P(H_2)$ with its first $H_2 - 1$ sets of components in $P(H_2 - 1)$. We may clearly continue backwards and ensure that the vector has its first J sets of components in $P(J)(J = 1, \ldots, H_2)$.

The construction is now clear and can obviously be continued in analogous fashion until $P(N)$ is reached, resulting in a vector in $P(N)$ whose first J sets of components are in $P(J)$ for all $J = 1, \ldots, N$. This completes the proof of part (A) of the theorem.

(B) Define $K(I)$ as in Theorem 4.1 $(1 \leq K(I) \leq I)$; then $\rho_J < \rho_I$ for $J = 1, \ldots, K(I) - 1$, and $\rho_J = \rho_I$ for $J = K(I), \ldots, I$. Further, $\rho_I > \lambda_J$ for $J = K(I) + 1, \ldots, I$, in view of Theorem 4.1 and the assumption that the λ_I are distinct.

Now, suppose that the statement to be proved is false for a particular process $(a^1 \ldots a^I, b^1 \ldots b^I)$. As observed in Fisher [3], this can only be true if $C(I)$ contains a full line through the origin so that both v and -v are in $C(I)$ where v is the vector corresponding to that process.[28] Thus, for some set of processes

[27] Since, clearly, $P(H_1 - 1)$ is closed under multiplication by a positive scalar.

[28] The construction of $\overline{p}$ in the proof of part (A) does not affect this statement, since it is easy to show that if $p(I) \in P(I)$ and

$$\sum_{J=1}^{I} \left[p(I)^J\right]' b^J < \rho_I \sum_{J=1}^{I} \left[p(I)^J\right]' a^J$$

for all processes $(a^1 \ldots a^I, b^1 \ldots b^I) \in S^I$ for which $a^J \neq \pi_J \overline{a}^J$ for some set of scalars $\pi_J \geq 0$ $(J = 1, \ldots, I)$, then there exists a vector $p(I + 1) \in P(I + 1)$ whose first I sets of components are $p(I)$.

$(a(r)^1 \ldots a(r)^I, b(r)^1 \ldots b(r)^I) \in S^I$, $(r = 1, \ldots, R)$, there is a set of nonnegative weights, $\beta_1 \ldots \beta_R$, with

$$\sum_{r=1}^{R} \beta_r = 1,$$

such that the point

$$\left(\sum_{r=1}^{R} \beta_r b(r)^1 - \rho_I \sum_{r=1}^{R} \beta_r a(r)^1, \ldots, \sum_{r=1}^{R} \beta_r b(r)^I - \rho_I \sum_{r=1}^{R} \beta_r a(r)^I \right)$$

is arbitrarily close to $-v$. Let

$$\tilde{a}^J = \sum_{r=1}^{R} \beta_r a(r)^J \quad (J = 1, \ldots, I).$$

Since T is superadditive, there exists a process $(\tilde{a}^1 \ldots \tilde{a}^I, \tilde{b}^1 \ldots \tilde{b}^I) \in S^I$ with

$$\tilde{b}^J \geqq \sum_{r=1}^{R} \beta_r b(r)^J \quad (J = 1, \ldots, I).$$

Then, for all $J = 1, \ldots, I$, $\tilde{b}^J - \rho_I \tilde{a}^J \geqq \rho_I a^J - b^J - \eta^J$, where $\eta^J > 0$ is a vector whose elements can be made arbitrarily small. By superadditivity, there then exists a process $(a^1 + \tilde{a}^1 \ldots a^I + \tilde{a}^I, b^{*1} \ldots b^{*I}) \in S^I$ with $b^{*J} \geqq b^J + \tilde{b}^J \geqq \rho_I(a^J + \tilde{a}^J) - \eta^J$ for all $J = 1, \ldots, I$.

Clearly, by Theorem 4.1, $\bar{a}^J = 0$ for $J = 1, \ldots, K(I) - 1$. Suppose that $a^J \neq 0$ for some such J; then, since all the η^J can be made arbitrarily small, there exists a process in S^J with growth rate arbitrarily close to ρ_I which contradicts the fact that $\rho_J < \rho_I$ for all $J = 1, \ldots, K(I) - 1$.[29] Hence the theorem is true for $J = 1, \ldots, K(I) - 1$.

Now, consider K(I). Obviously, $\bar{a}^{K(I)} \neq 0$. Further, $\lambda_{K(I)} > 0$, so that conditional strong superadditivity together with the fact that $a^J = 0$ for $J = 1, \ldots, I - 1$ combined with the proof of Fisher

[29] It is easy to show, following Furuya and Inada [5, pp. 97-98] that ρ_I cannot be a least upper bound for growth rates of processes in $S^J (J = 1, \ldots, K(I) - 1)$ unless $\rho_J = \rho_I$.

[3, Theorem 2'] yield the desired result for the $K(I)$th sector. If $K(I) = I$, this completes the proof. We shall thus assume that $K(I) < I$.

Now suppose that $a^{K(I)} = 0$. Then $a^1 \ldots a^{K(I)}$ are all zero. Suppose that $a^J \neq 0$ for some $J = K(I) + 1, \ldots, I$. Let a^H be the first such input vector, then an analysis similar to that already given for the case of $J < K(I)$ shows that λ_H is not less than ρ_I, which contradicts the assumption that the λ_I are distinct and the definition of $K(I)$. Hence, if $a^{K(I)} = 0$, all $a^J = 0$ $(J = 1, \ldots, I)$, and the desired result is trivial.

We may thus consider the case in which $a^{K(I)} \geq 0$. First consider any sector $H = K(I) + 1, \ldots, I$, if this exists, such that no process in S^H with $a^H \geq 0$ is associated with ρ_I. Then an analysis similar to that given for the case of $J < K(I)$ shows that this is contradicted unless $a^H = 0$.

Now consider $K(I) + 1$. If $\overline{a}^{K(I)+1} = 0$ for all processes associated with ρ_I, the desired result has been obtained in the last paragraph. Suppose, therefore, that this is not the case, and that $0 \neq a^{K(I)+1} \neq \pi_{K(I)+1}\, \overline{a}^{K(I)+1} \neq 0$. The facts that $a^1 \ldots a^{K(I)-1}$ are all zero, $a^{K(I)} = \pi_{K(I)}\, \overline{a}^{K(I)} \neq 0$, and T is von Neumann strongly superadditive, combine in a proof essentially that of Fisher [3, Theorem 2'] to show that there is a process in S^I which makes positive profits at prices $\overline{p}$ and interest rate ρ_I, contradicting part (A) of the theorem. The desired result thus holds for $K(I) + 1$. If $K(I) + 1 = I$, this completes the proof; if not, we continue.

Turn now to $K(I) + 2$. Suppose first that $a^{K(I)+1} = 0$. If every process in $S^{K(I)+2}$ which is associated with ρ_I for which $\overline{a}^{K(I)+1} = 0$ also has $\overline{a}^{K(I)+2} = 0$, then an argument similar to that already several times employed shows that $a^{K(I)+2} = 0$ also. If this is not the case, and $a^{K(I)+2} \geq 0$, then von Neumann strong superadditivity operates together with the fact that there is clearly a process in $S^{K(I)+2}$ associated with ρ_I for which $\overline{a}^{K(I)+1} = 0$ to show that the desired result follows for $K(I) + 2$ in the same way as it did for $K(I) + 1$.

We may thus suppose that $a^{K(I)+1} \neq 0$. As before, if $\overline{a}^{K(I)+2} = 0$ for all processes associated with ρ_I, we have already derived the desired result; we may therefore assume that there exists at least one process associated with ρ_I for which this is not the case. If $a^{K(I)+2} = 0$, the desired result is trivial, so that we may also assume that this case is absent. Now suppose that given $(\overline{a}^1 \ldots \overline{a}^I)$, $\pi_{K(I)} = \pi_{K(I)+1}$; then von Neumann strong superadditivity operates as before to show that the desired result holds for $K(I) + 2$. It thus remains only to consider the case in which $\pi_{K(I)} \neq \pi_{K(I)+1}$.

Suppose first that $\pi_{K(I)} > \pi_{K(I)+1}$. Then there exists a process

$$\left(0 \ldots 0 \left(\frac{\pi_{K(I)}}{\pi_{K(I)+1}} - 1\right)\bar{a}^{K(I)}\, 0 \ldots 0,\ 0 \ldots 0 \left(\frac{\pi_{K(I)}}{\pi_{K(I)+1}} - 1\right)\bar{b}^{K(I)}\, 0 \ldots 0\right) \epsilon\ S^I$$

and, by superadditivity and Theorem 4.2, there thus exists a process

$$\left(0 \ldots 0 \left(\frac{\pi_{K(I)}}{\pi_{K(I)+1}}\right)\bar{a}^{K(I)}\ \bar{a}^{K(I)+1} \ldots \bar{a}^{I},\ 0 \ldots 0,\right.$$

$$\left. 0 \ldots 0 \left(\frac{\pi_{K(I)}}{\pi_{K(I)+1}}\right)\bar{b}^{K(I)}\ \bar{b}^{K(I)+1} \ldots \bar{b}^{I}\right) \epsilon\ S^I.$$

However, this latter process is also associated with ρ_I and

$$a^{K(I)} = \pi_{K(I)}\ \bar{a}^{K(I)} = \pi_{K(I)+1} \left(\frac{\pi_{K(I)}}{\pi_{K(I)+1}}\right)\bar{a}^{K(I)},$$

while $a^{K(I)+1} = \pi_{K(I)+1}\ \bar{a}^{K(I)+1}$. The proof using von Neumann strong superadditivity can now go as before, using the constructed process in place of $(\bar{a}^1 \ldots \bar{a}^I, \bar{b}^1 \ldots \bar{b}^I)$ to demonstrate the contradiction.

The remaining case is that of $\pi_{K(I)+1} > \pi_{K(I)}$. In this case, there exists a process $(0 \ldots 0\ (\pi_{K(I)+1} - \pi_{K(I)})\ \bar{a}^{K(I)}\ 0 \ldots 0,$ $0 \ldots 0\ (\pi_{K(I)+1} - \pi_{K(I)})\ \bar{b}^{K(I)}\ 0 \ldots 0) \epsilon\ S^I$ and hence a process $(0 \ldots 0\ \pi_{K(I)+1}\ \bar{a}^{K(I)}\ a^{K(I)+1} \ldots a^I,\ 0 \ldots 0\ \pi_{K(I)+1}\ \bar{b}^{K(I)}\ \tilde{b}^{K(I)+1}$ $\ldots \tilde{b}^I) \epsilon\ S^I$ with $\tilde{b}^J \geqq b^J$ $(J = K(I) + 1, \ldots, I)$, and it is easy to see that such a process also makes zero profits. The proof using von Neumann strong superadditivity now proceeds as before, using the constructed process in place of $(a^1 \ldots a^I, b^1 \ldots b^I)$ to establish the contradiction. All possibilities being now exhausted, the desired result holds for $K(I) + 2$.

It is now clear how to proceed. If $K(I) + 2 < I$, consider $K(I) + 3$. Here the proof proceeds analogously to that for $K(I) + 2$, save that in the last two cases adjustment of the levels of two sectors rather than of one preceding sector is necessary. Proceeding in this way, we eventually establish (B) for $J = 1, \ldots, I$, and the theorem is finally proved.

Thus, under the stated conditions, there exists a set of positive prices such that when all commodities are valued at those prices and the interest rate appropriate to the subsystem under consideration is charged (recall that the full system is a subsystem of itself), processes associated with that rate make zero profits, and no process makes positive profits. Further, under the additional conditions, all processes with inputs not in the special von Neumann intrasectoral proportions actually lose money.

Since the special intrasectoral von Neumann proportions play the same role in the present case as does the von Neumann ray in other models, it will be convenient to define a distance concept which measures deviations from those proportions.

In all of what follows, $(\bar{a}^1 \ldots \bar{a}^I)$ will denote the input vector to a process in S^I associated with ρ_I, where we recall that it is understood that $\bar{a}^J \geq 0$ unless for every such process the Jth sector has only zero inputs $(J = 1, \ldots, I)(I = 1, \ldots, N)$. The $\bar{a}^J$ are thus the special von Neumann intrasectoral proportions in nontrivial form.

Now, for any $I = 1, \ldots, N$, and any vector $(a^1 \ldots a^I) \geqq 0$, consider $(\bar{a}^1 \ldots \bar{a}^I)$. Define $d^J(a^1 \ldots a^I, I)$ as zero if $a^J = 0$; as the Euclidean distance between

$$\frac{a^J}{\sum_{H=1}^{I} \sum_{j=1}^{n_H} a_j^H}$$

and $\bar{a}^J$ if $\bar{a}^J = 0$, but not all $a^H = 0$ $(H = 1, \ldots, I)$; and as the Euclidean distance between

$$\frac{a^J}{\sum_{j=1}^{n_J} a_j^J} \text{ and } \frac{\bar{a}^J}{\sum_{j=1}^{n_J} \bar{a}_j^J}$$

otherwise. Finally, define

$$D(a^1 \ldots a^I, I) = \sum_{J=1}^{I} d^J(a^1 \ldots a^I, 1).$$

Clearly, this last function measures the distance of $(a^1 \ldots a^I)$ from the special intrasectoral von Neumann proportions, $(\bar{a}^1 \ldots \bar{a}^I)$. Note that it approaches zero if and only if, when $(a^1 \ldots a^I)$ is normalized to lie in the simplex, a^J approaches zero for all $J = 1, \ldots, I$ for which $\bar{a}^J = 0$ and a^J approaches $\pi_J \bar{a}^J$ for all $J = 1, \ldots, I$ for which $\bar{a}^J \geq 0$, the π_J being nonnegative scalars.

The reason for this is that the intersectoral proportions of $(\bar{a}^1 \ldots \bar{a}^I)$ are determined for $\bar{a}^J = 0$, but that only intrasectoral proportions are determined for the nonzero $\bar{a}^J$.

We prove the extension of Radner's Lemma[30] to the present case.

Lemma 4.1: Under (1)-(6) of Theorems 4.2 and 4.3, for all $I = 1, \ldots, N$, it is the case that for any scalar $\eta > 0$, there exists a scalar $\delta > 0$ such that for any $(a^1 \ldots a^I, b^1 \ldots b^I) \in S^I$ for which $D(a^1 \ldots a^I, I) \geqq \eta$,

$$\sum_{J=1}^{I} \left[\bar{p}^J\right]' b^J \leqq (\rho_I - \delta) \sum_{J=1}^{I} \left[\bar{p}^J\right]' a^J .$$

Proof: We may obviously normalize $(a^1 \ldots a^I)$ to lie in the simplex. If the lemma were false, there would be a sequence of processes converging to some limit, say $(\tilde{a}^1 \ldots \tilde{a}^I, \tilde{b}^1 \ldots \tilde{b}^I)$ with $D(\tilde{a}^1 \ldots \tilde{a}^I, I) \geqq \eta$ and

$$\sum_{J=1}^{I} \left[\bar{p}^J\right]' \tilde{b}^J = \rho_I \sum_{J=1}^{I} \left[\bar{p}^J\right]' \tilde{a}^J .$$

However, it follows from Assumption 2.5 that $(\tilde{a}^1 \ldots \tilde{a}^I, \tilde{b}^1 \ldots \tilde{b}^I) \in S^I$, so that this contradicts Theorem 4.3.

We are now prepared to discuss the Turnpike properties of the von Neumann intrasectoral proportions. We follow Radner [9, p. 100] and assume a preference function to be maximized at the end of M periods over the set of feasible paths of order M starting from a given initial point. Thus $U^I = U(b^{(M)1} \ldots b^{(M)I}, I)$ will be taken as a utility function defined over the Mth period outputs of the Ith subsystem only. There will be N such functions, and we assume the following:[31]

Assumption 4.2: For all $I = 1, \ldots, N$, U^I is nonnegative and continuous in all outputs. Also, U^I is not constant over all outputs and is finite for any finite outputs.

Assumption 4.3: For all $I = 1, \ldots, N$, U^I is "quasi-homogeneous"; i.e., for any two nonnegative vectors $(b^1 \ldots b^I)$ and $(\tilde{b}^1 \ldots \tilde{b}^I)$ and any scalar $\pi > 0$, $U(b^1 \ldots b^I, I) \geqq U(\tilde{b}^1 \ldots \tilde{b}^I, I)$ if

---

[30] Radner [9, p. 102].

[31] These are Radner's Assumptions A.3 and A.4 [9, p. 100], respectively, in our notation and adapted somewhat. The reason for defining a different utility function for each subsystem will be apparent shortly if it is not so already.

and only if $U(\pi b^1 \ldots \pi b^I, I) \geqq U(\pi \tilde{b}^1 \ldots \pi \tilde{b}^I, I)$ and either both inequalities or both equalities hold. Without loss of generality, U^I may be taken to be homogeneous of degree 1.

Radner[32] gives examples of utility functions satisfying these conditions; we shall return to this later.

Definition 4.6: A feasible path of order M will be called U^I-optimal if and only if, given its starting point, U^I evaluated at its Mth period's output is not less than U^I evaluated at the Mth period's output of any other feasible path.

We shall show that, for every I, if (1)-(6) of Theorems 4.2 and 4.3 hold, if a starting point is given from which some process associated with ρ_I can be reached in a finite number of steps, and if from that process a set of outputs with positive utility can be reached in a finite number of steps, then no U^I-optimal path can be bounded away from the von Neumann proportions by any non-zero amount for more than a fixed number of periods. We shall discuss the meaning of these assumptions after the theorem. Suffice it now to observe that they are obviously close to those of Radner's proof of the Turnpike Theorem.[33]

Theorem 4.4 (Turnpike Theorem): If

(1) $\lambda_1 > 0$,
(2) T is conditionally primitive,
(3) T is von Neumann primitive,
(4) the λ_I are all distinct,
(5) T is conditionally strongly superadditive,
(6) T is von Neumann strongly superadditive,
(7) an initial commodity vector $(a^{(0)1} \ldots a^{(0)N})$ is given such that, for some $H(1 \leq H \leq N)$, there exists a finite s such that $(a^{(0)1} \ldots a^{(0)H}, b^{(s)1} \ldots b^{(s)H}) \in S^{(s)H}$ with $b^{(s)J} \geqq \tilde{a}^J$ $(J = 1, \ldots, H)$, where $(\tilde{a}^1 \ldots \tilde{a}^H)$ is the input vector to some process in S^H associated with ρ_H,
(8) for the same H, there exists a finite number s' such that $(\tilde{a}^1 \ldots \tilde{a}^H, \tilde{b}^{(s')1} \ldots \tilde{b}^{(s')H}) \in S^{(s')H}$ and $U(\tilde{b}^{(s')1} \ldots \tilde{b}^{(s')H}, H) > 0$,

then for that H and for any scalar $\eta > 0$, there is a number Q such that for any M and any U^H-optimal feasible path of order M starting from $(a^{(0)1} \ldots a^{(0)N})$, the number of periods in which $D(a^{(t)1} \ldots a^{(t)H}, H) \geqq \eta$ cannot exceed Q.

Proof: We shall not give the proof in any detail but shall merely point out that our earlier results in Theorem 4.3 and Lemma 4.1 make Radner's proof applicable with obvious modifications.[34]

---

[32] Loc. cit.

[33] [9, pp. 101-102].

[34] [9, pp. 102-103]. Radner's assumption (iii) follows in our case from the fact that $\overline{p} > 0$. See Radner [9, Remark 2, p. 104].

We add some remarks on the assumptions of the theorem:

Remark 4.1: If for $H < N$, (2), (3), (5), and (6) hold with T replaced by S^H and (4) is required to hold only for $I = 1, \ldots, H$, then the conclusion of the theorem also holds in view of the fact that S^H is itself decomposable. A similar result holds for Theorems 4.2 and 4.3.

Remark 4.2: If $\lambda_1 = 0$, then the first sector can never have a positive output, and we may as well begin the analysis with the lowest-numbered sector in which production is possible. This remark also applies to Theorems 4.2 and 4.3.

Remark 4.3: The assumptions of the theorem do not rule out the possibility that T is completely decomposable even if (7) and (8) hold for all $H = 1, \ldots, N$.[35] Again, this is clearly true for Theorems 4.2 and 4.3 also.

Remark 4.4: Assumptions (1)-(6) are not necessary; what are used in the proof are the results of Theorem 4.3, for which (1)-(6) are sufficient.

Remark 4.5: Assumptions (7) and (8) are stated as they are to avoid the possibility that the only paths associated with ρ_H which can be reached from the initial point are such as neither to yield positive utility themselves nor to allow a point with positive utility to be reached from them. This would be the case, for example, if the maximization of U^H required one to get out as far as possible on a given ray[36] (L-shaped indifference curves) and the only processes associated with ρ_H that could be reached from the initial point were such as to allow only the origin on that ray to be reached from them. (This could happen if T were completely decomposable or if nonzero points on the ray had nonzero components in sectors with lower numbers than K(H).) The nature of the utility function is thus implicitly restricted.

Remark 4.6: Since T is conditionally and von Neumann primitive, a sufficient condition for (7) to hold for all $H = 1, \ldots, N$ would be that there be at least one nonzero initial input in the first sector and that the following not too unreasonable condition concerning connections among sectors be satisfied:

Condition 4.1 (Hierarchic Production): For every $I = 1, \ldots, N$ there is a finite s such that for some $a^{(0)I-1} \geq 0$, there is a process $(0 \ldots 0\, a^{(0)I-1} 0,\ 0 \ldots 0\, b^{(s)I-1}\, b^{(s)I}) \in S^I$ and $b^{(s)I} > 0$.

Remark 4.7: Since $T = S^N$, the theorem holds for the system as a whole (a similar remark applies to Theorems 4.2 and 4.3). A natural question is thus whether in maximizing U^N the conclu-

[35] But see Remark 4.5 below.

[36] As in Radner's Example 3.2 [9, p. 100].

sions of the theorem will hold for all subsystems as well as for T so that U^N-optimal paths spend all but a fixed number of time periods close to the von Neumann proportions in <u>every</u> subsystem. Clearly this is always true for the K(N)th through Nth subsystems since the crucial proportions in all those subsystems are the same in all common sectors. It follows that this would hold in all subsystems if K(N) = 1 (a distinct possibility since $\lambda_I = 0$ for all I = 2, ..., N would occur if internal production in each sector were impossible because inputs from other sectors were needed). Further, even if K(N) > 1, there is nothing contradictory about such a circumstance, since if the K(N)-1st subsystem is growing at a rate close to $\rho_{K(N)-1}$ and the system as a whole is growing at a rate close to $\rho_{K(N)}$ which is higher, then the K(N)-1st subsystem will be <u>relatively</u> approaching zero, so that the whole system can still approach the von Neumann intrasectoral proportions. However, this is very unlikely unless U^N can be written as an additive function of utilities of certain subsystem outputs and running down the outputs of the first K(N) - 1 sectors to zero does not get one any farther up on a von Neumann ray than not doing so. (This latter circumstance would occur if T were completely decomposable.)

We now turn to the extension of the Furuya-Inada Relative Stability Theorem[37] to the present decomposable case. As is to be expected, most of the remarks just made concerning the Turnpike Theorem have their counterparts in this area, and we shall merely emphasize those which seem most important.

<u>Theorem 4.5</u> (Relative Stability Theorem): If

(1) $\lambda_1 > 0$,
(2) T is conditionally primitive,
(3) T is von Neumann primitive,
(4) the λ_I are all distinct,
(5) T is conditionally strongly superadditive,
(6) T is von Neumann strongly superadditive,
(7) $\{a^{(t)}\}$ (t = 0, 1, ..., ad inf.) is an efficient path of infinite order such that for some finite t there exists $(a^{(0)1} \ldots a^{(0)N}, \tilde{b}^{(t)1} \ldots \tilde{b}^{(t)N}) \in T^{(t)}$[38] such that $\tilde{b}^{(t)J} \geqq a^{(t)J}$ (J = 1, ..., K(N) - 1) and $\tilde{b}^{(t)J} \geqq \pi\tilde{a}^J$ (J = K(N), ..., N) for some scalar $\pi > 0$, where $(0 \ldots 0\ \tilde{a}^{K(N)} \ldots \tilde{a}^N)$ is the input vector to some process in T associated with ρ_N,
(8) for some finite s, and the same $(\tilde{a}^{K(N)} \ldots \tilde{a}^N)$ as in (7), there exists a process $(0 \ldots 0\ \tilde{a}^{K(N)} \ldots \tilde{a}^N, 0 \ldots 0\ b^{(s)K(N)} \ldots b^{(s)N}) \in T^{(s)}$ such that $b^{(s)H} > 0$ for all

[37] [5, Theorem 4, p. 102]. See also Fisher [3].

[38] Define, for the sake of elegance, $(a, b) \in T^{(0)}$ if and only if b = a.

$H = K(N), \ldots, N$ for which for some t, $a^{(t)H} \geq 0$,[39]
then $\lim_{t \to \infty} D(a^{(t)1} \ldots a^{(t)N}, N) = 0.$

Proof: Since $a^{(0)}, \ldots, a^{(m)}$ is intertemporally efficient for any m, it is obviously the case that there exist prices $(p^{(m)K(N)} \ldots p^{(m)N})$ such that $p^{(m)J} \geqq 0$ $(J = K(N), \ldots, N)$ and $p^{(m)H} \geq 0$ for at least one $H = K(N), \ldots, N$ for which $a^{(m)H} \geq 0$ with the property that

$$\sum_{J=K(N)}^{N} \left[p^{(m)J}\right]' a^{(m)J} \geqq \sum_{J=K(N)}^{N} \left[p^{(m)J}\right]' b^{(m)J}$$

for any $b^{(m)K(N)} \ldots b^{(m)N}$ such that $(a^{(0)I} \ldots a^{(0)N}, b^{(m)I} \ldots b^{(m)N}) \in T^{(m)}$ and $b^{(m)J} \geqq a^{(m)J}$ for all $J = 1, \ldots, K(N) - 1$. (In other words, there exist prices for sectors K(N) through N such that the output of those sectors on the efficient path has positive value and such that that value is greater than for any feasible path with the same starting point and at least as much output of every commodity in the first K(N) - 1 sectors as the efficient path.)

Given this result, the proof proceeds in essentially the same manner as that of Furuya and Inada's Theorem 4[40] to show that $D(a^{(t)1} \ldots a^{(t)N}, N)$ cannot exceed any arbitrary scalar $\eta > 0$ for more than a finite number of periods. This is done by using (7) and (8) and Theorem 4.3 to construct a path which has at least as much output in every period in the first K(N) - 1 sectors as does the efficient one and which (as in Furuya and Inada) lets the K(N)th through Nth sectors grow at a rate of at least ρ_N for a sufficiently long time so that when one moves in s steps to the output vector described in (8), the result of the preceding paragraph is contradicted. The proof is thus that of Furuya and Inada, mutatis mutandis, applied to the last N - K(N) + 1 sectors.

Remark 4.8: Remarks 4.2-4.4 on Theorem 4.4 apply here also and require no further comment.

Remark 4.9: Since S^I is itself decomposable for all $I = 1, \ldots, N$, the theorem shows convergence to the von Neumann intrasectoral proportions in any subsystem such that the efficient path is efficient considering only inputs and outputs in that subsystem. It is obvious that there may be some efficient paths which are also

[39]As is clear from writing out the proof below, this is stronger than necessary. It would suffice that $b_j^{(s)H} > 0$ for all $H = K(N), \ldots, N$ and $j = 1, \ldots, n_H$ for which, for some t, $a_j^{(t)H} > 0$.

[40][5, pp. 102-104].

efficient in some (or all) subsystems other than the full system, so that such convergence might occur in all subsystems.[41] On the other hand, it is equally obvious that (save under special conditions such as complete decomposability) there are paths which are efficient in the full system without being efficient in lower-numbered subsystems — the output of which may be sacrificed to provide higher outputs in higher-numbered sectors — so that there is no reason to suppose that such simultaneous convergence must occur (since sectors 1 ... K(N) - 1 need not converge absolutely to zero), and, indeed, it is easy to construct counterexamples.[42] It follows that save for subsystems K(N) ... N, it is not true in general that paths efficient of infinite order in the full system converge to the von Neumann intrasectoral proportions in subsystems as well.[43]

Remark 4.10: Since $T^{K(N)}$ is primitive by (2), a sufficient condition for (7) to hold is that, for some t, $a^{(t)K(N)} \geq 0$.[44] Since this is not necessary, it follows that (7) is a fairly reasonable assumption. It is required because no amount of growth in sectors K(N), ..., N can make up for lost output in sectors 1, ..., K(N) - 1.

If (7) does not hold and if for no t is $a^{(t)J} \geq 0$ for any J = K(N), ..., N, then the theorem should be applied to $S^{K(N)-1}$, since the efficient path is then necessarily efficient in that subsystem. If, on the other hand, (7) fails to hold and, for some J = K(N) + 1, ..., N and some t, $a^{(t)J} \geq 0$, then the whole analysis can be repeated leaving the K(N)th sector out of the technology to secure information on the convergence properties of the efficient path, and so forth.

Remark 4.11: A sufficient condition for (8) to hold is Condition 4.1 of Remark 4.6 above.[45]

This completes our discussion of the decomposable case.

---

[41] As stated above, there is nothing contradictory about this. If all subsystems are growing at their own von Neumann rates, sectors with numbers below K(N) will go relatively to zero.

[42] Note the difference between this state of affairs and that of Fisher [4, Theorem 3.2, p. 82]; this is a fundamental difference between the extension to decomposable systems of the Solow-Samuelson model [11] on the one hand and the similar extension of models involving choice on the other.

[43] It is true for subsystems K(N) ... N because the proportions in those subsystems are the same as in the full system. Cf. Remark 4.7.

[44] Cf. Remark 4.6.

[45] Cf. the parallel situation in Remark 4.5.

5. The Nearly Decomposable Case

The remainder of the story is quickly told, given the results of the last two sections. As in Section 3, let $\varepsilon \geq 0$ be a scalar parameter.[46] Let $T(\varepsilon)$ be a variable production set. We shall assume:

Assumption 5.1: $T(\varepsilon)$ is primitive for $\varepsilon \neq 0$ and decomposable for $\varepsilon = 0$. Further, if $(a, b) \in T(0)$, then $(a, b) \in T(\varepsilon)$ for all ε.

Denoting by $F(a, \varepsilon)$ the correspondence which assigns to a and ε the set of all b such that $(a, b) \in T(\varepsilon)$, we assume:

Assumption 5.2: $F(a, \varepsilon)$ is upper semicontinuous in ε at $\varepsilon = 0$.

Lemma 3.1 now follows as before. Once more accepting Assumption 3.3 (Free Disposal), Lemma 3.2 also follows.

As in Section 3, denote the maximal growth factor for processes in $T(\varepsilon)$ by $\lambda(\varepsilon)$ for any nonzero ε. Normalize each process in $T(\varepsilon)$ associated with $\lambda(\varepsilon)$ by requiring its input vector to lie in the simplex, and denote the set of all such normalized input vectors by $V^*(\varepsilon)$. As in the last section, denote the maximal growth rate for processes in $T(0)$ by ρ_N and observe that by Theorem 4.1, $\rho_N = \lambda_{K(N)}$. Normalize each process in $T(0)$ associated with ρ_N by requiring its input vector to lie in the simplex, and denote the set of all such normalized input vectors by $V^*(0)$. Finally, as in the last section, if (B) of Theorem 4.2 (uniqueness of von Neumann intrasectoral proportions) applies to $T(0)$,[47] denote by $(\bar{a}^1 \ldots \bar{a}^N)$ the von Neumann proportions in nontrivial form, and retain the distance concept $D(a^1 \ldots a^N, N)$ as in the last section.

It is clear that a proof parallel to that of Theorem 3.1 (and identical with it in part) yields:

Theorem 5.1:

(1) For any $\varepsilon \neq 0$, $\lambda(\varepsilon) \geq \rho_N$.[48] However,

(2) $\lim_{\varepsilon \to 0} \lambda(\varepsilon) = \rho_N$.

(3) Take any sequence of values of ε converging to zero and any corresponding sequence of elements of $V^*(\varepsilon)$ which approaches a limit. That limit will be a member of $V^*(0)$ so that $V^*(\varepsilon)$ is upper semicontinuous in ε at $\varepsilon = 0$.

---

[46] But see footnote 9.

[47] Note that this need not be a case in which (1)-(6) of that theorem holds nor a case in which the strong Assumption 4.1 holds, as these are sufficient but presumably not necessary. Note further that this is the only way in which Assumption 4.1 enters in this section.

[48] Remark 3.1 of footnote 11, on whether $\lambda(\varepsilon) > \rho_N$, applies here also.

(4) If (B) of Theorem 4.2 holds for T(0), then $\lim_{\varepsilon\to 0} D(a^1(\varepsilon) \ldots a^N(\varepsilon), N) = 0$ where $(a^1(\varepsilon) \ldots a^N(\varepsilon))$ is any sequence of members of $V^*(\varepsilon)$. In other words, for all J = 1, . . . , N and for any such sequence, if $\bar{a}^J = 0$, then $\lim_{\varepsilon\to 0} a^J(\varepsilon) = 0$, and if $\bar{a}^J \geq 0$, then either

$$\lim_{\varepsilon\to 0} a^J(\varepsilon) = 0$$

or

$$\lim_{\varepsilon\to 0} \left(\frac{a^J(\varepsilon)}{\sum_{j=1}^{n_J} a_j^J(\varepsilon)} \right) = \frac{\bar{a}^J}{\sum_{j=1}^{n_J} \bar{a}_j^J}.$$ [49]

This theorem provides the only extension of the principal result of Ando and Fisher [1] to the present model that seems possible without strong further assumptions. It parellels Fisher [4, Theorem 4.1, p.84]. It states that, as a nearly decomposable system approaches decomposability, the von Neumann ray (or rays) approach the von Neumann ray(s) of the limiting decomposable system and the von Neumann growth rate does likewise. Further, if the intrasectoral proportions of the von Neumann rays of the limiting system are unique (in the sense of Theorem 4.2), then those proportions are approached by any sequence of von Neumann rays. In view of Remark 4.9 above, it is clear that a result parallel to that of Theorem 3.2 above and to Fisher [4, Theorem 4.2, p.85] does not follow unless either every efficient path in T(0) is efficient in every subsystem of T(0) (which does occur in the case of complete decomposability and may occur otherwise) or a similar situation holds for members of $V^*(\varepsilon)$ for all ε in some neighborhood of zero. If either of these things does occur, then such a parallel theorem clearly holds, the proof being analogous to that of Theorem 3.2. [50]

---

[49] As in the case of Theorem 3.1, note that it is not required for $\varepsilon \neq 0$ that $V^*(\varepsilon)$ be single-valued or that (B) of Theorem 4.2 apply to $T(\varepsilon)$.

[50] It is thus wrong to suppose that we have hit on a case in which the Ando-Fisher result fails to hold. That result — that intrasectoral proportions are continuous at $\varepsilon = 0$ — does hold for sectors K(N) . . . N; we cannot extend it to lower-numbered sectors because the asymptotic behavior of efficient paths of infinite order in such sectors is not determined in the limiting decomposable case without such assumptions as indicated in the text. To the extent that intrasectoral proportions are determined in the decomposable case, the Ando-Fisher result does indeed hold.

REFERENCES

[1] Ando, A., and F. M. Fisher, "Near Decomposability, Partition and Aggregation, and the Relevance of Stability Discussions," International Economic Review, Vol. 4, No. 1 (January, 1963), pp. 53-67, and reprinted above.

[2] Dorfman, R., P. A. Samuelson, and R. M. Solow, Linear Programming and Economic Analysis, New York, McGraw-Hill, 1957.

[3] Fisher, F. M., "Balanced Growth and Intertemporal Efficiency in Capital Accumulation: Comment," International Economic Review, Vol. 4, No. 2 (May, 1963).

[4] __________, "Decomposability, Near Decomposability, and Balanced Price Change under Constant Returns to Scale," Econometrica, Vol. 31, No. 1-2 (January-April, 1963), pp. 67-89, and reprinted above.

[5] Furuya, H., and K. Inada, "Balanced Growth and Intertemporal Efficiency in Capital Accumulation," International Economic Review, Vol. 3, No. 1 (January, 1962), pp. 94-107.

[6] McKenzie, L., "Three Turnpike Theorems for a Generalized Leontief Model" (forthcoming).

[7] Morishima, M., "Proof of a Turnpike Theorem: the 'No Joint Production' Case," Review of Economic Studies, Vol. 28, No. 2 (February, 1961), pp. 89-97.

[8] Neumann, J. von, "A Model of General Economic Equilibrium," Review of Economic Studies, Vol. 13, No. 1 (October, 1945), pp. 1-9.

[9] Radner, R., "Paths of Economic Growth That Are Optimal with Regard Only to Final States: a Turnpike Theorem," Review of Economic Studies, Vol. 28, No. 2 (February, 1961), pp. 98-104.

[10] Simon, H. A., and A. Ando, "Aggregation of Variables in Dynamic Systems," Econometrica, Vol. 29, No. 2 (April, 1961), pp. 111-138, and reprinted above.

[11] Solow, R. M., and P. A. Samuelson, "Balanced Growth under Constant Returns to Scale," Econometrica, Vol. 21, No. 3 (July, 1953), pp. 412-424.

[12] ________________, "A Brief Comment," Econometrica, Vol. 22, No. 4 (October, 1954), p. 504.

INDEX